1701

CAPTAIN
GARRISON

ISBN: 978-1-949648-96-6

Cover and text layout design: Kristi Yoder

Maps of Europe and West Indies: Andrew Schwartz

Ship drawings: Merlin Yoder

Front cover painting: Peter Balholm

Printed in the USA

Published by:
TGS International
P.O. Box 355
Berlin, Ohio 44610 USA
Phone: 330.893.4828
Fax: 330.893.2305
www.tgsinternational.com

TGS002023

1701-1781
CAPTAIN GARRISON

Based on the life of Captain Nicholas Garrison

If I take the wings of the morning,
and dwell in the uttermost part of the sea;
Even there shall thy hand lead me,
and thy right hand shall hold me.
Psalm 139:9–10

Katrina Hoover Lee

Table of Contents

Acknowledgments

Thank you:

- To my husband Marnell, for his tireless encouragement, his interest in this writing project, and his irreplaceable presence on the research trip to Staten Island and Bethlehem, Pennsylvania.

- To Carlotta DeFillo, Historic Richmond Town, Staten Island, for her informative and fascinating tour of Nicholas Garrison's home area.

- To Peter Hoover, for the seed idea for this story, for his expert advice, and for his guidance on our tour of Bethlehem. Also, a big thank you to his assistant, Christopher Martin.

- To Thomas McCullough at the Moravian Archives in Bethlehem, for accommodating us so kindly at the archives, and for serving as such a valuable resource by email and telephone.

—Katrina Hoover Lee

Western Europe

NORTH SEA

Liverpool

ENGLAND

London

Amsterdam
Rotterdam

Plymouth · Portsmouth

GERMANY

Niesky
Herrnhut

Isles of
Scilly

ENGLISH CHANNEL

Herrnhaag
Marienborn
Ronneburg

Rhine River

Frankfurt

St. Malo

ATLANTIC OCEAN

FRANCE

Alps

St. Sebastian

Pyrenees Mts.

PORTUGAL

SPAIN

Gibralter

MEDITERRANEAN SEA

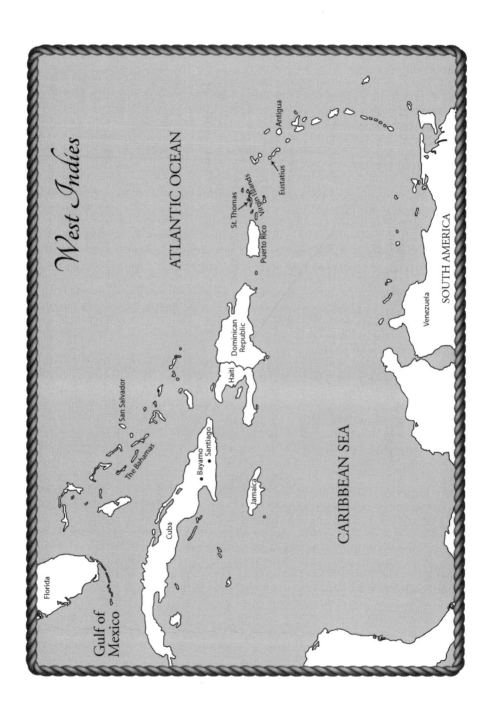

West Indies

ATLANTIC OCEAN

Gulf of Mexico

Florida

San Salvador

The Bahamas

Cuba

Bayamo
Santiago

Jamaica

Haiti

Dominican Republic

Puerto Rico

St. Thomas

Virgin Islands

Eustatius

Antigua

CARIBBEAN SEA

Venezuela

SOUTH AMERICA

Sails of a True Ship

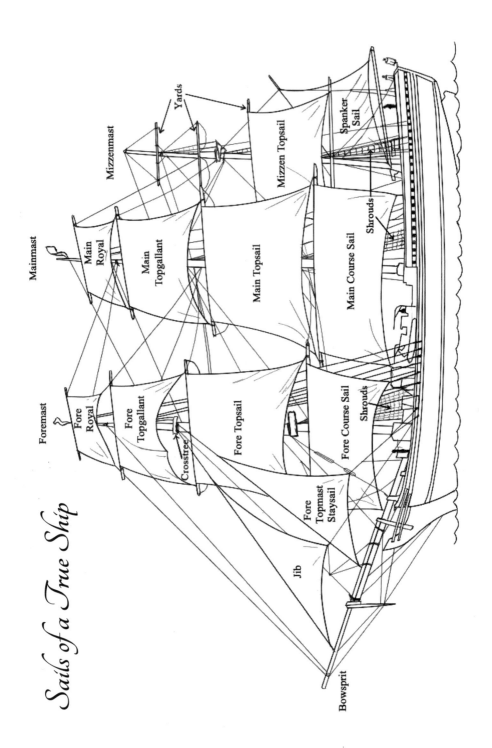

Decks of a Merchant Ship

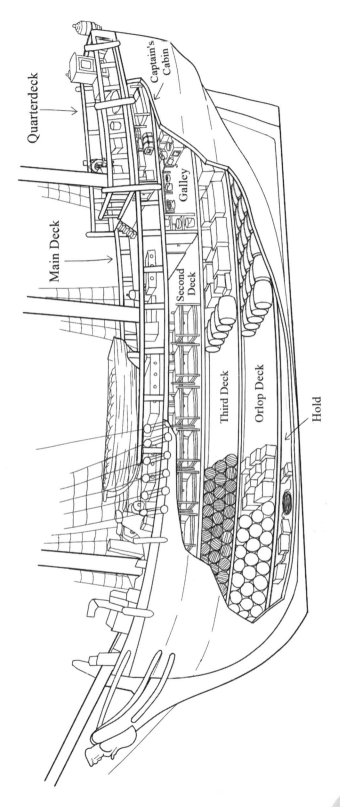

Quarterdeck

Captain's Cabin

Main Deck

Galley

Second Deck

Third Deck

Orlop Deck

Hold

Prologue

September 1712

Nicholas tested his weight on the rope. He was sure he could get in the warehouse window, because the shutter was slightly ajar.

"The till is on the main floor close to the front door," Daniel said. "I'll go behind that old rowboat over there so we don't attract attention." He disappeared from sight.

"What's wrong?" Daniel hissed as Nicholas continued to weigh his options, feet firmly on the ground. "You scared of the old pirate? Father will be back soon. There's no one watching. If you're going to do it, do it now!"

"No," Nicholas said evenly. "I am not afraid of your pirate."

He wasn't afraid of a pirate, but he was afraid. He was afraid of doing wrong, and stealing was wrong. He was afraid of the sting of the whip if his father, former Sheriff Garrison of Richmond County, Staten Island, should find out he had a son who was a thief. He was afraid of disappointing his mother, who had taught him the Ten Commandments.

But, right now, he was most afraid of disappointing Daniel. Anyway, Daniel had worked in a dusty warehouse for almost no pay. Maybe it wouldn't count as stealing if he was taking what was rightfully his brother's.

With a deep breath, Nicholas grabbed the rope. He climbed with no trouble to the second story window. The wooden shutters opened to the outside, and Nicholas pulled his legs through the window. He leaped to the floor of the loft.

Breaking into a warehouse is easy! Nicholas thought. Excitement tingled down his spine.

1

The Slate

October 1708

"I don't want to go to school without—"

Nicholas paused. He bit off another section from the apple in his hand. He chewed, then tried to swallow. It felt as if the entire apple had lodged in his throat and would choke him if he tried to finish the sentence.

"I just don't want to go to school," he said, hoping neither Pine nor Mary had noticed his unfinished thought. "I want to stay home and help Father."

Nicholas Garrison, seven years old, visited Pine and Mary's house often. It was only a few steps from the larger Garrison house. He came to escape his younger brothers or talk about things he could not bring himself to ask his parents. He came for an apple or a bowl of popcorn, and sometimes a popcorn battle with Pine.

Nicholas never thought of Pine as handicapped though he was missing part of an arm, and he never thought of Mary as a slave. Neither did he seem to notice that Pine and Mary had dark skin. Mary had cooked and baked for the Garrison family for as long as Nicholas could remember.

"Ah, are you afraid of the girls?" Pine teased. "Now tell me why a handsome young man like you would not go to school. Seems to me this same young man was over here most every evening last year, talking on and on about his lessons and that schoolmaster with the red beard."

Pine was right. Nicholas had loved the schoolmaster and he had liked school. He had enjoyed walking through the Staten Island countryside, past houses and barns and between trees on either side of the hilly path.

But that was last year, before Nicholas had to go alone. That was last year, when he and Seger had run to catch up with their older brother Daniel. That was when Nicholas had picked goldenrod for Mother because she said it lit up the kitchen like a lantern, and Seger, just older than he, had studied the birds and insects and watched for his favorite blue butterflies. They had dreamed of one day going to sea like their older brother Lambert.

But Seger and Nicholas had planned to go to sea together.

Mary sat in her rocking chair by the fireplace, stitching a patch onto a shirt. It seemed to Nicholas that Mary could tell what someone was thinking even when she was turned the other direction. As Pine talked with Nicholas, the rocking chair stopped. Mary put down the shirt she was working on and looked up at Nicholas. The whites of her eyes shone in the firelight.

"Pine, make that boy some popcorn," she said. "When Daniel and Lambert come home from sea, they are going to be so pleased. Here is their little brother, going to school and getting his learning and near smarter than both of them put together. Oh, yes, Pine, you wait and see if they won't be up on those masts next time they go to sea, a-*bragging* to the other sailors," and Mary drew out the word *brag,* "about their brother what can write and read and keep an account book as good as a captain, they will." She wiped the corner of her eye on the shirt she was mending.

Pine shelled popcorn from an ear of dried corn, feeding the kernels into a greased pan over the fire. Pine could do as much with one hand as most people could do with two.

"You know, Nicholas," Pine said as he emptied the popped corn into a bowl, "sometimes things—they look so bad. And then sometimes, it turns out that what we thought was bad worked for good."

Nicholas looked at Pine's empty shirt sleeve, neatly pinned together. He looked at the twisting scar on Pine's face, where a master's whip had cut into his flesh, far away on the Dutch island of St. Thomas. Nicholas had heard much about Pine's years as a slave. Pine had been sold to a sea captain and put on a ship to New York. On the voyage, he had lost his arm in a battle with a pirate ship. The captain had let him go free when they reached New York.

"Here I thought I lost my arm because God was angered with me," Pine would say. "But that arm floating out there in the West Indies Ocean is what made me a free man. I do not pine for that arm any more, oh no, I do not."

Pine had received his name on board the ship because he was so tall, although it was given in Dutch. When he learned that his name in English meant both a tree and to long for something, he began to use the verb form whenever possible.

"I am pining for a drink of water," he would say, just because it fit with his name.

Nicholas ate popcorn and thought about what Pine and Mary had said. He wanted to please his older brothers. If Pine could survive losing his arm, surely he could survive going to school. But it would not help to think of Seger or blue butterflies. The very thought twisted Nicholas inside until his stomach felt like a rock.

Would his father ever forgive him for what had happened that wet day last spring?

"Nicholas!" a voice called from the world outside the cozy house.

"It's your mama. Now run along," Mary said. "It's almost your bedtime, it is."

• •

On his first day back to school, Nicholas walked from the cluster of buildings on the Garrison farmstead to the footpath that led to the stone school building half a mile away. Ice crystals outlined the wood grain on the split rail fence around the property. Red and orange leaves carpeted the ground and filled the ruts made by his father's wagon.

Jonah followed, tail wagging, until Nicholas convinced his dog to turn back. The family's beloved English water spaniel looked handsome in the morning sunshine, bronze spots covering his white coat.

The schoolmaster showed Nicholas to a backless wooden bench beside another boy about his age. The girls sat in the back of the room, close to the warmth of the fire. But they were also close to the smoke that occasionally escaped from the chimney. Several of the girls were coughing, and a light haze of smoke filled their dusky corner. The shutters had been opened to let in daylight, but the room was still dark enough to require candles near the teacher's desk.

The day started with roll call. The schoolmaster checked off each name as the students responded, his quill pen making a scratching sound. He had kept his woolen cap on, as it was cool in the room. He lifted a prayer book, and the students bowed their heads as he read a prayer.

After a Scripture reading, they practiced the Dutch catechism.[1] From a small leather-bound book, the teacher read theological questions. The students answered the questions, the older ones leading the way.

"How do you come to know your misery?" the teacher questioned.

"The law of God tells me," the students answered.

The older students knew most of the answers by heart, and Nicholas joined them in the answers he remembered.

[1] "Heidelburg Catechism," <https://www.crcna.org/welcome/beliefs/confessions/heidelberg-catechism>, accessed on July 1, 2019.

"What does God's law require of us?" the teacher intoned, rubbing his woolen cap with his free hand.

"Christ teaches us this in summary in Matthew 22:37–40: 'You shall love the Lord your God with all your heart, and with all your soul, and with all your mind . . .' " Nicholas stumbled along. He remembered some of the words, but not all.

"Can you live up to this perfectly?"

"No," the students said. "I have a natural tendency to hate God and my neighbor."

The teacher held his book closer to the candle burning on his desk and flipped to another section.

Finally, the catechism was over.

The younger students grouped around the teacher's desk, where the hand *plak* lay beside the ink pot. The *plak* was like a wooden spoon, intended for swatting the hands of lazy or disobedient students.

"Where is your slate, Nicholas?" asked the schoolmaster.

Hot fear sprang up in Nicholas' stomach. He had completely forgotten his slate, even though his mother had reminded him just before he left for school. Most of the other students had been coming to school longer than he had, since his parents had allowed him to help with the harvest. Would the schoolmaster whip him with the *plak* and humiliate him in front of the other children?

"I forgot it," he said quietly.

The other children stared at him, frozen with suspense. A few sympathetic eyes warmed his heart, but most of the boys and girls looked eager. A whipping would break the monotony of a day at school.

Stern but thoughtful, the teacher's green eyes studied Nicholas. He got up from his rush-bottomed chair and walked to the back room, where his sleeping quarters were.

He returned with a slate, and handed it to Nicholas.

"This slate was left last spring by your brother. I believe he forgot it. I thought to bring it to your house to give it to him, but I am too late. Perhaps you will use it."

The teacher nodded toward Nicholas' bench with a look that was almost kind.

"Go sit down and write your alphabet."

Trembling, Nicholas walked to his bench. Tears of relief, joy, and sadness stung the back of his eyes at the same time. He gulped and swallowed to keep his chin from quivering. He could not cry at school.

He looked down at the slate. In one corner of the frame, someone had sketched three small butterflies.

• •

After school, Nicholas hurried home. He found Father in the barn, threshing oats. A cloud of dust hung in the air and Nicholas sneezed. He eagerly showed his father the slate and told him how the teacher had returned it.

For a moment Father said nothing. His eyes looked as if he were remembering a time he had hit his foot with an axe. Then he shut his eyes, opened them again, and turned back to the pile of grain.

"You should not have forgotten your slate at home. Take that one to Mother."

Nicholas turned away. His insides twisted as if they would curl up into a ball. Silently, he walked to the house, ignoring Jonah at his feet. He opened the bottom half of the Dutch door to let himself in.

Mother turned pale when he handed her the slate. Tears escaped her eyes. She took the slate, and went to the next room. Nicholas heard a drawer close with a soft clunk.

Nicholas ran blindly out of the kitchen. His feet pounded on the path to the house next door, where he fell into Mary's arms. As soon as he was old enough, he told Pine, he would do what Daniel had done. He would leave and go to sea.

2

The Home on Staten Island

"Mary, do you remember Mother before she married Father?" Nicholas asked, sliding Pine's carving knife beneath the bark of a piece of maple wood.

With his stomach full of cabbage stew and fresh bread from supper, Nicholas had made his way from the Garrison stone house back to Pine and Mary's smaller log cabin. He did not want to talk about the slate with the butterflies or about going to sea. He did not want Mary to sympathize with him or tell him everything would be okay. He wanted to forget about his father's pained face when he showed him the slate.

So he asked Mary about the days gone by. If Mary got started, she would talk on and on, and he wouldn't have to say a thing. Mary's words would fill the air and make pictures in his head.

Mary had a needle between her lips, preparing to thread it. Nicholas knew Mary much preferred the baking and cabbage-chopping she had done earlier in the day. But even though she disliked sewing, she could mend anything.

Mary snatched the needle from her mouth.

"Did I know your mama? Why Nicholas, I've told you a hundred times—" Mary struck at the air with the needle—"how I held your mama in my arms when she was only five years old and her Papa Morgan died of the fever, I did!"

Of course, Nicholas had heard the story. But Mary's dramatic voice soothed him deep inside. He fiddled with the knife, trying to separate bark from wood.

"Want me to find you a piece of dry wood so's you can make something decent?"

Pine asked from his chair, where he was cracking walnuts into a bowl.

"No, I'm just playing," Nicholas said. "Mary, what was Mother's papa like?"

This was a fair question, because Nicholas did not know much about his grandfather.

"Ah, your grandfather, Papa Morgan, was tall and fine, he was. Came from Wales with a bunch of money from his papa, and married your grandma Catalyntje. Your grandma was born here, Nicholas. She was born here in the New World, right there on Manhattan Island when there weren't hardly a white baby anywhere in this land! And then she married Charles Morgan and they went to the Church of England, and she learned to talk English, she did, and changed her name to Catherine, and then she had my dear Susannah, your mother, and we was the best of friends.

"When Papa Morgan died and your grandma Catherine married this Captain Nicholas Stillwell man, we says to each other, your mama and I, we says we was never going to look at him, we did. But then he gave your mama chocolates and told her stories, and we decided he was all right. Not like Papa Morgan, but all right."

"And then you married Pine, and Mother married Father," Nicholas said, gouging his knife into the green wood. "And they named me after Captain Nicholas Stillwell!"

"Your mama Susannah almost run me off when I was trying to wed Mary," Pine said with a wink. A shower of pieces fell around him as a walnut shell exploded. "I was telling stories about how my arm got blowed off and how the surgeon cut the rest of it off with a saw, and that Susannah girl nigh unto fainted. But then she up and married a rugged man herself, she did, and your papa Lambert Garrison wasn't no city man."

"Well, if you hadn't made those awful booming noises like them cannons make, and that scraping noise how the saw made cutting through your arm, she might not have been so upset," Mary huffed with a roll of her eyes. "But that's right, Nicholas, your mama Susannah married that tall Garrison man because she liked his kind eyes and his law studying over there in Holland, she did."

"Your papa told me 'twas the hardest thing he ever done, getting your mama to marry him," Pine added.

"Oh, but she loved him something awful, she did," Mary said. "She loved him something awful, so 'tweren't nothing nobody could say. We didn't none of us think she'd give up her tea parties and drawing pencils and fancy silk dresses and move out here to Staten Island with Lambert Garrison, we didn't. But when your mama makes up her mind, she makes it up, I tell you, Nicholas."

"Don't forget, she shed herself a few tears when she saw this here homestead with no house on it yet," Pine inserted.

Pine was a free black, and he had moved right along with Mary into the wilderness.

"So she did!" Mary snapped. "Who wouldn't a shed a tear looking at all them nettles and chipmunks every which way? But she quit crying and she started sewing and making soap and candles and having babies and she stayed right strong and elegant, even before the barn was built and them animals was living in the basement. And she still the most beautiful woman in all Staten Island, she is."

"Nicholas!" A faint call interrupted Mary's story telling.

"If that ain't your mama calling right this very minute," Mary said. "She wants you to take baby Elizabeth, if I don't make any mistake. If that baby isn't the best thing that has happened this year," she added, sighing.

Nicholas' parents had two older sons, Lambert and Charles, and two older daughters, Susannah and Catharine. Then five more boys had joined the family— Daniel, Seger, Nicholas, Isaac, and Jacob— and finally, baby Elizabeth.[1]

Born two weeks after that dreadful day last spring, Baby Elizabeth's shrill cry had somehow comforted everyone on the property. Here was a human being who had not experienced the horror of the last weeks. Here was someone who had to be taken care of—even if the rest of the world had collapsed around them. Here was an extra person on the farmstead, instead of a missing person; a new form in the cradle, instead of an empty bed in the loft. Elizabeth spent little time in the cradle. Everyone fought for her, from Susannah and Catharine, to the big boys and the little boys. Even Daniel, who snapped at everyone else, had spoken kindly to the baby.

In Mary's kitchen, Nicholas got up, shaking the maple bark from his clothes. He laid Pine's knife on the table and stepped into the twilight. His mother stood straight and tall at the door to the stone house. Ever since last spring, Mother's smiles ended much too quickly, as if they could not last long anymore.

Mother was beautiful, just as Mary had said, with high cheekbones and golden hair that escaped from her white Dutch cap. Her yellow dress brushed the blades of grass near the doorstep. She eased baby Elizabeth into Nicholas' arms.

"I'll put the little boys to bed and be back soon. Get ready to say your verses."

Nicholas carried his baby sister across the yard to the haystack close to the barn. He settled himself in the warm stalks, his summertime refuge for reciting. It had been a warm day, but it was growing cool. He wrapped the blanket around the baby, who looked up at him with bright eyes as if he was her one true hero. Her small fist escaped from the blanket and bobbed back and forth, finally grasping a piece of hay.

---

[1] Garrison Family Records are found in Addendum I on page 365.

Jonah folded his feathery white paws on Nicholas' knee. When Jonah ran, the fine hair on his legs and tail streamed behind him and the curls on his coat bounced. Jonah could swim and dive almost as well as the ducks in the Fresh Kills.[2] Lambert had brought the puppy home from Manhattan more than a year ago.

Nicholas watched the last reflections of daylight fade from the windows of the Garrison house that Father had built out of stone from his own fields. Now he was helping to build an Anglican church and making plans for a new jail. Father was sheriff of Richmond County.

If only Father would not blame Nicholas for what had happened to Seger. "We should have crossed the Fresh Kills at a different place," he whispered to Jonah and Elizabeth, tears rolling down his face.

Nicholas imagined that his baby sister had a special attachment to him. He spoke to Elizabeth as if she was his own age, whispering the entire account of that dreadful night into her silky hair. Elizabeth never told his secrets.

"It's easier to be good with Daniel gone," Nicholas whispered. *But I wish he had at least said goodbye.* Mother had found Daniel's note informing them he had taken a position as a ship's boy. Without asking for permission, he had left for sea. Like Seger, he had suddenly disappeared and now Nicholas was the oldest boy at home.

Jonah panted in Nicholas' face, full of admiration for his master. Elizabeth stared at her big brother, her eyes full of trust. Neither of them cared about what had happened six months ago. To them, Nicholas was big and strong and always right.

Nicholas blinked back his tears and set his jaw, looking at the sky and watching the fat full moon rising out of the east, the direction of the sea. He would prove Jonah and his baby sister right. He would prove to Father that he could be trusted. He would forget about the past and quit crying. He would not wish Seger and Daniel back anymore.

Mother was coming across the yard toward them, carrying a lantern. "Are you ready to say your verses?" she asked Nicholas.

At home the Garrisons had all learned Dutch, the language of Holland, but they also spoke English. Mother's stepfather, Captain Nicholas Stillwell, had bought an English Bible, the version King James had printed almost 100 years before. Father had asked them to learn their Scriptures in English because New York was an English colony now. Father had changed his last name from Gerritzen, which was Dutch, to Garrison, which was English. He had learned to speak English well, and he insisted his children speak it.

Nicholas recited the passage from Isaiah 53 that Mother was helping him

---

[2] *Kill* comes from a Dutch word meaning creek or channel.

memorize. She had seated herself beside him in the straw. The lantern light winked at Nicholas while he spoke.

" 'He was despised and rejected of men . . . All we like sheep have gone astray . . . He was wounded for our transgressions . . . He was cut off out of the land of the living.' "

When Nicholas finished reciting, they sat together on the haystack, enjoying the quietness of the night settling around them.

Then Mother asked, "Do you know who those verses speak of, Nicholas?"

"Jesus Christ who died on the cross for our sins," Nicholas said, remembering the answer he had memorized in school.

"Very good, my son," Mother said softly. "He suffered much for our sake. He took the blame for wrongs He had not done. Do you understand?"

"Yes, Mother."

Father came from the barn where he had been checking the horses. "We hardly need a lantern with a moon like this," he said, looking up. He had a way of looking over the sky, or a room, or a field, or a river, or a letter, or an island, as if he were a scientist taking notes.

"Have you said your verses, Nicholas?"

"Yes, sir," Nicholas said.

"Ah, the moon!" a voice called from the darkness. Pine had stepped out of his small house to empty a bucket for Mary.

"It's a bright one tonight," Father replied.

"As they say," Pine said, "how long can guests stay in the moon's quarters?"

"As they say?" Father asked. "Or as you say?"

"Guests can only stay until the moon is full," Pine chuckled, answering his own riddle.

Father laughed, a sound Nicholas had not heard much the last while. Pine went back into his house, and the little group at the haystack savored the moment of togetherness.

"The Lenape people[3] who lived on Staten Island before us keep time by the moon," Father commented. "They do not even have calendars.

"Nicholas, do you know what is it called when we do not see a moon?" Father asked.

Nicholas thought for a moment, anxious to find the right term. "Is it new moon?"

"That's right," Father said.

Mother looked down at Nicholas, pleased.

---

[3] The Lenape were also called the Delaware (Indians).

Nicholas had seen members of the native Lenape tribe a few times, but most of them had crossed the Arthur Kill and moved west to the land of New Jersey, maybe farther. He liked when Father told stories about Staten Island in the old days.

But mostly, he wished his father would be pleased with him too.

3

The *Ella*

September 1712

Daniel had been home all summer, but he was leaving for sea again. This time, he told Father about his plans, but like the previous time he did not ask for permission. Daniel was sixteen years old now, a tall man with a deep voice. He sometimes swore and sang rowdy sailor's songs. When Mother heard the songs, she bit her lip.

Father, Lambert, and Nicholas took Daniel to Manhattan to see him off. Lambert had come back from sea and had just gotten married. Father and Lambert rode up front. Daniel and Nicholas perched on baskets of squash they were hoping to sell at the trading post.

"It would be an easy drive to the ferry if it weren't for these hills," said Father as the wagon thumped over a tree root. A footpath used by the Lenape people had become a road, widened by carts and wagons.

The sun still shone warmly, and the leaves were turning orange and red. Ragged weeds stood high between rows of cabbage and pumpkins in the fields. The wood smoke from chimneys filled the air with an exhilarating scent.

"Howdy, Sheriff!" voices called from the fields and barnyards they passed.

Father called to the people by name and wished them a good day. He was no longer the sheriff, but he knew most of the families now living on Staten Island. He had been the census taker in 1706. According to the census, the island was home to 926 white people and 140 black people, for a total population of 1,066.

They began to descend to the flat land beside Darby Doyle's ferry, also called the Watering Place. Father pointed out the hillside where he and his brothers had watched a ship called *The Crossed Heart* sail away years before. The Dutch director, Peter Stuyvesant, had been on board, leaving his colony to travel to the Netherlands to explain why he had surrendered the city to the English.

The English had taken over New York in 1664 when Father was only four years old. English ships had sailed into New York harbor and demanded that the Dutch give up the colony. Defiant, Peter Stuyvesant had torn up the letter the English had sent. But the townspeople of New York did not want their houses and families destroyed in a battle and they convinced Stuyvesant to surrender.

"I heard that Peter Stuyvesant had only one leg, because the other one had been blown off in a battle. The wooden leg was decorated with bands of silver," Father said as he drove.

"One day I was with my father at a shop in Manhattan. In walked the former director and I got to see his silver leg."

"He came back from the Netherlands?" Nicholas asked.

"Yes, he did. He wasn't director anymore, of course. The English had their own government. He just lived on his own farm. But whenever he came into town, everyone called him General. They seemed to respect him even though they had once been against him."

They lurched down the path to the ferry and tavern at the water's edge.

Mr. Doyle had just taken a man across the Narrows and would be back shortly, his wife said. The Narrows lay between Staten Island and Long Island and all ships bound for Manhattan must pass through it.

A black slave stabled the Garrisons' two horses and secured their wagon in a shed. As soon as the sloop[1] pulled in, Father paid Mr. Doyle the fare and they all climbed aboard, hauling the squash with them. Nicholas tried not to rock the boat as he stepped aboard, but when Lambert handed him a basket of squash, he almost fell as the boat tipped his way.

"That's a landlubber there!" Daniel teased.

Nicholas felt his face turn red. Landlubber was a name for someone who knew nothing about the sea. But Lambert cuffed him on the shoulder as if to tell him not to worry.

Nicholas had been on the ferry before but never on such a fine day as this. The sun rose high above Long Island. But they were not going across the Narrows to Long Island today. Mr. Doyle set the single sail to pick up the breeze and pointed the sloop north into the Upper Bay. The water of the bay swelled gently as the

---

[1] A sloop is a sailing boat with only one mast.

boat cut a path, leaving a foamy white triangle behind it, which glistened in the sunlight. Gulls screamed above them, making almost the same sound the sloop made when Mr. Doyle adjusted the sail.

Ships lined the Manhattan harbor. Nicholas could not look away from their majestic masts and spars. Lambert pointed out the *Prince,* Daniel's ship. The ship closest to the ferry was a striking red and black, with the word *Ella* painted in white letters on her stern. Both were true ships[2] with three towering masts that reached the sky. The *Ella's* sails were down, but two sailors could be seen on the rigging, pounding and pulling at the wooden spar from which the sails were attached. More men walked the deck, shouting to each other.

"Ho, there!" Lambert bellowed as the ferry swung close to the shadow of the *Ella's* bow. "Is that John Gray?"

A man leaned his head over the side of the ship.

"Garrison!" he yelled back to Lambert. "Come aboard, old pal!"

"I will help carry some goods to the trading post first," Lambert called back. "But I will come visit the *Ella* after we unload."

The stench of fish and rotting waste met the ferry as it bumped against the dock. There were other ferries, likely from New Jersey or Long Island. Sailors, fishermen, traders, English soldiers, visitors, and townspeople were going about the daily business of this bustling port city.

Near the shore, several taverns welcomed visitors and locals alike. A few houses stood close to the water's edge, but most homes were built along a neat gridwork of streets farther from the shore. Some houses were sided with wooden clapboards, but most were stone or brick with red or black tile roofs. Neat gardens and orchards along with pigsties and chicken coops were behind the houses. Father said that years ago the Dutch government had put an extra tax on anyone who kept their pigsty close to the road.

Lugging the baskets of squash, the Garrison men started on foot to the trading post. It was muddy near the shore, but soon they stepped onto a cobblestone street lined with gabled houses. Huge warehouses stored the goods that arrived by ship. They passed a ship yard, where the hull of a future ship stood high and dry on the land. Nicholas heard pounding noises that sounded like a pond full of croaking frogs.

"What's that noise, Lambert?" he asked, staring at the huge hull rising above him.

"Caulking," Lambert said. "Men with wooden mallets are pushing oakum between the planks of the ship to make it watertight. Oakum is made by untwisting old

---

[2] "True" ships have three or more masts.

ropes that are not useful anymore."

At the trading post, the shopkeeper rattled paper and coins and called out cheery greetings to everyone who entered. Nicholas saw pewter spoons, forks, plates, and cups on the shelves. Forks were a new utensil that Father had not used as a child. Mother had, because her father had been wealthy. The post was cluttered with shutters, hinges, nails, Delft platters and plates, three-legged pots, paper, ink, account books, indigo, barrels of cinnamon and sugar and cumin, and huge bins of salt.

"I'm afraid I don't need more squash," the shopkeeper said, clearing his throat when he saw the boys with their baskets. "I can buy them, but I have such a stock right now, I can't give you much for them."

Daniel and Nicholas looked at each other. Any money would be better than nothing, and they didn't want to drag the full baskets back home. Nicholas could still feel the raw areas where the squash spines had cut into his fingers. All that work for almost nothing!

"There is a man across the street looking for someone to help him this morning," the shopkeeper said. "You could make a little more money that way. I told him I would pass the word. Grown men only," he added, shooting a glance at Nicholas. "He's stacking tobacco and the boxes are heavy."

"I'll work for a few hours!" Daniel said. "I need some spending money."

"I need to meet with some people at the fort," Father said. "We need to get a charter from England for our new church." They had already decided to name it the Church of St. Andrew.

Nicholas felt his heart sink. Lambert was going to the *Ella* to visit an old friend. Daniel would get the fun of working in a warehouse and making money. He would probably have to go with Father and listen to a boring meeting about the church charter.

He looked away, and saw that Lambert was watching him.

"Want to come with me to the *Ella* once I have my hinges picked out?"

"Sure!" Nicholas said, his insides quivering with excitement.

"Stay out of trouble," Father said.

From the neat cobblestone street, Lambert and Nicholas stepped into an alley and turned toward the water. Huge warehouses lined the narrow dirt path.

"The sail makers work in the upstairs lofts," he heard Lambert saying. "They need lots of space to spread out the canvas to cut the patterns for the sails. And here's a cooper's shop, where they make barrels for carrying water and goods. Barrels are easy to move because you can tip them over and roll them."

Lambert stepped across a cloudy pool of water, but Nicholas plunged into it, soaking his shoe. They were at the wharf.

Rounding the corner of the last warehouse, they saw the *Ella*, looking almost as high as the sky. The wharf was lined with ships from Europe and the West Indies and other English colonies. Beyond the ships Nicholas could see the fort, with the English flag flying. His father would be there soon, perhaps meeting old friends he had worked with as a sheriff of Staten Island.

But Nicholas had eyes only for the *Ella*.

Up the sloping gangway he followed Lambert.

The deck was a confusion of coils of rope, extra sails, barrels, and boxes. Men called to each other. A man in rough white clothing with a bandana tied around his head hurried past, bumping Nicholas with his elbow. Across the ship, Nicholas heard sailors singing. Crates and barrels were being carried up the gangway and high overhead a pulley creaked, hoisting a huge heavy box from the shore.

Nicholas looked up at the rope work—black ropes and white ropes and ropes knotted into a grid like a ladder. Oh, what he wouldn't give to climb them! Nicholas could barely see the tops of the masts, which seemed to move against the white clouds. It made him dizzy, and he quickly looked down.

"Garrison!" a voice shouted to Lambert.

"Hey, old pal!" Lambert shouted back.

"What did you do, bring a landlubber with you?" asked the darkly tanned sailor. He stood with his hands on his hips, his legs spread wide on the planks, his white shirt loose at the throat. He winked at Nicholas.

"My brother Nic," Lambert said.

"Bosun says the captain's going to be up here shortly so we can't stand around talking," Lambert's friend said, with a dry roll of the eyes. "Come help stack boxes in the hold."

Nicholas followed them down a ladder into the storage part of the ship.

"Stand back, Nicholas," Lambert said. "Best to stay out of the way."

As the men talked and worked, Nicholas sniffed the air. Vinegar? Newly cut wood? Dead animals? He wondered if the boxes the boys were stacking contained beaver pelts, or some other animal skin. Furs and tobacco and popcorn and squash were some of the things people in Europe liked to import from the New World of New York.

A gray cat strolled past them, gliding among the boxes. Nicholas watched its tail disappear between two boards. Of course there would be mice on a ship, especially one that carried grain. *If there are mice, there should be a cat.*

"You have been to the Bahamas, yes?" the sailor asked Lambert. "Beautiful country down there and beautiful girls at the shore, aren't they? Ah, but we had best leave that talk until later," he said, with a glance at Nicholas.

"Nicholas," Lambert called, "you can go up on deck and get some fresh air. Stay out of the men's way."

Nicholas knew Lambert wanted to get rid of him so they could talk about their secrets. Lambert and Daniel used many words that Nicholas had heard before in church, like *God, damnation, hell,* and *devil.* But Reverend Mackenzie spoke them seriously. His brothers and their friends spoke as if the words were a joke, or to make themselves sound important or to make other people sound bad.

Nicholas had just arrived in the open air, blinking in the sunshine, when he heard sharp footsteps and a sudden quietness.

"Good morning, Captain Parker," someone said.

The captain nodded in greeting. He was dressed in blue with gold edging on his coat and hat. A red silk handkerchief dangled from his hand.

"Morning, men. Who's that boy?" he asked next. "Come here, boy."

With a choking sensation, Nicholas realized that he was being addressed. He stepped around a pile of circular pieces of wood with holes through them.

"You want to come on this voyage? What's your name? Ah, maybe you're a bit too young to live on a ship."

"Ah, Nicholas. Garrison, sir. I am here with my brother who is down . . . there," he said with a nod to the ladder.

"Ah. I could use a boy. Are you going to come to sea sometime?"

The answer sprang out before he thought. "Oh, yes sir, I am!"

"Very good," Captain Parker said. "Perhaps we will see you in a few years. When the time comes, remember to check in at the *Ella.*"

4

The Pirate's Warehouse

When Lambert and Nicholas returned to the trading post, neither Father nor Daniel had returned. Lambert told Nicholas to wait at the post while he made a quick call on a friend.

Nicholas stood on the porch, leaning against one of the wooden posts. Men clattered in and out with a rattle of foreign languages.

Nicholas studied the tops of the masts that he could see above the buildings. *Captain Parker asked me to come to sea with him!* Nicholas thought with a shiver of delight. Captain Parker, Nicholas was sure, was the best man alive.

Nicholas snapped out of his dreaming when Daniel stomped up the porch steps. "That old pirate," Daniel snarled. "Nicholas, come do something for me. He won't know you, and if I—" Daniel swore.

"What happened?" Nicholas asked, staring at Daniel. He had heard Daniel swear plenty of times, but he had never seen him so angry.

"Sure as can be, the man who hired me is a thief and a pirate. I wish I could turn him in to the crown. He agreed to pay me hard cash at the beginning of the day—I need *money* for the sea ports on my voyage, not tobacco! Look at this flea-bitten bag of tobacco he gave me!"

Nicholas swallowed. He felt bad for Daniel, but he wondered what Daniel wanted him to do about his predicament.

"He's left the warehouse now, and I know where his till is," Daniel said in an undertone. "And I know there's money in it. Look, it's that third warehouse down.

There's a loft, and I opened the window at the back of the warehouse before I left. You're small enough to fit through and you can climb anything."

Nicholas felt the warm stimulation of his brother's praise. Daniel, who on that dark day four years before had said, *You saw the log. You should have warned him,* was asking for help. Nicholas wanted to be an honest man. But more than that, he wanted to please Daniel.

"Sure, let's find a rope," Nicholas said, all business. "I saw one on a fence."

"I'd never send you in if he were still there," Daniel said. "Meanest man alive. Got a scar along his left arm and two missing fingers. But he's gone. You'll be fine."

Nicholas ran to the edge of the next warehouse and ducked down a narrow alley. Near the wharf, over a wooden fence post, he found what he had remembered seeing: a piece of abandoned rope.

Back at the warehouse, he tied a loop and threw the rope toward the window. After several tries, it caught on the hinge of the shutter. Above the shuttered part of the window was another section of glass with no shutter.

"Was there anyone else in the warehouse?" Nicholas asked, remembering Lambert's words about sailmakers using the upper lofts.

"No," Daniel said.

The road in front of the warehouse district was busy, but the building where Daniel had been working was small and out of sight from the main streets.

Nicholas tested his weight on the rope. He was sure he could get in through the shuttered part, because the shutter was slightly ajar.

"The till is on the main floor close to the front door," Daniel said. "I'll go behind that old rowboat over there so we don't attract attention." He disappeared from sight, although he must have disturbed several chickens, judging from the sudden clucking.

"What's wrong?" Daniel hissed as Nicholas continued to weigh his options, feet firmly on the ground. "You scared of the old pirate now? Father will be back soon. There's no one watching. If you're going to do it, do it now!"

"No," Nicholas said evenly. "I am not afraid of your pirate."

He wasn't afraid of a pirate, but he was afraid. He was afraid of doing wrong, and stealing was wrong. He was afraid of the sting of the whip if his father, former Sheriff Garrison of Richmond County, Staten Island, should find out that he had a son who was a thief. He was afraid of disappointing his mother, who had taught him the Ten Commandments.

But, right now, he was most afraid of disappointing Daniel. Anyway, Daniel had worked in a dusty warehouse for almost no pay. Maybe this wouldn't count as stealing.

What if the pirate came back to the warehouse and spotted Nicholas? Could he escape before being recognized as the son of Lambert Garrison?

Taking a deep breath, Nicholas grabbed the rope and climbed easily to the second story window. The wooden shutters opened to the outside, and Nicholas pulled his legs through the window. As he balanced on the sill, the sweet, woody aroma of the dried tobacco plants rushed into his nostrils. He leaped to the floor of the loft.

Breaking into a warehouse is easy! Nicholas thought. Excitement tingled down his spine.

He scrambled down the stairs, leaving shoe prints in the dust. He didn't care. By the time the ill-tempered pirate returned to his warehouse and saw the tracks, Nicholas would be gone. Daniel would have shillings in his pocket.

In the dimness, Nicholas bumped against a stack of wooden tobacco crates. A dirty window let in enough light to guide him to the front counter under which he found a heavy wooden box. He tilted it and coins clanked inside.

Nicholas tried the latch, but the box was locked. Probably the pirate carried the keys with him. Should he try to break into the box? Or just take the whole box and risk being seen with it outside? It was heavy, but he could carry it.

He spotted a canvas sack close to the front door, and he had his answer. He would drop the box into the sack and take the whole thing.

It would be a lot easier to go out the front door. Getting down the rope with the box would be tricky, but the front door opened into the street, where he would risk being recognized. He decided to go back up to the loft and down the rope.

Nicholas carefully tugged the canvas sack from behind the canoe paddles near the door. As he turned to take it back to the counter, he heard the door latch click. Nicholas jumped behind the paddles and flattened himself.

The door opened with a scream of metal on metal. Light flooded the entrance, forming rays of dancing dust. Nicholas inched closer to the wall, and then he knocked over a canoe paddle. It fell to the floor with a clatter.

The paddle nearly struck the face of a man as it fell. The light disappeared, blocked by the shape of the merchant pirate. A vice-like hand clamped onto Nicholas' shoulder. For such a huge man, his voice was thin and shrill.

"There you are!" he shrieked. "Rope up over my window. Aha, says I, I'm being broke into. Never trust a boy."

Nicholas darted forward, striking the man's ribs. The man's three-fingered left hand closed over a metal mat hook. Nicholas felt his stomach tighten in fear. Was the man going to beat him?

Although at eleven years old he was too young to use a mat hook, Nicholas knew what it was. The iron handle with a flat-hooked end was held in the left hand at harvest time to grab stalks of grain and position them for cutting with a scythe. His father had informed him with pride one sweaty afternoon that the mat hook was a Dutch tool.

The man wrenched Nicholas backward, turning his face to the light.

"Aye, not even one I hired today. He's a little one, he is. A friend, maybe? Maybe we find . . ."

"You didn't *hire* him! You made him your slave!" Nicholas snapped.

Never before in his short life had Nicholas contradicted an adult. But now, he was caught. There was no use showing respect. He would be sent to jail, perhaps the jail his father was planning for Staten Island. Perhaps he would be put in a jail right here in Manhattan and never see his family again.

The man looked at the pegs along the side of the building, searching for something. He curled his lips and spit a stream of tobacco juice between his yellow teeth onto the dirt floor.

Nicholas saw his chance. He pulled at his shoulder with all his might, dropping to the ground. His forehead collided with a wooden cart wheel, but his shoulder was free. He rolled across the floor, knocking over more canoe paddles and an empty barrel, which in turn toppled a stack of empty boxes, making an awful racket.

"Can't even be safe in me own building. If you come back," the thin voice threatened, "I'll ask Captain Parker to make room for you on his yard arm."

Nicholas ran up the loft stairs, blood dripping from his forehead. He was sliding down the rope before the pirate could get out the front door. He didn't stop running when he reached the boat where Daniel had been hiding. As he expected, Daniel was gone. Most likely he had fled when he saw the pirate walking toward the warehouse. Nicholas did not slow until he was nearly to the ferry stop.

"Are you all right?"

Nicholas jumped, nervous, but the voice was kind. He recognized Mr. Van Woogelum, who owned a field on Staten Island next to his father's.

"Yes—I am—all right," Nicholas spoke, too quickly.

Mr. Van Woogelum scratched his hair, which was so blond it was almost white. "It looks to me like you are running very fast from something sharp," he said gently.

Nicholas touched his forehead and looked at his fingertips. They were red and sticky. "I-I was running and—didn't see a tree limb," he said. "I need to wash it."

"I have a bit of water," Mr. Van Woogelum said. "Let me help you."

Hearing the gentle voice, Nicholas could not help asking the question that he would not want to ask his father.

"Mr. Van Woogelum, what is a yard arm?"

"On a ship, my boy?" The man pulled out his handkerchief and poured water onto it.

"I think so," Nicholas said. "He just said, 'I will ask Captain Parker to make room for you on his yard arm.' "

Mr. Van Woogelum placed a big hand on the back of Nicholas' head and swabbed his forehead. He rubbed a spot on Nicholas' cheek. He rinsed the handkerchief, and then looked Nicholas in the eye.

"Who said that?"

Nicholas looked at the cobblestones.

Seeing that Nicholas was not likely to answer, Mr. Van Woogelum answered.

"The yard is the wooden piece that crosses the mast of a ship and holds the sail," he said. "See, yonder? The cross pieces on the masts. I believe the arm is the end of the yard. Sometimes murderers or mutineers are hanged on the yard arm. But surely you have not gotten yourself into trouble with Captain Parker, my boy?"

"No," Nicholas said. He touched his forehead. "Thank you, Mr. Van Woogelum."

When Daniel showed up, he was less gracious.

"Sending me off with no money," he snapped. "Why didn't you hide? I'm going to my ship. Might see you at Christmas time."

Nicholas used his fingers to comb his hair down over his forehead. Perhaps he could hide the cut. Father and Lambert returned, but they were so busy talking that they did not notice Nicholas' injury. For once, Nicholas was glad to be ignored. They climbed onto the ferry and headed home.

"We should receive a charter from Queen Anne for the church before too long," Father said.

The committee Father was part of had helped bring the Church of England to Staten Island. They had decided to call it the Church of St. Andrew, but they needed official recognition from the English government to be part of the Church of England.

At home around the supper table, the September sunset filtered in through the open top of the Dutch door and the lead-lined windows, but the heavy ceiling beams and the plastered walls of the kitchen were already shadowed. A candle burned in the middle of the table casting flashes of light across the faces of the Garrison family.

But even in the shadows Mother noticed the cut. "Nicholas, what did you do to your forehead?" she asked.

Nicholas concentrated on scraping his wooden spoon across his bowl. "I was running and hit a tree limb."

The red fire in the brick oven glowed behind Mother's head. The firelight lined her high cheek bones and the wisps of hair escaping from her white cap. Nicholas could not see her eyes.

Nicholas glanced at the others to see if they were watching him.

Nine-year-old Isaac and seven-year-old Jacob on the wooden bench beside him stared at the cut on Nicholas' forehead. Elizabeth was four now, and she and Nicholas were still great friends. Her big eyes were full of sympathy.

At the fire, Mary stopped stoking the coals in the beehive-shaped oven. She let her red poker die down to nothing in the air. She continued to face the oven, but Nicholas knew she would tend to his cut later.

"Perhaps if you start watching where you are going you will be able to avoid danger," Father said sharply.

Nicholas felt his stomach twist. His relief that his parents believed his story vanished at the fresh reminder of his father's disapproval.

I won't think about it. I will not think about it. I will not, Nicholas told himself. *I will go to sea as soon as I am able and I will show Father that I can be a man on the water.*

5

The Snowy Night

December 1712

"Why don't we make some taffy tonight, Mary?" Nicholas heard Mother say. "Bring your family over. It is almost Christmas!"

Nicholas and Isaac and Jacob had walked through fresh snow on the way home from school. As they fed the cows and horses, more snow fell. They had just eaten supper, and now the wind whistled around the house, driving the snow before it. It was wonderful to live in a snug stone house. Nicholas thought of Daniel. Was he warm and dry, far out on the water?

Everyone around the table brightened at the mention of taffy and Mary's family. Life had lost some sparkle with Lambert married and Daniel gone to sea. Daniel had said he might be back for Christmas, but there had been no sign of him yet.

But the prospect of Pine and Mary and Jack and Sarah coming for the evening was delightful. Mary and her family were almost part of the Garrison family. They ate, played, and laughed together, not just at Christmas time but throughout the year.

Mary had just hung a long wooden spoon on a hook by the fireplace. As she considered Mother's invitation, she cocked her head and rolled her eyes. "Well, if I don't think Pine is over home snoring already," she said, "but I'll go see what that man is up to."

Mary wrapped herself in her thick shawl and put on her boots. Within minutes, the children heard the sound of her returning, and the voices of Pine, Sarah, and Jack. The Garrison children all cheered.

"You do sound like a pack of wolves," Mother said. But she was smiling.

Everyone scurried to arrange the kitchen for a party. Father put more wood on the fire. "Let's bring feather ticks from upstairs—to sit on!" Nicholas suggested to the other boys.

"Yes!" shouted Isaac and Jacob.

They came bumbling back down from the cold loft, lugging their bulky feather beds. Mother raised her eyebrows but let it pass. *She must be feeling happier than usual tonight*, Nicholas decided.

Father poured cold cider into a kettle. The open hearth now had three kettles hanging from the iron bar, one each for taffy, popcorn, and hot cider. Pine stirred his popcorn with a big spoon and Father stirred his apple cider with another big spoon—and both of them got in Mary's way.

"If there isn't a man on every stone of this hearth," Mary fussed.

"Man the mizzen kettle, Captain Lambert!" Pine shouted in reply.

Father was not a captain. That was just Pine's way of playing with words. Sometimes Nicholas almost forgot that Father's real first name was Lambert. To Nicholas he was always Father.

Pine and Father talked about the war in Europe. England had been fighting, afraid that France and Spain would join forces because the king of Spain had died without an heir and left the throne to a Frenchman.

"Reminds me of the Dutch and English passing this country back and forth," Father said with a shake of his head and swirl of the spoon in the cider. "I've always wished I could have that calf back. Used to eat carrots out of my hand."

There was a plopping noise and the fire in the hearth sizzled. A ball of snow had fallen in through the narrow opening of the chimney. Dutch chimneys had no covers.

"Aloft there!" Pine hollered into the chimney. "Set the topgallant sail! Sorry to interrupt your story, Cap'n. Back to the calf you lost to the Dutch."

Father had been only four years old when the English took the colony of New Netherland from the Dutch in 1664, but nine years later the Dutch had tried to take it back from the English. On a hot August day, fifteen Dutch ships landed on Staten Island. After eating mostly sea biscuit on the long voyage, the Dutch were hungry. They helped themselves to the settlers' cows and sheep so they could have fresh meat. They took the calf Father had been raising and slaughtered it for the evening meal. Then they went on to Manhattan and claimed the territory for the Dutch, calling it New Orange this time.

"The governor was out of town, and it took over a year for them to decide that the territory still belonged to the English," Father said. "Mary, do we have any cinnamon? I think a little cinnamon might be good in this hot cider."

"Why, Lambert Garrison, since you just brought some yourself from Manhattan, of course you know we have cinnamon!" Mary cried, whisking the paper bag of cinnamon out of the cupboard.

Nicholas heard the wooden doors of the *kast* opening in the next room. The *kast*, a fixture in many Dutch homes, was a tall and deep wooden cupboard with two upper doors, two lower doors, and two shallow drawers at the bottom. Mother kept all kinds of things in her *kast:* linens and lace her mother had made, wooden shoes she had painted red and yellow and worn as a teenager, pencils and drawing paper, and a few small jars of paint.

"Nicholas," Mother called.

Nicholas ran to the next room, Elizabeth following. The children were not allowed to open the *kast,* so Nicholas always enjoyed helping Mother get things out of it. Beside the cupboard, Mother's drawing of the sun setting over Manhattan hung on the wall. Mother posted it in the bedroom, where visitors were less likely to see it. Mother had always said it was a poor drawing. People made good drawings and paintings in Europe, but not in America.

"Here is the checker board," Mother said. "You take it, Nicholas. I will find the checkers."

Mother reached into the drawer, beside the pair of wooden shoes. She lifted a small bag of checkers that clacked against each other. At that moment Nicholas spied the familiar slate, partially exposed to reveal the corner with the three butterflies. He had not seen the slate since he had given it to Mother four years before.

Mother shut the wooden door, and Nicholas followed her to the next room. The little boys cheered and reached for the checker board.

"Take turns," Mother said. "Jack and Nicholas can play first because they are the oldest."

"I am pining for a popcorn battle," Nicholas heard someone say. A kernel of popcorn whizzed past his face.

"You missed me!" Nicholas yelled, knowing Pine was trying to hit him in the nose. That was their game.

Nicholas and Jack, each resting on a feather tick, set the board between them on the floor. The two younger boys crowded in to watch. Nicholas brought a candle in a tin holder and set it beside the board since the spectators blocked the fire light.

It was late when the taffy was gone and the cider mugs were empty and all the popcorn had been picked up off the floor. Isaac and Jacob had taken their feather ticks upstairs. Pine and Mary had just gone home after Nicholas beat Pine 5–3 in a popcorn fight. The checkers game was a different matter, however. Nicholas picked up the checkers slowly. He was still puzzling over the pattern on the board and what he could have done to keep Pine from beating him.

"All right, my son," Mother said. "It's time for you to go up to bed. Say your psalm to me as you pick up the checkers."

" 'If I take the wings of the morning, and dwell in the uttermost part of the sea, even there shall thy hand lead me and thy right hand shall hold me,' " Nicholas quoted from Psalm 139. " 'If I say, surely the darkness shall cover me, even the night shall be light about me. Yea, the darkness hideth not from thee, but the night shineth as the day. The darkness and the light are both alike to thee.' "

Nicholas tried not to think about the warehouse. *Could God have seen me breaking into the building and taking the money? Because I would have taken it, if I had not been caught.* Nicholas handed the checker board and the bag of checkers to his mother.

"God has given you a bright mind, Nicholas," his mother said softly. "I want you to grow up to be an honest and God-fearing man."

Nicholas didn't answer. How could his mother know so much when no one had told her?

"Good night, Nicholas."

"Good night, Mother." Nicholas trudged up the stairs to the loft. He stepped around his brothers, who were already fast asleep. As he lowered himself to his feather tick, Nicholas thought once more of the slate he had seen in the drawer. *I will take Seger's slate to sea with me when I go,* he told himself.

6

The Last Question

Spring 1713

"Boys, wake up!" Father said. "I want you to go down to Lambert's house. Tell him Mother is sick."

Nicholas rolled on the feather tick. He forced himself to focus on his father's voice at the foot of the stairs.

"Yes, Father," he called.

Isaac and Jacob woke sleepily. They were getting big, now ten and eight years old. Daniel was home from sea for a visit and was sleeping in the garret as well. Winter was barely over, so the boys still slept on feathers. They would trade them for straw in the warmer months when the garret grew stuffy and hot.

It was Sunday. Rain was plopping on the wooden shingles just above their heads. Normally, the boys were expected to go to the St. Andrew church with their parents and occupy themselves with quiet activities the remainder of the day. Nicholas felt badly that his mother was sick, but he was glad to have a chance to do something exciting on a Sunday. Mother had been sick five years before, but in the morning she was fine and baby Elizabeth had arrived. Maybe there would be another baby when they came home this evening. Maybe his mother would be smiling as she had when Elizabeth was born.

He folded his blanket and headed down the stairs. He was nearly to the bottom when he heard coughing from the room where Mother slept. Nicholas felt his stomach tighten, almost like it had when he saw the mat hook in the pirate's hand. The coughing and wheezing had an odd quality of authority, as if they were in charge of Mother's body and there was nothing she could do to stop them.

Catharine, now married, had come home to help out. She sat sleepily in Mother's rocking chair. A finger over her lips, she looked sternly at the four boys. Five-year-old Elizabeth sat beside Catharine, sleepy and scared, her small hands clutching her blanket. Nicholas saw the track of a tear on her cheek.

Over the fire, Mary's largest kettle steamed, hanging from its iron hook. He could smell no meat or porridge, so it must be full of water. Mary was probably bustling about in Mother's bedroom, making her comfortable.

"Take your coats and something to eat," was all Father said to the boys. Nicholas understood that they were expected to keep to themselves the rest of the day. "But stay quiet. No climbing trees, Nicholas," he added with a stern look.

It was Sunday, after all. His father, as sheriff and county judge, had already punished people for working on the Sabbath day. Just the spring before, Father had reported that three cases of Sabbath-breaking had been presented in one court session. Two men were accused of making cider on the Sabbath, one had allowed his slave to carry iron to the blacksmith, and a third had gotten drunk on the Sabbath and made a spectacle of himself. All were punished with fines.

Quietly, Nicholas lifted a pewter kitchen knife and cut into the apple pie that Catharine had made the day before. He was careful to avoid hitting the white and blue Delft china platter. The pie was a delightful treat made with white sugar and cinnamon from Manhattan and wrinkled apples from the crop last fall. In Catharine's pie, the old apples had come back to life. He took a generous section to share with his brothers for lunch. They each took a handful of venison jerky and several pieces of bread. Daniel, Jacob and Isaac stepped out the front door.

Nicholas slipped back to the table and broke off a piece of the pie. Stepping over to Elizabeth, he offered the treat to her. She took a bite and her eyes brightened. Nicholas still told Elizabeth things he would tell no one else, just as he had whispered stories into her soft baby hair.

Nicholas slipped away, ignoring Catharine's frown. He ran out the door after the others, then slowed his pace as he remembered that it was the Sabbath. Jonah rushed up, turning in delighted circles.

Pine's head appeared through the upper half of his front door. "How is your mother this morning, me fine young lads?" he asked. "This old one-armed man has been pining for a little news."

Mother had been sick for a few weeks. It started with an occasional harmless cough. Then one afternoon, her cheeks had been flushed with fever and she took to her bed. Yesterday, Father fetched the doctor, who immediately tipped a few drops of medicine onto her cracked and swollen lips.

"Water," he had growled at Mary. "You need to give her all the water she'll take. Can't you see she's drying out?"

"As if I haven't been begging and pleading with her to drink some water or some soup!" Mary wailed when the doctor left, "and putting a wet washcloth in her mouth for some little wetness."

"Be quiet, Mary," Father had snapped.

The eyes of the boys had widened; Father *never* scolded Mary. It was far more common to have Mary scolding Father, although always in jest.

"And do you think I let my Susannah marry someone only to watch him bring his muddy boots right into the kitchen?" she would say, waving the wood-shaving broom at him.

If Father was snapping at Mary, he was either angry or very worried about Mother. But Father had never been angry at Mary.

Daniel, Nicholas, Isaac, and Jacob stared back at Pine's face in the doorway.

"Father told us to go tell Lambert that Mother is sick," Nicholas said.

"Ah." Pine frowned.

Jack appeared beside his father, and the boys invited him to join their morning walk. They took the road that skirted Iron Hill and kept to the lower, swampy ground close to the Fresh Kills. Jonah darted in and out of the underbrush, and came to Nicholas with a long, thin object in his mouth.

"Jonah!" Nicholas scolded. "That's an eel basket! Go put that back so the trappers can get their eels."

Jonah just wagged his tail, pleased with his find. Nicholas took a detour into the woods to return the trap.

At Lambert and Elizabeth's house, the boys pounded on the heavy door.

"Who's there?" came their oldest brother's voice.

Lambert let them in and added wood to the fire. He arranged chairs close to the blaze and draped the coats over them to dry. Elizabeth cut pieces of bread and cheese for them all.

"Father sent us to tell you that Mother is sick," Daniel said.

Lambert chewed thoughtfully. "We will come visit after church," he said. Lambert and Elizabeth attended the Dutch Reformed Church.

Leaving their brother's house, the boys passed the clapboard house that had been a school house until 1701. Their older brothers and sisters had gone to school there. The school room had been upstairs and the bottom floor had been used for a church. Farther up the road, the boys could see the steeple of the St. Andrew church. They turned the other direction, toward the ocean.

"It's only a couple of miles," Daniel said. "Let's go to the sea. Maybe catch something. I have some fishing line in my pocket."

Nicholas knew he should object. Their father would not approve of fishing, nor of walking all the way to the ocean on a Sunday. But he did not want to go to the Fresh Kills in the rain—it would bring back memories he was trying hard to forget. So Nicholas did not object to going to the ocean, and neither did the younger boys. They spent the day fishing from the sand of the Great Kills beach. As the tide came in around their feet, they backed up into the marsh grasses.

They arrived home at dusk. They had fed several fish to Jonah, and thrown the remainder of their catch back into the sea.

Their father met them at the door.

"Go see your mother," he said.

What is happening? Nicholas wondered. *Why is Father so stern and quiet?*

Daniel, Isaac, and Jacob went immediately. Nicholas looked down at his feet, stalling for time. His feet were muddy.

Nicholas went to the well that Father had dug. He drew water, scraped mud from his feet, and tried to wash them. He straightened and looked at the familiar homestead around him. Everything seemed to be weeping today. The barn dripped with water, and the animals huddled inside.

Nicholas thought of how Father had first dug a room under the house for the animals before he could build the barn. The horse and cow and a few sheep and pigs had crowded into that basement for warmth on winter nights. Mother had grown up in a rich house in Manhattan. Had she fretted about the animal smell in the house?

Today, water dripped over each brown, gray, and black field stone of the house. It caught in the lime mortar made from oyster shells from the Fresh Kills. When the sun was shining, the two Dutch chimneys, wide at the bottom and narrow at the top, radiated orange light. But now the yellow Holland bricks were a mournful brown color, rising above sopping wood shingles. The window glass from Europe reflected the gloomy gray sky, and the open wooden shutters did not let much light in today. The rounded half circle bumping out of the stone wall showed where Father had built the huge Dutch oven, but the oven was not in use lately because Mary was busy caring for Mother.

Nicholas stepped inside. The kitchen was dusky and smelled of herbs in Mary's tea. It was so dark he could barely see the ceiling beams. He washed his hands in the basin on the wooden table inside the door. He washed each finger separately, as if stalling would keep anything bad from happening.

When his brothers came out of the other room, sober-faced, Nicholas walked in.

Nicholas had not seen his mother for a week, and the change in her appearance shocked him. Nausea rose inside his stomach. Mother's eyes were sunken in her white face. Her golden hair lay against the pillow, damp and forgotten. Mary, at the head of the bed, bathed Mother's forehead with a cloth.

She's dying, Nicholas thought. *That's why Father is so sad. But it can't be true. It can't be true. We can't lose someone else!*

He had known for days that something was wrong. But he had convinced himself that surely it was something simple, something that could be fixed by a doctor or by Mary.

Now, he knew he was mistaken.

"Mother," he whispered.

"Put your hand in hers, Nicholas," Mary said.

"Seger," Mother said, looking at the ceiling.

Nicholas jumped as if Mother had slapped him.

"No, Mother, it's me! Nicholas!"

"Ah, I think she knows you," Mary said. "She keeps telling me she sees Seger."

"Nicholas," Mother said. "Are you going . . ." She stopped to catch rapid raspy breaths every few words, but she seemed determined to ask her question. ". . . to be like Daniel? The sea has not been good . . . for his soul."

She paused again. A strange brightness glowed from her eyes, but it was not the energy of good health. "Will you follow him, Nicholas?"

Mother's hand tightened around his wrist.

Nicholas wanted to tell his mother that he would never go to sea like Daniel had, but he could not. Instead, he found himself quoting Isaiah 53, the chapter his mother had taught him just before Christmas.

" 'Surely, he hath born our griefs,' " Nicholas said, "and carried our sorrows.' "

He didn't know if he should finish the entire chapter, but Mother seemed to be listening. He kept going.

" 'He was wounded for our transgressions . . . and with his stripes we are healed.' "

When he said the last words, Mary's eyes filled with tears.

Mother squeezed his hand. "I love you, Nicholas."

A few days later, Mother's eyes closed for the last time.

7

The Cherry Pie

The Garrison family sat at the supper table in the evening light, but nothing was right.

Nicholas had thought that perhaps when Mother's funeral was over and the relatives went home, the house would feel more normal again.

It did not. The empty chair had been taken from the table but that kept no one from feeling its absence. Mary, who had cooked the beans and cornbread for supper, was preparing to go to her own house. But even Mary was not right. She was quiet, and twice that evening Nicholas had seen her wipe her eyes on her apron.

Then, Father pushed back his chair, and the world shuddered again.

"Mary," he said, without looking at her. "I don't want you to leave, but I know you came with my wife. I'll not keep you from going elsewhere if that is your wish."

Nicholas felt his muscles go rigid with terror. Would they lose yet another person? Elizabeth gave a sharp cry and flung herself into Mary's arms. Isaac and Jacob stiffened beside him. Only Daniel, who would be leaving soon anyway, remained unmoved. Nicholas felt that he was suffocating with the horror of suspense.

"Now, Lambert, don't be talking like a crazy man!" Mary said. "If you think I'm gonna go off and leave my Susannah's family to do their own cooking and laundry at such a time as when she barely been put in the ground—." Mary broke into wailing, and covered her entire face with her apron, until she could gain control. "All I say is, your head must be touched with the grief. If you ever decides to get yourself another woman, then we'll talk, but there's not one bone in my body, not one bone in my *body*, Lambert Garrison, what thinks about leaving my dear Elizabeth and her big brothers in such a time as this!"

The relief of the big brothers was tempered slightly by the idea of their father "getting another woman." But enough to know that Mary was staying.

"All right, Mary," Father said, and he too sighed as if a heavy load had fallen from his shoulders. "Thank you."

Daniel went back to sea a few weeks after Mother died. He had achieved the role of midshipman, and he was full of confidence and pride as he buttoned his white vest and trousers.

Father, Pine, and the boys took Daniel and his sea chest to the ferry by horse and wagon. They lurched down the path to the water's edge.

"We'll wait to see you off," Father said.

They sat on the wagon, waiting for the ferry and watching the Narrows. A number of small vessels moved on its surface. A ship was coming in from the ocean.

"Did you boys know we lived on Long Island for a few years?" Father asked.

"What's Long Island?" Jacob asked.

"That land across the water," Nicholas whispered, pointing. He whispered because Jacob was interrupting Father and Nicholas wanted to hear the story. Sometimes Father went for days without talking to the boys.

Lambert Jr. had been a toddler when riots broke out in Staten Island. The Governor of New York was Catholic, and the settlers were afraid he wanted to push his religion on the Protestants. They may have been right, since much blood had been shed in Europe in religious battles. Since Governor Dongan lived on Staten Island, some of the residents hid in the woods or fled.

To be safe from the riots, Father took his family across the Narrows and lived on the property Mother had inherited from her father, Captain Stillwell. When Governor Dongan finally moved away, Father moved his family back to Staten Island. By the time Daniel was born in 1696, the family had settled on forty-four acres of land by the system of creeks called the Fresh Kills.

Father's voice broke several times as he told the story. Nicholas felt his eyes fill with tears.

Mother could not be dead! They needed her so much!

Father had just finished the story when Darby Doyle returned with the ferry. The boys helped Daniel carry his sea chest from the wagon to the ferry. He was allowed space for a sea chest, now that he was an officer. As the ferry pulled away, Daniel waved his handkerchief. They watched him grow smaller and smaller as the ferry caught the wind and sped across the harbor to Manhattan. Soon, he was no bigger than one of the screeching gulls.

Father's eyes followed his son until he could no longer be seen. He seemed to be surveying sorrowful things hidden from Nicholas' sight. Then he turned to the boys.

"Let's go," he said.

It was only midmorning, but Father's voice sounded like he was ready to go to bed after a hard day's work.

Nicholas had thought today might be a good time to tell his father how much he wanted to go to sea too, but he simply could not get up the courage. His father had never liked sea travel. He had been on the sea only twice, going to the Netherlands to university and returning to Staten Island. He had been seasick for most of both voyages, and he had witnessed someone die at sea.

If Father had been a sailor, Nicholas thought, *he would understand how much I want to go to sea.*

Now, with his father grieving over Mother and Daniel, how would Nicholas ever ask? Maybe it would be easier to do what Daniel had done the first time and simply disappear.

Nicholas thought of Mother's last words to him. Mother did not want him to go.

It was time for the noon meal when Father and the boys arrived home.

"If it's not fresh fish from Catharine's man!" Mary said, waving a grease-coated spoon. The fish sizzled in the three-legged iron griddle that stood directly over the fire. "And Elizabeth picked a summer cabbage which we almost have whisked into a slaw."

"No rush, Mary," Father said, washing his hands in the basin inside the door and drying them on a sack towel. "Isaac, when we've all washed up, empty this basin and get fresh water for the afternoon."

Father did his best to think of the small things Mother had always done that no one had noticed. Mary tried too. But no one could take Mother's place.

As soon as the fish was fried, the family sat around the heavy oak table. Father said a prayer and began to serve the food. He poured himself a large glass of beer from a pitcher, and smaller portions for Nicholas, Isaac, and Jacob. Because the water was often contaminated, the settlers often drank beer instead.

Mary heaped huge portions of cabbage slaw and boiled potatoes onto the plates after Father dished out the fish, still almost sizzling in their coats of flour and oil. Nicholas sighed and dug into the fish, which fell into flakes under his fork. He burned his mouth on the first bite, so he turned to his piece of thickly-buttered bread. He took a large, satisfying bite.

"I do believe I hear footsteps," Mary said as Jonah began to bark. She went to the window and peered through the leaded glass. "I believe it's Mr. Van Woogelum's little Christina."

"Run to meet her, Nicholas," Father said. "See what she wants."

Nicholas was not accustomed to speaking with young ladies, but Christina was only a little older than Elizabeth, and the family lived close by. It was Christina's father who had spoken with Nicholas on that fateful day when he had broken into the warehouse.

Nicholas burst out the door, and hurried around the house to where Christina was walking carefully through the tufts of summer grass, closely cropped by the Garrison livestock. Nicholas spotted Christina's brother on a horse out on the cart path and gave him a hearty wave.

"My mother sent this for your family," little Christina said, handing over a paper parcel.

Nicholas knew that Elizabeth and Christina had played together, before Mother died. Mother had let them draw with her pencils. Christina looked like Elizabeth, too, with golden curls and blue eyes.

"Mother said to give it to you because you don't have a mother anymore," Christina added softly, looking up at Nicholas with big eyes.

"Thank you," Nicholas said. "You can come inside the house."

"I need to go with my brother," the little girl said. "My father is going to the mill tomorrow. If one of you is going you can return the dish."

Mary placed the parcel on the table and unwrapped the paper. It was a cherry pie, covered with a lattice-work crust. Everyone inhaled with anticipation. Mary went to the cupboard to get a knife.

"That Van Woogelum family," Mary said fervently. "If they isn't about the nicest people on this side the Atlantic."

8

The News at the Mill

If Mary had not run out of flour the next day, Nicholas would not have gone to the mill. He would not have heard the latest gossip from Manhattan. Father sent Nicholas on horseback with one bag of wheat. Mary sent the empty pie pan as Christina Van Woogelum had suggested.

Nicholas set out up Forest Hill Road. He could not see much due to the thick undergrowth and the leafy branches of late summer. The trees had been trimmed to make these hill roads passable, but he still had to duck his head at times. Jonah trailed along, darting from one side of the woods to another.

They descended the other side of the hill, and Nicholas changed his posture to keep from sliding off his horse. Finally, they reached the St. Andrew church on the beautiful green slope at the side of Iron Hill. The horse swung onto the wider, more level path. On the hillside a few stones marked the graves of those who had died in the four years since the building of the church had begun. Nicholas turned his horse onto the path along the creek and soon approached the mill.

"Mr. Van Woogelum!" he exclaimed in surprise.

He leapt off his horse, cheeks burning as he realized that he had interrupted Mr. Van Woogelum as he talked to the miller. He tied his mount loosely to the hitching post beside Mr. Van Woogelum's wagon and hoisted the sack of wheat over his shoulder.

"Nicholas," Mr. Van Woogelum said, turning toward him. "Lambert Garrison's son," he added to the miller.

"Aye, yes," said the miller, pleasantly, and Nicholas sighed with relief that they were not holding his interruption against him. "Just one sack today?"

"Yes," Nicholas said to the miller. "And a dish for you, sir." He handed the empty pie pan to Mr. Van Woogelum.

They walked into the dim interior of a clapboard shed. It smelled of fresh pine boards and newly ground corn and wheat. The miller hurried to a side door, and Nicholas heard the screeching of a sluice gate being opened and then the groaning and squeaking of the water wheel as it turned in the stream. The miller scrambled up a stone step and held the sack of wheat high above the hopper as the heavy millstone began to turn. The kernels rained into the hopper and through the hole in the center of the stone. The miller placed Nicholas' empty bag at the end of a wooden trough under the stones, and soon the flour began to trickle into the sack.

For the rest of his life, whenever he heard a grist mill or smelled freshly crushed wheat, Nicholas recalled the miller's next words to Mr. Van Woogelum.

"Did you hear that Captain Parker is back on Manhattan rounding up men for another voyage?"

The squeaking and grinding and dripping sounds faded into the background. Nicholas faintly heard the men talk on about the latest news and the peace treaty being worked out in Europe. The war had been going on since Nicholas was born.

But Nicholas wasn't thinking about a peace treaty. He was back with Lambert on the *Ella*. He was back under the masts that reached for the clouds. He was back in a world of ropes and ladders and pulleys and shouted orders and song. He was back with Captain Parker in his trim blue and gold suit, captain of one of the biggest merchant ships on the seas.

"It seems like the English are here to stay, and that's fine with me—as long as they don't force their beliefs on us. They say Captain Parker came straight from England this time and brought a charter from Queen Anne for the new Church of St. Andrew. Fancy big piece of parchment with the names of all the men who helped to get it around, including Nicholas' father, Lambert Garrison."

The miller gestured toward the church, which stood behind the mill. He looked at Nicholas, who smiled and nodded to show he was listening and had heard his father's name.

The church was the one topic on which his father and Mr. Van Woogelum disagreed. Lambert supported the Church of England and Mr. Van Woogelum was a staunch supporter of the Dutch Reformed Church. To Nicholas, the churches seemed similar, other than the language used to preach the sermon.

The miller handed Nicholas his sack of flour. Nicholas got the half-penny from the leather purse where he had put the money from Father and then turned to go, anxious to get back on his horse and into the woods where he could think.

Elizabeth was standing at the kitchen door when Nicholas reached home. Mary had opened the upper half of the door, and Elizabeth was tall enough now to see over the lower half.

It hurt to think how much Elizabeth must miss Mother. Elizabeth had been the baby longer than any of the others, so she had spent more time with Mother. They had cuddled together on the rocking chair on cold mornings, wrapped in the warm wool blanket Mother had knitted. Even though Elizabeth was only five years old, Mother had taught her letters and allowed her to use her drawing pencils.

"Ah, yes," Mary had said when Nicholas had mentioned Elizabeth several weeks earlier. Mary's hands were full of bread dough and Elizabeth was outside scattering scraps for the chickens. "She misses your mama something dreadful. Does she know how to tell us? Oh no, she do not. But when she complains that it's too hot or too cold or her shoes are too tight, that's when she's missing her mama. But here's the thing, Nicholas, my boy. Little children can move on faster. Oh yes they can. Old people like me . . ." here Mary dissolved into tears and ended in a wail. "The world ain't never gonna be right without your beautiful mother in it! It ain't never gonna be right, Nicholas!"

She paused to sob some more and wipe her eyes on her sleeve.

"I'm sorry, my dear boy, I shouldn't cry these tears in front of you. Oh no, I should not. But even you, my dear, even you will be able to live again. Oh, you'll never forget your mama, don't get me wrong. But you will find a way to live, much quicker than old Mary. So don't feel too badly for Elizabeth. She has you and me and her father, and she'll be all right. Susannah and Catharine live close by, and Lambert, and soon . . . Soon Elizabeth will be the happiest little auntie that ever walked on this island."

Mary's words had made Nicholas feel better at the time.

Now, arriving home from the mill, certain he would soon go to sea, Nicholas was not so sure. Elizabeth would miss him too!

That night after supper, Isaac and Jacob and Elizabeth ran outside to play in the sunset. Nicholas might have gone too, but his father was still sitting at the kitchen table, mug in hand. Mary had gone to her own house.

Nicholas got up as if to go outside. He walked to the door and looked out the top half, almost hoping for an interruption so he could not talk to his father. The brilliant red of a stunning sunset was leaking onto the purple clouds clustered across the blue-green sky. Nicholas had always loved the sky.

Are you going to be like Daniel? Nicholas could almost hear his mother's voice from the bedroom where she had breathed her last, just a few yards from where he stood.

Mother had not wanted him to go to sea. He should respect her wishes and stay home.

"Father." He turned with determination. "I want to ask you something."

His father looked up at him. His eyes measured Nicholas as if he were estimating the hairs on his head.

Nicholas grabbed for a wooden spoon drying on the wash cart by the door. He clutched it with both hands, as if it would help him form the right words.

"Captain Parker is on Manhattan looking for men for his next voyage. May I go?"

Father looked down into the depths of his mug, and studied its inside for a long time. Nicholas could not bring himself to move. Finally, Father took a drink.

"I was wondering when you would ask," he said.

9

The Cook's Hand

1713

Everyone was moving, except Nicholas.

On the main deck of the *Ella*, sailors pulled together on the thick ropes that lifted the yards. High on each of the three masts, top men stood on ropes dangling from the yards and let out the topsails. Men clambered up and down the black rope ladders sewn together into a webbing, their white shirts billowing in the breeze. The mates, in smart white vests, shouted orders from the deck, frustration edging their voices when a new hand made a mistake.

Nicholas stood to the side, where he had been told to observe. Would he ever get to climb those ropes? To get to the standing rigging, a sailor must climb the rope ladders that hung over the water, but Nicholas wanted to try it. He wanted to feel the black, tar-smeared rope beneath his hands, and see how quickly he could climb.

"Braces, men!" shouted an officer. The huge sail on the bottom of the center mast turned and filled with wind. Nicholas realized they were moving, and he turned his eyes to the dock, where just yesterday Father, Isaac, Jacob, Elizabeth, Pine, Mary, and Jonah had said their goodbyes.

"You, boy! Get your eyes off the shore and watch the men!" the first mate snapped.

Nicholas hurriedly took his eyes off the docks and warehouses of Manhattan, and studied the scene before him. He wanted to be a seaman, but at twelve years old, he was not strong enough to take on the heavy labor of the men before the mast.[1] He had signed on with the merchant ship as a cabin boy. Captain Parker had two cabin boys already. However, he was short on seamen, and one of the boys was now fifteen years old; as soon as Nicholas was trained, the fifteen-year-old would begin as a seaman. For now, Nicholas' job was to watch everything that went on as the ship moved away from port.

Captain Parker stood on the quarterdeck near the stern, tall and confident, his dark hair rippling in the breeze. He wore a blue coat with gold buttons. Over his clean-shaven face, the captain wore a matching blue tricorn with gold trim, one corner above his brow flaring to two corners at the back of his head. He wore a red handkerchief around his neck. Nicholas still remembered it from their first meeting.

Nearby, the helmsman stood at the wheel, turning its spokes with a practiced hand. The *Ella* swung away from the dock, its bow headed to the Narrows between Long Island and Staten Island and then to the sea. A pilot from Sandy Hook, the last piece of land before the ocean, stood beside the helmsman and told him where to go. They would drop the pilot off on Sandy Hook, where he would wait to guide the next ship in.

Nicholas didn't understand all the lingo the sailors used. He did know that the bow was the front, the stern was the back, starboard was the right side, and the left side was called either port or larboard, depending who was yelling orders.

"Stay out of trouble," Father had said gruffly when they parted on the pier. "Obey orders."

"When will you come back?" Elizabeth had asked. Her big blue eyes had filled with tears, which made Nicholas concentrate to keep back his own.

"Keep hold of both arms." Pine said.

This made everyone laugh, which was what Pine wanted.

"Now don't you forget to eat your vegetables," Mary instructed loudly, then burst into tears, right there on the dock. "Pine says—Pine says—Pine says that people—"

She wiped her entire face with her apron, before her dark eyes reappeared and looked sternly at Nicholas. "Pine do say that sailors who eat fruits and vegetables be getting over their little illnesses," she finally managed. "But here, put this in your bag yet. And be a good boy and say your prayers and your Scriptures like your dear mother taught you."

Mary opened the bag over Nicholas' shoulder and stuffed something in, wrapped in paper. The packet made a bulge, since the bag was already full with the few

---

[1] "Men before the mast" refers to ordinary seamen, rather than officers.

possessions that Nicholas could take with him on the ship. Nicholas smelled something that made him think of sweet bread and Christmastime.

Nicholas felt the hard edge of Seger's slate poking his shoulder. He had slipped into the *kast* one day and taken it from the drawer.

On the dock, Nicholas had squatted down to run his hands through Jonah's white and brown curls. The dog licked his face in delight, and Nicholas felt the ache to take him along. He knew his family couldn't come, but there would be animals on the ship; couldn't Jonah go? But Jonah was a big dog, and Nicholas knew it was better this way.

"I'll watch Jonah," Isaac promised.

"Here," said Elizabeth. "I made this for you!"

As she handed him a folded paper, Nicholas heard the metallic ringing of the ship's bell and he knew it was time to go.

"Thank you, Elizabeth!" He kissed her, then turned and headed up the gangway.

He pushed away his tears. He would prove himself here on the *Ella* and make his father proud. He had fallen asleep the night before dreaming of his father saying, "Good job, Nicholas."

Now, standing on the deck and watching the men, his stomach growled. He thought of the treat Mary had put in his bag. He would eat it soon.

"Nicholas!" called Gilbert, the cabin boy who would train him. "Captain wants us to help get the water casks ready. We'll stop at the Watering Place along Staten Island for fresh water. We will fill containers from the hold and from the cook's galley."

Nicholas followed Gilbert's flying white form. All the boys wore white shirts made of coarse, loosely-woven cloth. Each of them had received a white linen handkerchief to wear around his neck. Gilbert had tied his handkerchief around his head.

They went through the hatch, down a ladder, between the sailors' bunks, through another hatch, and down another ladder. They scrambled past boxes of furs, through another hatch to the orlop deck. Gilbert showed Nicholas the hatch leading to the hold at the very bottom of the ship. The pumps were down there, ready to be put into action if the carefully caulked planks of the hull sprang a leak. The heavy water barrels would be lowered into the hold, where they would help steady the ship, Gilbert explained.

"We'll pass empty casks up the fore hatch to the deck," Gilbert said. "The full ones will come down the main hatch."

"Fore" must mean the front of the ship, and "main" the middle, Nicholas thought.

"Goes with the masts," Gilbert said, seeing Nicholas' confused expression. "The foremast is the front one closest to the bow. The mainmast is the tallest one in the middle, and the mizzen mast is back by the captain's quarters. That spar pointing out the front of the boat with the jib sails attached? That's called the bowsprit."

Nicholas felt dizzy from the tour and all the new information. The slight rolling and swelling motion fogged his brain. He was glad when the second mate barked at them.

"Up to the cook's galley, boys. Get those buckets and casks out first."

"Aye, aye, sir!" Gilbert said, and they scrambled up the ladder.

"Always say 'aye, aye, sir' when receiving an order," Gilbert hissed to Nicholas. "If you don't, you'll find yourself in trouble sometime. Are you feeling fine so far?"

"Yes, just a little stuffy and hungry," Nicholas said. "But I have a pastry from home."

"I was sick as a dog my first three days!" Gilbert said. "But I hardly ever get sick anymore."

They hurried through the rows of bunks in the second deck to the galley astern.

"New cook," Gilbert said. "I'll go into the galley and hand the buckets out to you. I don't know this one, but most cooks don't like too many people in the galley."

Gilbert handed out the wooden buckets bound with metal bands, and Nicholas focused on running them up to the main deck. He tried to ignore the foggy feeling in his head. The fresh air on the main deck felt wonderful and he took a few deep breaths before plunging back down the ladder. This time he was able to do it without holding on. As he landed on the planks, he heard a high-pitched, tinny voice giving instructions to Gilbert.

Nicholas grabbed the buckets Gilbert had put outside the galley, and made another trip to the weather deck.

Gilbert handed him a huge copper kettle with an iron handle. Nicholas could see a shadowy reflection of himself in the bright sides of the kettle. Behind Gilbert, he saw the form of the cook, lifting another kettle from a hook on the galley ceiling. He saw the cook's right hand reach up to take the handle, and his left arm went around the bottom of the kettle. Nicholas saw the dark line of a scar disappearing around the curve of the kettle.

Nicholas forgot his threatening seasickness in a sudden new twist of his stomach. Why did this man's voice remind him of the pirate who owned the warehouse? The scar looked so familiar. Nicholas could not see the man's left hand, but it surely would be a normal hand with five fingers, he assured himself.

The cook turned toward Gilbert and Nicholas.

Nicholas saw the man's yellow teeth, and he saw his left hand. It was missing two fingers.

10

The Cat-o'-Nine-Tails

Nicholas stood along the portside bulwarks, watching the faint strip of shore-line disappear. He had learned the word *bulwarks* from Gilbert.

"The wall that keeps you from falling off the deck," Gilbert had laughed. "But different people use different words."

The *Ella* was three days out of New York, and Nicholas was beginning to feel more comfortable. He learned that by planting his feet wide apart like the others, he could stand on the deck without falling. His stomach had not quite adjusted to the motion of the waves, but it was feeling better than it had a few days before. Unlike several of the men on board, he had never been thoroughly seasick.

Nicholas knew the names of quite a few sailors and had observed the skilled men on board. The cook, though he scowled often and served crude words with his soup, had not seemed to recognize Nicholas. He had given no hint that he remembered the boy sprawling across his warehouse floor. Nicholas was not planning to remind him.

At the beginning of the voyage, the sail maker, the carpenter, and the surgeon on board usually had plenty of free time. As sails ripped and planks leaked and sailors fell ill, they all became busier. The first weeks were a good time to show Nicholas their trades. The sailmaker let Nicholas push one of the big needles through a scrap of canvas. The carpenter showed him the flat tool used to stuff oakum between the planks of the hull. The surgeon told stories of men who had died of scurvy, their bodies oozing blood.

"Eat your vegetables," the surgeon told Nicholas. "Seems to help."

The men before the mast helped Nicholas learn the techniques required of sailors. They taught him the names of the ropes. They quizzed him on the difference between a brace and a halyard. They told him to never grab the white running rigging for support, only the black standing rigging. They explained that the black ladder-like ropes were called shrouds by some sailors and ratlines by others.

"I guess they are called ratlines because the men look like rats when they climb," a sailor named Old Pete said. "You need to know both terms. If you don't, one day someone will yell the word you don't know and you'll be confused."

Nicholas looked longingly at the standing rigging leading to the upper sails. He was glad to know that those ropes were called shrouds or ratlines. But mostly he wanted to climb them.

"You'll be up there soon enough," Old Pete laughed. "Find your footing on the deck first."

Pete was an able seaman from Whitby, England, who had been at sea for many years. His kind eyes and patient teaching endeared him to Nicholas. He spoke without the coarse words used by most of the men.

Nicholas was beginning to understand the routine of the watches and bells. The boys and the men before the mast were divided into two groups called watches that answered to either the first mate on the larboard watch or the second mate on the starboard watch. Captain Parker was not part of either watch, but at any time of the day or night, he might be needed.

From eight o'clock at night until midnight, one watch was on the weather deck, exposed to the wind and waves and rain. Nicholas wondered about the pen of pigs and the wired coop of chickens at the fore. He could understand why they would be kept in the open air, but he wondered how they would do in a storm.

The watch bell rang every half hour. When eight bells rang at midnight, the watch below came on deck. The watch on deck went down to sleep until 4 a.m. when eight bells were rung again. During the day the watches continued to alternate every four hours. The two-hour evening dogwatches changed the schedule so it was different than the night before.

Nicholas followed Gilbert's watch, the starboard watch. The other cabin boy, Thomas, was in the larboard watch. Captain Parker would have a boy available at all times.

This morning, as Nicholas stood watching the land disappear, Gilbert arrived at his side. His mouth bulged as he stuffed the remainder of a pastry into it.

"Where did you get that?" Nicholas asked in wonderment at the white crust and apple filling.

"Cook made it for the captain's meal tonight and gave me a piece," Gilbert said. "Captain always gets better food than us, but sometimes we get leftovers since we clear their table. When are you going to eat the pastry in your bag?"

It seemed strange to Nicholas that the cook had given the treat to Gilbert. First, the cook was known to be irritable in his best moments. Second, by his own words, Gilbert usually got only leftovers.

Nicholas remembered the package Mary had handed to him on the dock in Manhattan. Nicholas had wanted to save Mary's pastry, but soon it would spoil. He decided to eat it during his afternoon watch.

That night, at the beginning of the second dogwatch, the first mate blew his whistle. Nicholas had already learned that the captain didn't do much talking to the men. He let the mates do that.

"A theft is brought to my attention by the cook," the mate bellowed. "Apple pastry intended for the captain's cabin disappeared from the galley this morning."

"If anyone knows who did this, please report to me. Per the captain's orders, such a person will receive ten lashes. We cannot have a thief aboard the *Ella*."

Nicholas turned pale, and dared not look at Gilbert at his side. Had Gilbert really stolen the pastry?

The men hurried to their places. Nicholas and Gilbert had just eaten with their mess group. Nicholas was relieved when the second mate called him to watch the helmsman. He didn't want to talk to Gilbert. He would never betray Gilbert's trust by accusing him of stealing the pastry, but he didn't know what he would say to him.

Nicholas stood off to the side behind the big wheel. The *Ella* was making good time this evening, the helmsman said. The steady trade wind would take them across the Atlantic Ocean to England. He kept an eye on the compass, rocking on its gimbals in a wooden box just ahead of the helmsman.

"This here case for instruments is called the binnacle," the helmsman growled.

He was a man of few words, so Nicholas watched the water and the sky and the white wake sliding out behind the *Ella*. It was early September, and the sun was nearing the horizon. Clear sky roofed the world with a tinge of bluish-purple on the eastern rim. A light breeze fanned Nicholas' back and hair. The sea reflected the beauty of the sky.

Just as I thought, Nicholas said to himself. *I love being at sea!*

"Nicholas! The first mate wants to see you," a sailor said to him. "Maybe you get to meet the cat?" The man threw back his head and laughed.

Nicholas stared at him. He looked up at the helmsman, who jerked his head toward the forecastle, the front of the ship, where he saw the first mate. Nicholas headed that way.

The first mate saw Nicholas coming and stooped to pick up a coil of rope. Perhaps the mate wanted to teach him some knots.

"I've heard word from numerous sources that you were seen eating pastry in your bunk this afternoon," the first mate said. "You'll receive your ten lashings at four bells when the watch ends. You will sit down now on this crate and separate the strands of this rope to make the cat. A thief who steals from his own captain certainly cannot be tolerated at sea, and if we were still in port you would immediately be put off the ship."

Nicholas was so stunned he could not speak for a moment. He stared up at the first mate's face.

"But, it was mine from home," he gasped. "From Mary!"

"You will say, 'Aye, aye, sir,' when spoken to," snapped the first mate, whipping the rope against the crate, cracking an oath along with it. "The boy expects me to believe he brought pastry from home," he mumbled as he turned away.

Nicholas wasn't even sure what to do with the rope. His face aflame, he sat on the crate and dug his fingernails into the end of the rope, trying to separate the strands. They were rough and bit at his fingers, even though his hands were toughened from farm work.

Thoughts raced wildly through his head. He had not done wrong, but he was about to be flogged and possibly put off the ship. Should he report that Gilbert had been eating pastry? But he didn't want to accuse Gilbert of stealing. Also, as far as he knew, he had been the only one to see Gilbert. Nicholas, on the other hand, had eaten his pastry on his bunk in plain sight. The sailors had teased him about his "woman" on shore who had sent him treats. Everyone knew he had been eating pastry. But surely they also knew that he had gotten it from his bag. And why, if he had stolen it, would he eat it in front of everyone?

With a flash of understanding, Nicholas remembered Gilbert asking him when he was going to eat his pastry. Gilbert knew about the pastry because Nicholas had told him. Gilbert must have set him up.

Shocked and angry, Nicholas' hands tightened on the rope. He had trusted Gilbert. How could this happen? When the captain heard about it, would he not put him off at the next port? Nicholas relaxed his hands on the rope and found that they were shaking so much he could not unravel the strands.

He heard the first mate striking the bell. Two bells. It would be four bells in one hour, and Nicholas would receive a flogging. He didn't know where it would take place or if it would be done in private.

A distant story from Daniel came to mind. If Daniel had been right, beatings took place in front of the entire crew. Daniel had said they tied the guilty party to a mast, and stripped him to the waist.

How Nicholas wished he could be at home in the stone house on Staten Island! If only he could see Mary, or Pine, or Jonah, or Elizabeth. He did not want to see Father because then he would know for sure that Nicholas was a useless boy.

Jonah. If only Jonah were here now! If only he could throw his arms around Jonah's neck and bury his face in Jonah's hair, things would be better. *Don't think about Jonah. Don't think about Jonah,* Nicholas said to himself.

Daniel had been right. In a blinding terror, Nicholas found himself positioned, shirt-less, arms around the mainmast. His arms were not long enough to go around the mast, so they were secured by a rope around both of his wrists, jerked tight. The sailors stood nearby, watching, silhouetted by the pink western sky. Captain Parker stood front and center in his fine hat and coat, arms folded, red silk hand-kerchief neatly tied.

Powerful arms swung the cat-o'-nine-tails to which nine buttons of wood had been fastened. Nicholas realized he had never experienced real pain before. Even his father's whippings had been nothing in comparison. The first blow lit up his back with fire, and he cried out in sudden pain even though he had meant to be silent.

Two! Pause. *Three!* Pause.

Nicholas pressed his mouth against the wood of the mast to stifle his cries, slicing his lip open. Equally dreadful to the blows was the awful space of time between them. The red hot suspense of the pause flogged his mind just like the cat-o'-nine-tails tore the skin of his back.

Four! Pause. *Five!* Pause. *Six!* Pause.

All thought escaped from Nicholas' mind except that he would die of this beating which clawed through his body.

Seven! Pause. *Eight!* Pause. *Nine!* Pause. *Ten!*

The rope around his wrists fell away, and Nicholas fell backward to the deck. He stumbled toward the fore hatch where he could get down to his bunk and away from the spectators. At the hatch, he nearly bumped into the cook before blindly falling down the rungs of the ladder.

"That'll teach a thief," the cook gloated behind him.

He fell into his bunk in agony. He wished he had obeyed Mother and never come to sea.

11

The Orange Cat

Three thoughts quivered in Nicholas' mind when he awoke the next morning to the sound of eight bells and the men stirring.

First, he had managed to sleep. He had slept through both watches without being awakened. He had been certain the night before that he would not sleep at all.

Second, the smallest movement created a painful explosion in his back.

Third, he remembered the words of the cook. *That'll teach a thief.* Nicholas knew that, to the cook, he was a thief. He had not stolen the pastry. But he had intended to steal from the cook that day in the warehouse.

The berths grew quiet. Several men began to snore. Then Nicholas heard a voice above him.

"Is there anything I can get for you, Nic? It's Old Pete. No, don't move."

Old Pete gently restrained Nicholas from sitting up by touching his right arm.

"Water," Nicholas said.

"Right."

Nicholas heard footsteps disappear and then return. He saw lantern light falling on the curved side of the hull against which his bunk was built. He heard two voices this time, talking softly.

"A rum thing for a new boy," he heard someone say.

"The surgeon's here with bandages, Nic," Old Pete said. "We are going to have you sit up—"

"Let's take him to my berth," the surgeon said. "He's as light as a feather and can rest better there."

In the dimly lit room near the stern, below Captain Parker's quarters, Pete gave Nicholas a big swallow of water. Next, the surgeon gave him a sip of something hot that burned a track down his throat. Then the surgeon went to work cleaning his back.

Nicholas' back seared with pain, and he bit his throbbing lip again to hold back the whimpers that threatened to escape. Then he felt a cool ointment land on the raw areas, and the stinging grew worse. The surgeon wrapped a bandage all the way around him, and arranged several feather pillows for him on the straw tick.

Leaning against the pillows in the fresh bandage, Nicholas felt almost comfortable. Whether it was the drink or the ointment or the bandages, he sighed with relief. The searing pain was gone.

"Thank you," he whispered.

"Nic," Old Pete said, sitting beside him on the straw tick. "Did you steal the pastry?"

"No."

"I didn't think so. Neither did most of the men on our watch. But don't talk about it or you might get in worse trouble. You can stay below today if you wish. Even grown men stay below for a few days after a flogging."

When light began to fall through the hatch, Nicholas woke again. The surgeon brought him a bowl of porridge and a spoon. Nicholas wasn't sure that he was hungry, but he stiffly sat up and ate it. The surgeon took the empty bowl and left, leaving Nicholas alone.

As the room grew brighter, Nicholas saw a rounded mound of fur in the far corner of the bed. It was the back of a calico cat, with a large patch of orange fur that reminded Nicholas of the brown of Jonah's coat. A warm stream of affection for the cat circled inside Nicholas.

He was not alone!

In the afternoon, when Nicholas' watch was below, Gilbert came into the room. Nicholas bristled and lay as still as he could so Gilbert would think he was asleep. He simply could not talk to him.

"Nic," Gilbert hissed. "Nic!"

Nicholas opened one eye.

"I'm sure you think I was the one who stole the pastry, and set you up, but really, I didn't! The cook did give it to me, I swear! Nicholas, did you know that cook before you came here?"

Nicholas opened both eyes now. Gilbert's voice sounded sincere.

"Ummm . . . not really," Nicholas said. "But I saw him before."

Why didn't Gilbert stick up for me? Nicholas wondered. But on the other hand, how could Gilbert talk back to the first mate?

"He said something today about 'once a thief, always a thief.' It was like he thought you stole before. I don't know why he would say that. You don't seem like that kind of person. I think he set you up, Nic. But don't talk about it. It might just get you into more trouble."

Relief washed through Nicholas like medicine. If Gilbert was speaking the truth, then he still had a friend aboard the ship. No, he had two. Old Pete had taken care of him during the night. And then there was the white and orange cat, still snoozing on the bed.

Still, most of the men on the ship, including Captain Parker, probably believed the first mate and the cook. And it didn't seem that anyone would be likely to inform the captain, for fear of getting into trouble themselves.

And, Gilbert was wrong about one thing. Nicholas *was* that kind of person. He *had* stolen from the cook—or had intended to.

The next day, Nicholas determined to join his watch at noon. The surgeon re-dressed his back, and Nicholas shakily pulled his shirt over his head. The bandage could be seen beneath his shirt, but he didn't care. Everyone already knew he had gotten a flogging. He climbed the ladder slowly. The sunlight struck his face, and he felt better immediately.

Gilbert approached him.

"Captain wants to see you," he said. "Don't worry. He's not upset."

Nicholas tried to walk quickly to the quarterdeck where the captain was looking out at the horizon.

"This way," Captain Parker said, pointing to the door of the companionway.

Nicholas followed the captain down the narrow stairway. They entered a low room crammed with a table and benches.

"Sit down," the captain said.

Nicholas relaxed on the bench. His back scraped against the wall behind him and he jerked forward in pain. The captain blinked and called to the closed door.

"Gil, a shot of brandy!"

"Aye, aye, sir!" Nicholas heard his friend say, followed by the sound of flying footsteps.

"Did you steal from the galley?" Captain Parker looked Nicholas straight in the eye.

"No."

"How do you address a captain?"

"No, sir."

"Fine. Good."

Gilbert handed down the brandy. Captain Parker handed it to Nicholas, who lifted the cup to his lips. He felt it burn down his throat as the surgeon's drink had.

"That's all," the captain said when the small tin cup was empty. "For the rest of the day you can observe whoever you wish. What would you like to do that you haven't done yet?"

"Climb the ratlines, sir."

The captain's eyes widened. His mouth quivered as if he was going to tell Nicholas to choose something easier. Instead he picked up his red handkerchief which he had unwound from his neck and smoothed it between his hands.

"Gil," he yelled, "go get Old Pete."

It occurred to Nicholas that standing at the door waiting for orders would soon be his job. It appeared that the captain believed him and would not be kicking him out at the next port.

Old Pete descended the stairs.

"This boy wants to climb the ratlines," the captain said.

"Aye, aye, sir," Old Pete answered with a twinkle in his eyes.

Nicholas followed Old Pete up the stairs and across the deck.

Pete looked down at him.

"Are you dizzy, boy?"

"No," Nicholas said. "And I've been climbing things since I was—little."

"I'll go after you," Pete said.

He showed Nicholas how to spring from the bulwarks onto the tarry, black lines.

"Remember what I said? Some folks call 'em ratlines, some call 'em shrouds, some call 'em standing rigging. They're tarred and they stay fastened to whatever they are tied to. All the white ropes move with the sails."

Even with his back stinging, Nicholas came alive on the ratlines. He shot up the ropes.

"Slow down, lubber," Pete called from below, chuckling. "If you fall and I'm not close enough to catch you, we'll both be in trouble."

Nicholas looked down. He could easily fall and land in the water, depending how the ship rocked. It made him a little dizzy, so he looked up, up, to the masts above and even higher to the majestic expanse of sky.

The ratline they were climbing ended at several vertical bars attached to the mainmast.

"Do you know the names of the sails?" Old Pete asked Nicholas.

Nicholas shook his head.

"At the very bottom of each mast is the course sail. So on the foremast, it is called the fore course sail. On the mainmast, it is called the main course. On the mizzen mast, it is the mizzen course. Above the courses are the topsails. We are right above the topsails now. Above the topsails are the topgallant sails. The very highest ones, up by the lookout, are the royal sails."

"How do we get up there?" Nicholas asked, looking up at the man posted near the royal sail.

"Ah, this isn't far enough on your first day with a stinging back?" Old Pete asked. "If you're a landlubber, you go up there through the safe hole between those cross trees. If you're a true seaman, you go around the cross trees and grab the ratline from the outside. You should probably—"

Nicholas knew Pete was going to say he should probably go between the cross trees. Before Pete finished speaking, Nicholas scrambled around the outside of the wooden bars. He grimaced at the burning as he stretched the skin on his back, but he kept climbing. Soon, he was at the top of the ship, right beside the lookout sailor.

The lookout was Clark, his red hair rippling in the breeze.

"Ah, men!" Clark bellowed from his speaking trumpet. "Landlubber in the mast head!"

Nicholas heard a cheer go up from below. It took a second for him to realize they were cheering for him. He looked down to see if the cook was on deck. There was no sign of him, although it was hard to see from so far up.

If only Father could see me now! Nicholas thought.

Nicholas felt like he was flying among the clouds. To the horizon on all sides, he saw nothing but sea. The masts swayed with the rocking of the boat, tipping forward, then aft.

"You know what I like to do to pass the time, if I have chew with me?" Clark said. "I like to see if I can spit on one of those chaps down on deck. It's harder than you'd think!"

"How can you aim?" Nicholas asked in amazement. "The ship is rocking back and forth."

"Oh, today is easy," Clark said. "Already hit a man."

"It's a different matter when the sea's up," Pete said. "Isn't that right, Clark?"

"Aye, that's right! I been hanging onto this mast already when I think the masts are going to kiss the water."

Nicholas tried to imagine what it would be like in a storm. What would it be like to fall down, down, down toward the water? How fast would the mast spring back up? How hard would it be to hang on? But it was such a beautiful day that he could not imagine it very well.

"A man usually slips going down," Clark said. "But Old Pete will keep an eye on you."

Nicholas descended without incident. A ship's ratlines were made for climbing.

When he reached the bottom of the shrouds, Nicholas felt a wave of exhaustion wash over him. He felt Old Pete grab him and lift him over the bulwarks and safely to the deck. The pain from Pete's hands pressing Nicholas' sides brought Nicholas back to full alertness.

"Best to sit and work on some knots," Pete said. "Here, take this line and show me a clove hitch around this rod."

The orange cat padded up and passed between Nicholas' legs. She circled him a few times, then curled up beside him on a coil of rope.

What a wonderful thing it was to be a sailor at sea!

12

The Art of Sailing

As cabin boy, Nicholas stayed close to the captain to take orders. This was perfect because Nicholas wanted to learn about latitude and longitude, degrees and angles, knots and velocity. He had liked arithmetic in school, but Captain Parker used a field of arithmetic that even the schoolmaster would not have understood.

Nicholas tied knots, scrubbed decks, fed the animals, and served Captain Parker his meals. Gilbert soon moved to the role of an ordinary seaman, and Nicholas was officially on his own.

Every day Nicholas learned something new. He observed Captain Parker and the first mate taking measurements. At noon, they met on the quarterdeck and measured the angle between the sun and the horizon. The closer they sailed to the equator, the more directly overhead the sun would be. Here in the winter months in the north, the sun appeared to be closer to the southern horizon.

Nicholas also watched the method for measuring the ship's speed. Every time the ship's bell signaled another half hour, a sailor threw a triangular board off the stern. The board contained a spool of rope, with knots tied every so often. As the ship pulled away from the triangle, the rope unwound. The seaman would count how many knots were unwound in thirty seconds, measured by a sand glass.

Every day the first mate recorded the estimated latitude and longitude in the log book. He wrote down the speed and direction the ship had traveled. Captain Parker looked through the log, compared it to the charts and maps in his chart room, and made any corrections he saw fit.

A barometer, a thin glass tube with mercury in it, hung in the chart room. The mercury level varied with the air pressure. Captain Parker told Nicholas that if the level of mercury dropped very low, it was almost certain that there would be a storm.

Besides learning about navigation, Nicholas began to learn the songs of the sailors. The rhythmic working songs kept the men together as they hauled at the sails. Everyone on the rope pulled at the same word.

Seagull Sal, a tall Norwegian with a mane of golden hair, led the singing. He was the chanteyman on Nicholas' watch. Sal would sing the first line, in his confident tenor voice, and the men at the rope would answer:

> Sal: Our boots and clothes are all in pawn.
> Men: Go down, ye blood-red roses, go down!
> Sal: And it's mighty drafty round Cape Horn.
> Men: Go down, ye blood-red roses, go down!

Every time they sang the word *down,* the men pulled at the rope, lifting the sail or yard.

"A song is as good as ten men," Old Pete would say.

Sometimes when Nicholas was scrubbing the deck, he timed his mop to the rhythm of the songs, making a hearty swipe across the planks every time the men pulled on the ropes.

Seagull Sal had brought a cittern with him, carefully wrapped in linen. The cittern had a pear-shaped body with a long wooden neck. Taut strings stretched down the neck and across the wooden body. Nicholas loved to watch Seagull Sal as he played. The fingers of Sal's left hand danced from string to string on the neck of the cittern, and the fingers of his right hand plucked the strings above the body of the cittern. The music bouncing off the strings spread happiness on the ship.

During the dogwatches after each mess had eaten their salt pork and sea biscuit, the men would sing on deck with Seagull Sal leading. He was nicknamed "Seagull" in jest, because the men told him he shrieked like a sea gull. But everyone enjoyed his music, and many of the men secretly wished for his voice and his cittern.

Off-duty singing in the forecastle berth was different. Here, the songs were thick with filth. Often, lines were changed to ridicule the cook or the captain. They were received with shouts and guffaws.

Songs were not the only crude part of sea life. The men did little to shelter the boys from what went on at the sea ports. Seagull Sal made up songs about dark-eyed women in dance houses in Plymouth and Portsmouth and London. He sang about dark-skinned women coming to meet the ships in the West Indies ports. Clark, the red-headed lookout, was the first to join in. Clark boasted about what he planned to do when they reached Plymouth.

Nicholas wanted to be a man, so he laughed along with the men. The crudest men were funny and made life sound exciting. Old Pete kept out of these conversations, and sometimes he invited Nicholas to a game of checkers away from the talk.

Everyone sang a hymn on Sundays. Nicholas or Thomas covered the binnacle with a cloth and placed Captain Parker's prayer book and Bible on it. Captains always led the services, Gilbert told Nicholas. All the men except the lookout gathered in the waist of the ship to listen to the Scripture. They sat on boxes or barrels or coils of rope.

"Keep, we beseech thee, O Lord, thy church with thy perpetual mercy," Captain Parker read from the quarterdeck, from the Book of Common Prayer.

Usually, each Sunday's selection was a psalm, a short prayer, a reading from an epistle, and a reading from a Gospel. After that the men would sing a hymn together and church was dismissed.

Meals were eaten in groups called messes. Each watch was its own mess. Each mess had a mess cook. The mess cook did not cook, but he carried the ingredients to the kitchen and retrieved the prepared food.

The first few days of the voyage, the men ate stews with fresh meat and fresh vegetables. After that, they ate foods that could be preserved on long voyages, like hard tack.

When Nicholas first received the four-inch square bread, he nearly chipped a tooth on it. His mess was eating on their bunks in the forecastle because it was raining up on deck.

"Hard tack," Old Pete said to him. "Soak it in your tea."

"Some people call it sea biscuit, but that's an offense to biscuits," Seagull Sal said. "These things are indestructible."

He picked up his hard tack and with it tapped out a tune on the bunk above his head.

"Made to last for months. They bake 'em three times so they're hard as a rock," Old Pete said. "You can nibble around the edge, but it would take awhile without liquid."

"Good thing is, no worms yet," said another.

"Worms?" Nicholas asked.

"Yup," Seagull Sal said, slurping bean soup out of his bowl. "Gets in the water too."

A trickle of soup escaped over the edge of the bowl onto his bunk. Seagull Sal leaned down and licked the soup right off the bed, his mane of golden hair flopping.

" 'Nother reason we call him Seagull. He leaves a mess wherever he goes," Old Pete told Nicholas.

When Seagull Sal got up from his bunk, a track of crumbs remained.

One day when Nicholas awoke, they could see land on the horizon. After five weeks on the North Atlantic, they were almost to England! Nicholas tingled with excitement.

As the ship neared Plymouth, the sailors began sounding. Nicholas watched with fascination as the men stepped out onto a wooden platform called the *chains* to measure the distance to the ocean floor. The sailor on the chains picked up the lead line, a thin rope with a lead weight on the end. The rope was marked with pieces of colored string and leather.

"You can't see it from here," Seagull Sal said beside him, "but they put animal fat on that lead so it picks stuff off the sea floor."

"Why?" Nicholas asked.

"Oh, I guess it don't matter much here, because so many ships come through. But t'other side of the globe, where nothing's mapped? You want to know what's down there. There's a difference. Sand, rocks, mud . . . watch him drop that line now!"

Nicholas, pressed against the side of the ship, watched the lead line rush into the water and drop like a stone. The sailor fed the rope until the lead struck bottom.

"By the deep, nineteen!" the sounding man bawled.

Nicholas looked up at Seagull Sal.

"See, those little pieces of leather and string mark out every second or third fathom," Sal said. "If the measurement is right at that mark, they say, 'by the mark, twenty' or 'by the mark, five.' But this time the measurement is between two markers, so he has to guess. That's what 'by the deep' means."

"Oh," Nicholas said. "How many feet is a fathom?"

"Aye, that a cabin boy should know!" Seagull Sal said. "It is good you asked me and not the captain. Six feet to a fathom, and don't ever forget it!"

Nicholas stayed on board when they anchored in Plymouth. Whenever they did not have to keep watch, the men plunged into the smaller boats and rowed to shore, dispersing to the taverns and dance houses about which they had sung. Captain Parker was one of the first to leave the ship.

Nicholas tried to remember the steadiness of the earth and wondered how it would feel to walk on streets and paths again. The busy port was much older and dirtier than Manhattan. What secrets were hiding in its streets and alleyways? The smell of fresh beef cooking came through the fishy smells of the wharf. He saw the steeple of Charles Church. The men told him of yarn markets and leather markets in Plymouth, and one of the men bought a leather writing book that Nicholas eyed with longing. But Captain Parker told him to stay on board. Old Pete stayed on board too.

Fresh mutton came back from the Plymouth meat market. The cook, who by this time had made enemies of most of the sailors, made a stew with fresh vegetables and served fresh, soft bread. He even took a small bit of the meat and fed it to the orange cat.

When he saw the cook on deck later, Nicholas wanted to walk away like he always had before. Instead, he thanked him. "That was good stew!"

The cook turned his head and spit a stream of tobacco juice over the side of the ship.

Once the furs had been unloaded and English goods and fresh water and meat taken on, Captain Parker instructed the men to make ready to sail to the West Indies. When the wind was right to move out of the harbor, the men set the sails and weighed anchor to a song.

> What shall we do with a drunken sailor?
> What shall we do with a drunken sailor?
> What shall we do with a drunken sailor?
> Early in the morning.

> Haul away, and up she rises.
> Haul away, and up she rises.
> Haul away, and up she rises.
> Early in the morning.

"We really do need to ask that question today," Old Pete said, nodding at Clark who was hanging in the shrouds, cursing as his foot caught on a piece of rope. His eyes were bloodshot and his red hair was wild. "I hope he can keep himself aloft."

Clark wasn't the only seaman with this problem. Two of the men pushing the capstan bars to lift the anchor from the water were bleary-eyed and slow in matching the rhythm of the song.

"Avast, there!" cried the second mate finally. "Let's have some men who can stand upright at the capstan."

Gilbert had taught Nicholas the meaning of the word *avast*. It meant *stop,* and Gilbert said that *Avast!* was shouted at new hands quite frequently, so he had better learn its meaning straightaway.

The weather had grown cold, and the men wore coats in the mornings and evenings. Nicholas slept with his coat on and wrapped his blanket around him, remembering his old spot under the eaves at home. He wondered how Isaac and Jacob were doing up there now and how Elizabeth was faring in the other loft. He wondered about Mary and Pine and his father. He realized that he had yet to write a letter.

I should have written them while we were in Plymouth, he thought, looking at the endless water on all sides.

Now they had left Plymouth far behind, headed for a place Nicholas had heard so much about, the warm green islands of the West Indies.

13

The Chart Room

Nicholas began to think that life at sea could be boring. When Lambert or Daniel had told stories around the open hearth on a cold winter's night, there seemed to be constant drama. They told of fights, floggings, captures, strange sails, pirates, and men overboard. Even Pine, who was not given to making things up, had seen enough bloodshed and shipwreck that he could have written a small novel if he had known how to write.

From Staten Island to Plymouth, England, Nicholas had been so busy learning the men's names, the daily schedule, and the ship lingo that he had no time to be bored. He had a flogging to heal from, a cook to be afraid of, and a captain to please. Now that his back had healed and he had learned some of the captain's requirements and routines, his mind was more at ease. There was still the unsettling presence of the cook, whose shrill, whining voice rang in the ears of the sailors every day as he scolded everyone in sight. But Nicholas was beginning to feel competent and comfortable.

His senses no longer alerted him to the sounds and sights that had impressed him so much in the first few days. He no longer watched the sails come alive or heard them crack as they were unfurled and caught the wind. He no longer heard the masts creak as they were pressed forward by the billowing sails. He no longer noticed the red paint on the bulwarks or the hundreds of lines, cables, and ropes connecting sails and pulleys and masts. The sights and sounds had become part of the normal routine.

He still loved to climb the ratlines. Climbing was not part of his job, but the men allowed him to scramble up nearly every time he asked.

Nicholas continued to watch the captain and first mate take readings to determine the position of the *Ella* on the Atlantic Ocean. Several days, the *Ella* had scarcely moved due to the absence of wind. Nicholas learned that the term for this was *becalmed*. He wished he could ask questions but decided that if Captain Parker wanted to talk to him, he would.

"Done cleaning the decks?" the captain asked him one morning several weeks into the voyage. "Go get me some beer from my locker, and let me show you a few things on the chart."

"Aye, aye, sir!"

Nicholas went to the wooden locker under the stern windows in the captain's cabin and opened the metal latch, his fingers trembling with excitement. The captain was going to give him a lesson! He heard rustling as the captain picked several charts from his chart box, then unrolled one on the wooden table in the low-ceilinged chart room. Even Nicholas could not stand up fully in this half deck room, but that was why a table and stools were placed here.

Captain Parker took a noisy drink from the mug Nicholas put before him.

"Sir? May I run and get the slate I brought with me?"

"If you wish, boy."

Nicholas was back in a flash, with the slate from the *kast* at home. "Latitude isn't a problem when the sun shines," the captain explained, undoing the red kerchief from his neck and tossing it on the table. "All we need to do is find the angle between the sun and the horizon at noon. Then, we can look on our chart and determine our latitude. Here, look at this chart. These lines that go across the map are called lines of latitude."

As Nicholas bent over the captain's wooden table, he thought he would burst with excitement. The captain took another long swallow from his mug.

"Longitude is a bigger problem," the captain went on. "The lines of longitude are far apart at the equator, but grow closer and closer as you travel toward the poles. It is not a mere matter of distance, it is a matter of degrees. There are differing opinions about the best way to find longitude. Some people look at the stars and moon. Others want to use clocks, but no one has yet developed a timepiece that can keep accurate time at sea."

Nicholas puzzled over this. How could their position relate to time?

"Lines of longitude are the lines we draw on the map to divide the globe into sections up and down, like cutting an apple into slices. These," Captain Parker pointed to the chart with his divider, tracing the line of longitude from the top of the map to the bottom. "Now, at noon today, we will see the sun above us. If we knew exactly what time it is in Plymouth or London we could know exactly what longitude we are at here. Do you understand, boy?"

Nicholas frowned. He wanted to say yes, but he could not understand how time and longitude could have anything to do with each other. Worse, he did not have a slate pencil, and therefore could not write down what he was learning.

"No, sir," he said quietly.

"Longitude goes from 0 degrees, all the way around the world to 360 degrees. Do you understand this, that a circle has 360 degrees?"

"Yes, sir!" Nicholas answered hastily, filled with gratitude for arithmetic lessons from the schoolmaster in the old classroom at home.

"And we know that the sun rises every 24 hours, Nic. So how many degrees does the sun appear to move per hour? You can do a little math, can you not?"

"Yes, sir."

Nicholas began the division in his head, but Captain Parker plunked a slate pencil in front of him. Nicholas wrote 360 divided by 24.

"The sun moves at 15 degrees per hour, sir," he said.

"The earth actually moves, not the sun," Captain Parker said. "But yes, 15 degrees is correct.

"We have an English almanac that tells us what time the sun rises over London every day of the year."

The captain reached for a leather-bound book. The books in the chart room were on shallow shelves with slats of wood across them to keep the volumes from sliding out when the ship turned or rolled.

"Today is November 20, 1713," the captain said. "I check the book to see the time of the sun's movements in London on November 20, and here they are."

He moved the book closer to Nicholas.

"Sunrise," Nicholas read, "November 20, 7:25 a.m."

"Okay," the captain said. "We will give you an easy one to start with. Let's say that the sun rises here at our position at 7:25 as well. We look at our London watch and it says 9:25. We are two hours different from London time. What longitude does that make our ship?"

Nicholas fingered the slate but wrote nothing. Fifteen degrees per hour. Two hours.

"We are 30 degrees east—uh, west—of London, sir."

"Good work, Nicholas." A hint of a smile crossed Captain Parker's face, and he picked up the red handkerchief.

"The problem is, clocks won't keep accurate time at sea. Even if a clock loses a minute per day, by the end of our journey we can be most inaccurate with our longitude, which can be dangerous. Still, it gives us a general idea. Now, here is the chart of our destination."

The captain unrolled another map. Nicholas could tell it had been newly printed. It still smelled like fresh ink and was creamy white with neat edges. It had no bends or tears.

In a box on the lower left side of the map, he saw *WEST-INDIES* in large block letters. He read in smaller letters, *A MAP of the WEST-INDIES or the Islands of AMERICA in the NORTH SEA; with ye adjacent Countries; explaining what belongs to SPAIN, ENGLAND, FRANCE, HOLLAND &c also ye TRADE WINDS, and ye sevral Tracts made by ye Galeons and Flota from place to place. According to ye Newest and most Exact Observations.*

"Our destination is Jamaica," the captain said. "The English captured Jamaica from the Spanish in 1655, a few years before I was born and long before you were born. Our challenge will be to get there. We will need to navigate through the islands of the Bahamas, which also belong to England. Then we pass between Cuba, a Spanish territory, and the western half of Hispaniola, which belongs to the French. To the south of Cuba is Jamaica. We have records stating it is between 76 and 79 degrees west of London."

Nicholas quickly scratched the numbers on the slate.

"What is the latitude, sir?"

"The latitude of Port Royal, Jamaica, is 17 degrees, 57 minutes, 24 seconds north. Have you heard the story of Port Royal?"

"No, sir."

"Ah. The clergy said it was because it was the most wicked city in the world. A terrible earthquake and tsunami sank the town and killed 2,000 people. I believe it was toward the beginning of the 1690s. Before you were born, eh? I was on the coast of West Africa at the time, but ask around. Some of these sailors were likely close by. But now I need to go over the first mate's work in the log book. You will begin to take a turn at the helm in calm waters. Go now and stand by the helmsman and study the compass. Next watch you will take the wheel."

"Aye, aye, sir," said Nicholas, sliding off the bench and saluting as he ran up the steps of the companionway. He clutched Seger's slate under his arm.

"Nicholas!"

"Sir?"

"Take this. Practice writing our location each day. Return it to me at the end of the voyage."

Nicholas took the slate pencil.

"Thank you, sir!"

He bounded up the steps, and into the bright sunshine.

Nicholas was sure Captain Parker was the best man who had ever sailed the seas. What a wonderful world of mathematics and science was required to navigate a ship. And best of all, the captain had spent time explaining these things to a mere cabin boy. If he could only talk to Seger now! Seger would be so glad that Nicholas enjoyed the science of navigation, too.

Nicholas was standing beside the helmsman, studying the compass, when Captain Parker came up from his cabin.

"Mercury's been dropping," he said shortly.

Nicholas looked at the sky in surprise. It was a bit hazy but the sun was shining. The boat was sailing with the wind, making good time.

That night on the dogwatch, one of the men pulled out a checker board he had purchased in Plymouth. All through the watch, the men played checkers. Nicholas played Clark and lost, but barely. The orange cat sat beside the board, twitching her tail. It seemed to Nicholas the cat was watching each move.

Some of the men began to tease Nicholas.

"Aye, the boy can play a game of checkers, he can. A smart one, this boy!"

"But he don't know anything about rough waters," another said. "Can't let him be thinking a voyage is always this calm!"

"Sometime, you're going to have to learn to hang on," another said.

"Hang on to what?" Nicholas asked.

"Whatever isn't going overboard," the man replied, and everyone laughed.

A MAP of the
WEST-INDIES
or the Islands of AMERICA
in the NORTH SEA; with ye adjacent
Countries; explaining what belongs to SPAIN,
ENGLAND, FRANCE, HOLLAND &c.
also ye TRADE WINDS, and ye several Tracts
made by ye Galeons and Flota from place to place

According to ye Newest and most Exact Observations
By Herman Moll Geographer

ATLAN-

Variable Winds

LUCAYOS or

Lucayos or

BAHAMA

ISLANDS

-TICK

Barmudes Isl. English

LA VERA CRUZ

A Draught of St AUGUSTIN and its Harbour.

CUBA ISLAN.

Ilha Cagada

DARIEN

Porto de la Nave

The Bay of Porto Bella

PONTO BELLA

A Draught of ye City of CARTAGENA its Harbour & Ports

The Lake of Cartagena

OCEAN

Spanish Miles

English and French Leagues

Dutch Miles

HISPANIOLA

GREATER ANTILLES ISL.

NORTH SEA

CARIBBEE

BARLO VENTO

or the WINDWARD ISL.

SOTO VENTO or Antilles

LEEWARD ISLANDS

NEW GRANADA

NEW

PARIA

St. FE or CASTILLA

ANDALUSIA

TERRA FIRMA

GUIANA

POPayan

DEL ORO

ZUELA

14

The Rocks

Captain Parker didn't say he was worried about the dropping mercury, but Nicholas was beginning to understand his handkerchief gestures. As the captain paced the quarterdeck, he undid the red handkerchief from around his neck. He twisted it in his hands, then shoved it into a pocket where it dangled against his leg. He folded his arms and looked at the sails flapping gently in a slight breeze.

Nicholas was brushing up on knotting lessons with Pete. The men off duty had taken to the checker board, sitting on the deck behind them. Even the cook was watching the game, turning his head every now and again to spit tobacco juice into the waves.

"Not bad," Old Pete said. "Look at this, men! If our ship's boy isn't whipping out bindings and hitches and bends like an old hand."

"Old Pete, Captain Parker said you might know something about a port in Jamaica that sank in an earthquake," Nicholas said. "I forgot to ask you."

"Aye, Port Royal. It was a terrible thing," Old Pete said. "I was north of there, off of the Bahamas at the time, but we felt that earthquake. Then a tsunami came into Jamaica—"

"That's what he said! What's a tsunami, Pete?"

"Wall of water. Great big wave that starts in deep water, and when it gets into shallow water—you know what happens to waves in shallow water—they get high. Well, this one got fifty or a hundred feet high, people say, and Port Royal just disappeared. Must have been twenty years ago now."

At the mention of Port Royal, the cook had looked sharply at Old Pete. As Pete continued to talk, the cook walked away and stood at the edge of the ship. He was still within earshot, but facing the water.

"Twenty-one," the cook said.

"I beg your pardon?" Pete said, not even sure the cook was speaking to him.

"Twenty-one years ago."

"Ah."

The men around the checkers game looked up at the cook, whose back was turned. One of the players raised an eyebrow.

"Were you there, my good man?" Old Pete asked the cook.

The cook didn't answer. His head had dropped and the three fingers of his left hand gripped the bulwark. His shoulders jerked.

The man was crying.

Nicholas stared in astonishment. He had never imagined the cook capable of tears.

The men around the checker board looked at each other and shrugged. A player moved a black checker. The sea was so calm tonight that the pieces were mostly staying in their squares. Each square was bordered by a small ridge, but the pieces were still known to leap off their squares when playing at sea.

"In port," the cook gasped out. "I was in port with my . . ." An audible sob escaped between the words. "With my son!"

Old Pete rubbed his nose in perplexity. He knew how to run up the rigging, how to cling to a thin footrope in a storm, how to weigh an anchor at the capstan. But he was baffled by the tears of a bitter old seaman.

"Gone!" the cook went on, flinging his right arm across the water as if to trace the entire harbor of Port Royal, its houses and taverns and ships. "Gone, like that!"

Nicholas felt himself grow cold inside. For a moment—a very short moment—Nicholas was standing at the mouth of the Fresh Kills where it poured into the Arthur Kill, searching, searching the black water. He could feel the cold spring rain on his face and the mud around his toes, and he could see nothing but water because the person he was looking for was gone!

Gone, like that!

The cook's right hand came crashing back, smacking the top of the bulwark. Nicholas' thoughts crashed back onto the *Ella,* and he was glad to escape the Fresh Kills.

The men around the checkers game had paused again to listen. They echoed the cook's words with a smattering of subdued blasphemies. Cursing in response to misfortune was the best way they knew to offer sympathy.

"What happened to your ship?" Pete asked. "Were others saved?"

"No one!" the cook shouted. His son had perished in Port Royal, under the massive wave.

The cook came back to the circle of men, scowling as if he wanted to rescue his reputation as a man who had no soft feelings.

"A man wishes he wouldn't have been saved when everyone else goes down, he does," the cook growled. "I went up to New York, but I ain't been to sea again, 'til now. Don't know why I came," he said, then repeated the words with a string of foul language. "Except maybe to find the wave that missed me."

"Aye, man, not such talk!" Old Pete said. "Some of us would like to live a little bit yet. Young Nic here has a whole life ahead of him!"

"I thought young Nic was someone else when I first saw him," the cook said. "Reminded me of a boy who broke into my warehouse a few years back."

That night during his entire four-hour watch, Nicholas wondered if he should tell the cook that it had been he. Some of the men were playing checkers between jobs, but Nicholas paced a distance from the game, his eyes searching the darkness for answers.

What would that help? he asked himself. *Why should I apologize? He falsely accused me of stealing and I got a flogging I didn't deserve.*

He fell asleep, still wondering. And then he dreamed.

A giant wave crashed over a harbor lined with ships. The mainmast of one of the ships cracked like a twig and was falling, falling. The cook was diving to get out of the way, his left arm and hand pinned by the falling mast. The cook banged on the mast.

Bang! Bang! Bang! Nicholas jerked. The banging was real. It was not a dream. Someone was banging on the hatch above his head.

"All hands!" He heard the first mate shouting.

Nicholas sat up, and the ship pitched, flinging him against the hull to which his bunk was fastened. The first of the starboard watch was tumbling up the ladder and through the trapdoor. A sharp wind whistled down to Nicholas' bunk.

"Nic!" Gilbert called. "Grab your oilskin."

Nicholas was glad for the reminder. He snatched the raincoat off its peg and turned to the ladder. He bolted up and nearly fell when the wind hit him.

"Watch it, boy, or you'll be going over!" the man behind him yelled.

Nicholas was not experienced enough to help much in a crisis. The first mate was hanging on to a length of standing rigging, yelling, but the sound vanished into the wind. He held a lantern above his head to draw the men to him and beckoned to a group of sailors from the starboard watch. He then pointed to the foremast and yelled again.

The men turned to the shrouds, their hands grazing the ropes and wood they passed, ready to grab for solid objects at the next roll of the ship. Nicholas saw them leap onto the shrouds. Each piece of rigging was a moving target in the blackness. He knew they must be swarming up, one after another, but he lost sight of them, since he was close to the stern and they were at the other end of the ship.

He could barely get his bearings in the suffocating blackness. The lanterns cast a fuzzy glow, swinging wildly on their hooks. Blurred figures ran through the fuzzy glows. Above him, silhouettes of men stood on the footlines of the mizzen mast yard, reaching for the canvas sail. The men on one end of the yard had their part of the sail furled and were bringing the ties together to fasten it when a mighty gust of wind caught the other end of the sail. With one powerful snap, the wind snatched the wrapped end from the men's hands, throwing the sail open again.

Nicholas heard an explosion of oaths close to his ear and realized that Captain Parker was beside him and had been watching too.

"Did you men never learn to work together?" the captain yelled.

Nicholas suspected that the men heard nothing, and he was glad. He could not imagine standing on a thin rope in such a wind, trying to furl the sail.

"Nicholas, up with you," Captain Parker said. "You know how to tie knots. And for the love of life, don't let go!"

Nicholas was speechless with fear and excitement and forgot to acknowledge the order. He leaped onto the mizzen shrouds. The men were only halfway up the mast. They were taking in the mizzen topsail, the second sail from the bottom of the third mast. In the fierce wind, the huge sail had become a living monster. Nicholas leaped to the footrope just as the men again brought in the sail by fistfuls. Without pausing to wonder if he was doing the wrong thing, Nicholas put one arm around either side of the yard, snatched the ties, and began to knot.

He successfully tied a knot while the stronger men held the sail.

"Nice work, Nic. Duck under my arms and move down!" the sailor beside him shouted.

Pleased, Nicholas ducked and moved down the footrope just as the ship took a plunge into the trough of a wave. He had kept his hands around the yard, but suddenly the foot rope was gone out from under him and his feet were dangling free and his mouth was full of salt water.

Stay calm, Nicholas told himself.

He tightened his grip on the yard and kicked with his feet to find the footrope. A sailor guided his feet back to the rope. Without pausing, Nicholas secured his footing and continued tying.

When Nicholas and the men returned to the deck, the first mate was yelling, the pigs were shrieking, and the masts were groaning as if they would snap. A wave hit the *Ella* on the port side and the entire vessel heeled to starboard. A loose crate rattled across the deck and disappeared overboard.

"Now, into the wind!" the captain yelled to the man at the wheel.

Nicholas saw Old Pete move to the wheel to help the younger seaman steer. He grabbed Nicholas on his way.

"Tie yourself to the binnacle with a hitch knot," Pete hollered at Nicholas.

The rain drove into the ship first from the side and then from the front. It pushed under his eyelids and into his ears and nose. The weather deck was earning its name tonight, heaving first to one side and then to the other and becoming slick with rain.

Captain Parker stood beside them and a bit to the starboard side, left hand on the binnacle. His red kerchief was clasped in his right hand.

From one of the cabinets in the binnacle, Pete snatched three coils of rope. After maneuvering the tiller into the wind together, the two helmsmen took turns tying themselves to a stationary object. Nicholas wrapped the coil around himself and then pushed the other end of the rope through a bar on the side of the instrument cabinet close to Old Pete's. He fumbled, suddenly confused . . . *Half hitch, slippery hitch, lark's head hitch . . .*

He was about to give up when Old Pete's hands snatched the rope. In the lantern light, Nicholas saw Pete's fingers fly as he wrapped the rope twice around the bar. He slipped the rope's end over the long end and under the wrapped part, wrapped the end once more around the long end connected to Nicholas, and pulled the knot fast.

Nicholas stood and hung on, watching the men struggle to keep the *Ella* turned into the face of the wind. The sails had all been furled, except for one on the foremast which was double reefed. Reefing, Nicholas knew, made the sail smaller so it would take up less space and catch less wind.

Nicholas lost track of time, but when one bell was rung, he knew that the first half hour of the new watch had passed. The fact that he heard the bell at all was a sign of the quieter weather, for he had not heard the eight bells marking 4 a.m. The seas were still high, but the port watch was ordered below to get some sleep. The younger helmsman was from the port watch, so he left the wheel to Old Pete.

"Let's take a sounding!" Captain Parker shouted.

"Aye, aye, sir," a sailor replied, running for the lead measuring line.

"Many an experienced seaman has gone over on a night like this," Old Pete said.

A wave hit the bow at the other end of the ship, and spray flew high in the air.

"I did slip on the footrope," Nicholas admitted.

"You were in the rigging?"

"Aye, just above helping tie the mizzen course. Captain sent me up."

"Did you do some of the tying?"

"Yes, because the men were hanging on. But that's when I lost my footing."

By the light of the dancing lantern, Nicholas saw Old Pete break into a delighted grin.

"You'll be a mate one of these days," Old Pete said.

Nicholas smiled too.

"How's your back been lately?"

"All healed up."

"Sea life is not too glamorous sometimes," Old Pete said. "I've seen captains hang the wrong man."

"That's . . . terrible," Nicholas said, inhaling sharply.

Hung!

Then he added quietly, "Not Captain Parker?"

Old Pete's eyes drifted somewhere to starboard in the churning sea. "I want you to make your own opinion of a man without listening to my opinion," he said. "And I'm sorry you have scars on your back that do not belong to you."

Scars that don't belong to me? Nicholas thought. *But I really did try to steal from the cook once. I'm going to tell him. Yes, yes. Tomorrow I will tell him.*

Old Pete and Nicholas heard a scream. It was the man on the chains platform sounding with the lead line.

"By the mark, seven!"

"Seven fathoms!" Pete said to Nicholas under the roar of Captain Parker's swearing and shouting. "Forty-two feet! We must have come upon a bank. This, my young friend, will not be good. In this wind, we're liable to run aground if we are close to land."

Sailors dashed for the anchor and heaved it overboard into the blackness, almost sending one of the men with it. But the anchor was barely out of the ship when there was a mighty collision. The *Ella* shuddered and groaned, throwing men to the deck.

They had struck rock, and the *Ella* was breaking to pieces.

15

The Cape Verde Islands

"Get ready to get on the boat," Old Pete shouted to Nicholas.

But Nicholas had just thought of the slate. He heard Captain Parker calling for the small boats to be lowered and filled with men, but he dashed for the nearest hatch and shot down the ladder. The ship was sinking lower and lower, and no doubt the lower decks were already filling with water. Nicholas could hear a creaking noise. Perhaps the wood planks separating the decks were about to burst. Perhaps the hull was ripping in a new place. Perhaps he would soon be carried away by the water or trapped below deck.

But he must get Seger's slate.

Nicholas leaped to his bunk and reached under the mattress. He grabbed his bag. He was hurrying back toward the ladder when, by the light of the swinging lantern, he got a glimpse of something white in the farthest corner of a top bunk.

The orange and white cat! He pulled her out of her refuge and held her firmly as he scrambled back on deck.

Captain Parker screamed at Nicholas for going below, but Nicholas couldn't hear most of the words. He clambered over the side of the *Ella* into the boat where Gilbert was waiting for him.

Nicholas clung to the cat and his bag and Gilbert as the boat tossed toward shore. It seemed impossible that they would make it to land.

But they did. The boat was unloaded, and four sailors took it back to the *Ella*. Only when they touched solid ground did Nicholas release the cat.

Nicholas, Gilbert, and the others who had come ashore waited with ropes and a lantern, ready to pull in the next boat. They watched the fuzzy light of the lanterns on the boats, fearing the four sailors would come back empty-handed or not at all. Standing on land for the first time in weeks, Nicholas thought it seemed as if the land was rocking.

He clutched his bag, feeling the edges of the slate through the cloth.

In the darkness they saw the boats returning, lanterns held high, filled with men.

Nicholas snatched up a lantern and circled among the men, relief following relief as he saw first one face, then another.

Captain Parker was there with his box of charts and instruments.

Clark, the redhead, was there, whining as usual.

"If I couldn't use a draught of Plymouth whiskey about now," Clark said.

Old Pete!

Old Pete had waited to be the last man on the boat. He threw an arm around Nicholas.

"I told you it wouldn't be good, and I was right," Old Pete said. "But we are safe, and that is more than I thought possible on a night like tonight."

Seagull Sal, with his cittern!

Nicholas kept circling the groups of men, as they walked up the beach to a cluster of thatched-roof buildings. Finally, he could not help himself.

"Where's the cook?" Nicholas asked.

"Overboard," someone said.

Nicholas stopped walking. His lantern fell to his side. The men continued to pass him in the sand. A figure broke from the moving body and came back.

It was Old Pete. "Aye, Nicholas. He wanted to go. Didn't you hear him yesterday?"

"But," Nicholas said, "I was going to tell him something. Did he go over on purpose?"

"No. Big wave, swamped the deck right before the boats came back. We easily could have all gone with him."

But maybe, Nicholas thought, *maybe he didn't even try to hold on.*

Nicholas followed Old Pete to where the other men had gathered. A stout Portuguese man had been roused from bed. He spoke enough English to inform the men that they had shipwrecked on the Cape Verde Islands. Since the French had invaded last year and destroyed the city, the man said, not many people lived on this part of the island. He was a plantation owner, however, and they were welcome to camp in his barn.

As the captain made arrangements, the sailors sat in groups on the cliff. The eastern sky grew lighter, and plantation slaves emerged from thatched-roof huts.

Palm trees grew farther inland, and birds were singing, unlike any Nicholas had ever heard on Staten Island. An unfamiliar orange, white and black bird perched in a bush, watching the men. For a brief moment, Nicholas was back on the island at the mouth of the Fresh Kills. He was standing in the marsh grass with his brothers and a heron was lifting into the air, flapping its wings, and beside him a voice said—

Nicholas shook himself. He must not think about nightmares.

Below the gray rocks to the west, they could see the *Ella,* not so far from land. She lay there, black and red and broken in the churning water. The stump of her foremast pointed to the sky. The rigging that had connected the foremast to the ship had been cut during the night by the last men to leave. These cables and ropes hung from the ship like orphans, without purpose now that their parent mast was no more. A barrel had burst, probably filled with sea biscuit, and a whirl of water birds had descended on the scattered bits washing toward shore.

Nicholas scanned the wreckage for any sight of the man who had gone overboard. He searched what was visible of the red and black ship he loved, watching for a lone hand clinging to the wood. Finally, near noon, the *Ella* completely disappeared. Only a few floating planks and barrels bobbed in the blue water.

In the stickiness of midday, black slaves passed out mugs of strong drink sweetened with molasses. They ladled a thick stew into bowls for the sailors.

"*Cachupa,*" a pleasant woman said to Nicholas as she handed him the bowl.

"I don't understand you," Nicholas said.

"*Cachupa,*" she said again, this time pointing into the dish.

"Oh! The stew! Thank you!"

Beside him, Seagull Sal wolfed down the cachupa, brown juice trickling out of one corner of his mouth. Plymouth was several weeks behind them, so fresh ingredients were a treat, even in a foreign dish. Nicholas tasted green bananas, corn, sweet potatoes, beans, and fish in the stew.

Stretched out beside the orange cat, Nicholas fell asleep in the muggy afternoon.

He awoke, confused. He heard snoring around him in the darkness. The bed on which he was lying seemed to be rocking. He raised himself on his elbow and rubbed his eyes.

No. Not rocking. He was lying on the ground, which was completely still. That was what seemed so strange. He wished he were waking from a dream. But he was not. He was remembering a nightmare that had really happened. The *Ella* was gone.

She had held on longer than anyone expected, good ship that she was. She had saved the lives of most of the men on board by giving them a place to cling.

Noiselessly, Nicholas stood and stepped around the snoring men to the open end of the thatched building. Though on solid ground, he found his steps still clumsy.

The first thing he saw was the moon. It was almost first quarter, and Nicholas remembered his father teaching him about its phases. He remembered Pine saying, "The moon must be able to keep a great many guests in her quarters, but only until they are full."

So strange that the very same moon was here, in the middle of the Atlantic Ocean on an isolated island where palms and tropical birds lived. Nicholas wondered if anyone on Staten Island was looking at the moon at that moment, and an ache filled his heart. He should have written to them in Plymouth. Now, there was no *Ella* to write about.

"What awakens you, Nicholas?"

Nicholas jumped and found Old Pete nearby.

"Just woke up, I guess," Nicholas said. "Tell me about Whitby!" he added hastily. "You said you would some day."

"Ah," Pete said. "My hometown. It's a beautiful town, old abbey high on the cliffs, a little like these cliffs here! Nigh two hundred steps going up the hill to it. Old graves in there, hundreds of years old. Daughter of mine, she'd walk up there every night. She just loved those steps."

Nicholas wondered if his daughter was still alive but decided not to ask.

Hearing Old Pete talk of his home made Nicholas think of the cart path to the old stone house. How he would run down that path if he were there now! How he would leap over the split rail fence and knock loudly on the Dutch door. Jonah would come running, wild with joy. Father would wake up and ask, "Who's there?" and he would reply, "Nicholas," and Father would open the door and say, "Nicholas, you are a sailor and I'm so proud of you." Elizabeth and Isaac and Jacob would tumble down in their night clothes and Mother . . . Nicholas shook himself and inhaled a huge gulp of air to swallow the tears that threatened.

Mother would not be there, fussing over him and stirring up the fire so they could have tea. He had not thought of her much in the busy life aboard ship, but now he felt a pain as if he had swallowed a knife. He had left home so soon after Mother's death that he could not imagine the stone house without Mother.

The silhouette of a giant mountain rose high behind Pete's head. Nicholas quickly thought of something to say so he would not be alone with his thoughts. "How did we not see this island last night?" Nicholas asked. "It is so tall."

"Storms can't be reckoned with, Nic," Old Pete said. "Most likely Captain Parker thought our longitude was farther to sea than it was. There is no good way to measure longitude, you know."

"I know," Nicholas said. "Why doesn't someone find a way?"

"Aye, it isn't for not trying, boy. There are ways, but they are too expensive or too complicated for ordinary seamen—or not accurate. You should ask Captain Parker. He knows more than I. But I know that a few years ago, four British warships went down off the Isles of Scilly because they miscalculated their position."

"Did anyone die?" asked Nicholas.

"Nearly 2,000 men," Old Pete said. "The story goes that before the disaster, a seaman came to the captains and begged them to listen to him. He felt sure they were about to shipwreck on the rocks near Scilly."

"They didn't listen to him," Nicholas said, more as a statement than a question.

"They hung him. That's the story anyway. It might just be sailor's gossip. They say he was from the Isles of Scilly so he recognized the land. Who knows?"

Nicholas gulped.

"Remember, I told you that I also have seen the wrong man hung. The sea is not a civilized place. Each ship becomes its own country and the captain its king."

They were both quiet as Nicholas thought of how wonderful it would have been if the man had not been hung and had been able to see that he was right. Of course, he probably would have died anyway when the ships went down.

"What will happen to us here on this island, Pete?"

"Ah. Perhaps we can get word to an English ship. But right now? We are at the mercy of the Portuguese. I am hoping they treat their visitors well."

16

The Goodbye

"We are on top of the world, I think," Gilbert said as they reached a lookout and stopped to catch their breath.

"Oh," one of the men gasped. "Even Yorkshire can't hold a candle to this."

Seagull Sal began a song.

"Quiet!" hollered Clark. "Do you think we have breath enough for a song?"

The Portuguese plantation owner had packed the forty men off, claiming he did not have enough food to feed so many men. Considering the lush fields and pineapple groves, Captain Parker was not convinced. Still, he had accepted directions to the sea port on the other side of the island.

"How far?" Captain Parker asked.

"One day, one day," the portly man assured him, jowls shaking. "Captain take horse."

On their way up the mountainside, Nicholas found out that one day of hiking in the Cape Verde hills was a different matter than one day of walking on flat land. The two black slaves leading the way scrambled up the inclines without stopping to catch a breath. Captain Parker's borrowed horse was quite nimble as well. The rest of the men, though accustomed to climbing, quickly discovered that mountain-climbing muscles were different than rigging-climbing muscles.

Now for a moment, every man enjoyed the view. The hillside was terraced with stone walls, forming a giant stairway of cultivated strips of crops such as beans, onions, and squash. Sweet potato vines grew at their feet. Each terrace was several feet lower than the one beside it. Fog lay like a fleece at the bottom of the mountain, and beyond the fog, the ocean.

"My soul would find more pleasure in this view if I were here visiting on purpose," Clark said.

They all turned to keep climbing. Everyone would be happier when they reached the port with its familiar ropes and anchors and ships. Captain Parker had ridden ahead on the horse to make arrangements.

Going down the other side was easier. Nicholas decided that the rain must fall only on the west side of the island because the east side was brown and dry. The men finally arrived at the sandy port. Though it was scarcely evening, the hills cast a huge shadow over them and on out over the water. Their feet ached and their stomachs rumbled. Captain Parker met them and led them to a large bonfire where the people of the village were preparing a stew.

"*Cachupa,*" Nicholas said to the orange cat, for practice. He fed the cat bits of chicken from his bowl.

"Nicholas, come with me," Captain Parker said. "I may need a runner. I want to talk to this Spanish captain."

Nicholas ate his cachupa at the heavy wooden table of the tavern with Captain Parker, Captain Pedro, and their officers. Outside, the rest of the men lounged around the fire, gazing out to sea. Two ships were anchored in the deep water of the bay.

"Captain Pedro will take you and your men to an English port if you pay," the translator said to Captain Parker. "And he expects the men to help with the daily work of the ship."

"Can he take us to Gibraltar?" Captain Parker asked. "I can pay him in full there."

The translator, whose name was Joaquin, consulted with Captain Pedro. "Yes, yes, señor, he can."

That evening, the men discussed their options. The other ship was a Dutch East Indiaman, returning from India. It would go directly to Amsterdam, and it was offering payment to any able seaman since it was short on hands. Some of the men thought this would be preferable to the Spanish ship, which would only take them halfway to England and would not pay them. Old Pete arranged for passage on the Dutch ship.

Amsterdam held appeal for Nicholas; his father had visited there. But he was not an able seaman.

"They will take a boy, I think," Old Pete said.

Nicholas considered his reply. He felt he could not leave Captain Parker, who had taken him under his wing and taught him navigation. Captain Parker had spoken to him when he was much too young to go to sea. Captain Parker had commanded the beautiful *Ella,* now on the Atlantic floor or washing up against the Cape Verde cliffs. Nicholas would stick with Captain Parker.

Old Pete and Gilbert were both going on the Dutch ship. Bidding them good-bye was not easy.

"Perhaps we will see each other again," Old Pete said, slapping Nicholas on the shoulder, and then giving him a warm hug. "Keep your guard up, Nicholas. The sea is a tough place. It's filled with men who say one thing but mean another."

"What do you mean?" Nicholas asked. Old Pete's words irritated him. Why did Old Pete have to be so gloomy?

A bell behind them began to clang. The Spanish ship was boarding and Nicholas heard Captain Parker calling for him. "Take good care of your stowaway," Old Pete said, rubbing the cat's head and giving Nicholas' shoulder a final squeeze.

They left on the evening tide. Not until the ship cleared the island did Nicholas allow the cat out of his bag. He didn't think anyone would care if she were along, but he didn't want to give anyone a reason to put the cat on shore.

* *

Nicholas found himself relieved to be back at sea, even on the green and yellow Spanish *Valencia.* The wind blew steadily from the east, which would have been excellent for their original voyage to Jamaica. Now, they would head north to Spain and Gibraltar.

The *Valencia* was bigger than the *Ella* had been. There were sixty Spanish sailors, and a number of passengers in the hold. Captain Parker was permitted an officer's room in the stern. Nicholas and the other seamen from the *Ella* were given hammocks and shown where to hang them. There were only fifteen of them with Captain Parker. They were divided into watches and given instructions by Joaquin, the young translator. Seagull Sal was along. Nicholas was glad there would be English songs.

It was not Nicholas' watch, and the hammock quarters were cramped and dirty. Back on deck, Nicholas looked behind them for a final glimpse of the islands but he couldn't see them. Something seemed odd. The ship was sailing with the wind. He crossed to the port side. There was Cape Verde. The ship had come north out of the port, and was crossing back, heading due west with the wind.

Nicholas frowned. Perhaps the Spanish had different ways of sailing than the English. He looked for Captain Parker, but he was at dinner with the Spanish captain. Joaquin directed him to the room where the captains were eating.

The men were sitting in the low dining area, similar to the one on the *Ella*. Nicholas was surprised to see a woman serving the meal. He sat on the companionway steps, trying to blend into the wood paneling until the meal was finished.

The Spaniards pressed Captain Parker to drink and he did.

Captain Parker looked at Nicholas. "I will be up on deck in a few minutes," he said.

Nicholas nodded, understanding that was his dismissal. He climbed the stairs and walked to the bulwarks. The men were singing rowdy Spanish songs and a few were dancing around the mainmast.

Captain Parker arrived on deck, slightly giddy with drink. With an effort he forced himself to focus on the water. He looked up at the sails.

Nicholas wanted to ask him what he thought about the east wind. Were they really heading west? But Captain Parker knew so much more than he about navigation. He dared not bring it up first.

"A fine evening, Nicholas," Captain Parker said. "But I believe I'll turn in below and get some rest. When do you go on watch?"

"At eight bells, sir."

Midnight.

"Wake me up when your watch ends. My cabin is down the companionway, second door to the left."

"Aye, aye, sir!"

Nicholas found his hammock for a quick nap before his next watch. He kept thinking about the east wind filling the sails.

I must have been wrong, Nicholas thought as he drifted off to sleep.

17

The Cuban Castle

Nicholas had more time to think on the *Valencia*. He wished he had told the *Ella's* cook that he was the boy who had broken into his warehouse. He wished he would not be disobeying his mother by being at sea. He wished Old Pete had come with the *Valencia*. He wished his father would see how much he was learning.

To keep back the troubling thoughts, Nicholas decided to roam the ship. The Spanish sailors were even cruder than the men of the *Ella*. Their captain had brought his wife with him, and the men made frequent jokes about her. Actually, Nicholas wasn't sure she was his wife, as Joaquin interpreted the term *mujer* to mean *woman*.

In one of the rowdy dogwatch conversations, Nicholas heard the word *Cuba*. Where had he heard of Cuba before? Then, he remembered the chart of the West Indies Captain Parker had shown him. Perhaps the *Valencia* had just returned from Cuba.

On deck only a few days into the journey, a few of the *Ella's* crew were talking about Gibraltar. Captain Parker came toward them.

"Good to hear a language I understand," he said to the men. "But it is bad that I only now took a reading of our position. I trusted our progress to the Spaniards, but I am perplexed with our latitude. We appear to be farther south than we should be."

Nicholas stiffened.

"Maybe we're not going to Gibraltar," he said before he could stop himself. Then, seeing Captain Parker's face, he knew he might as well finish and hope he would not be hanged. "When we left Cape Verde, we seemed to be sailing with the east wind, sir."

Captain Parker stared at him. "I was at dinner with the Spanish men pouring drink into me," he finally said. "Are you sure, Nicholas? Why did you not tell me?"

"I–I am quite sure, sir, but I thought I might be wrong and that the Spanish might have different methods of sailing."

"Not even the Spanish sail west when they mean to go north," Captain Parker snapped, laughing in a way that was not humorous at all. He pulled the red handkerchief from his neck and smashed it into a ball. He spun and headed straight for the captain's cabin.

Soon raised voices were heard from below. Captain Parker reappeared on the steps of the companionway.

"Nicholas! Find that stubby-nosed translator and get him down here."

Nicholas hustled to find Joaquin, wondering why he hadn't noticed Joaquin's nose before. It *was* stubby, as were his fingers.

Joaquin talked the whole way to the cabin and was still talking when they joined the arguing men.

"Stop talking and listen!" Nicholas hissed.

The Spanish captain had reverted to pure Spanish in his attempt to explain matters to Captain Parker. Joaquin translated.

"He says, 'We will take you to Gibraltar if that is where you wish to go, but we must deliver our goods to Cuba first.' "

"Tell him," Captain Parker said, "that he is a weevil-bitten, green-livered liar." He rushed past Nicholas and up the steps to the deck. Nicholas stood rooted to the spot, then decided to follow Captain Parker. Joaquin followed Nicholas.

"I did not tell our captain that last message from your captain," Joaquin said confidentially to Nicholas.

Nicholas wanted nothing more than to be alone at that moment. "Please, Joaquin, I need to be alone with Captain Parker. He might have orders for me. Just stay close in case we need you again."

"Perhaps I can help you carry out the orders," Joaquin suggested.

Nicholas saw a fellow Englishman listening and laughing. Nicholas sighed. He could not shake his shadow.

"Couldn't tie a knot to save his life, that one," one of the *Ella's* men had growled, watching Joaquin. The sailor had forgotten that the boy spoke English, and Joaquin snapped an insult back about the man's torn and dirty uniform. Shipwreck had not been kind to the men's costumes.

As it was, there were no orders to receive. Captain Parker crumpled his red hand-kerchief and paced back and forth along the deck. Nicholas kept nearby, but just far enough away so as not to intrude.

His face was somber, but inside he felt smug. He had been right. He had noticed something that Captain Parker had missed. Captain Parker had scolded him for not sharing the information, as if Nicholas was a person whose opinion was reliable.

Captain Parker continued to pace.

The orange and white cat padded along close to Nicholas. By now, everyone knew that the cat belonged to him, and no one seemed to care. Nicholas squatted to pet her, running his hand across her back. The cat kept going, curling her tail against his fingers. She leaped onto a barrel to avoid the captain's booted feet. She balanced easily on the rounded side of the barrel and twitched her tail.

Captain Parker had reached the end of his pacing track and turned. Nicholas saw the captain's eyes flit toward the cat and narrow into slits. But there was no time to act.

The captain grabbed the cat's tail and threw her in a wide arc over the side of the ship. She screamed as she tumbled through the air and landed with a splash.

Nicholas gulped in horror. He clutched the side of the ship. He stared at the cat, tossing in the waves. He glanced up at Captain Parker in disbelief. The cap-tain looked back at him with a bitter smile, as if inflicting pain on other creatures was the only balm for his own pain. When the cat finally went down, Nicholas ran below deck, his eyes stinging.

It doesn't matter, Nicholas told himself. He pinched himself to keep from crying. *It was just a cat. It doesn't matter.*

But Nicholas wept in his hammock all the same.

He had let the orange cat die because he had not told Captain Parker the ship was going west. He had drowned her because he had been smug about noticing something before Captain Parker. Perhaps the captain had sensed his attitude and felt he should be disciplined.

Nicholas heard feet shuffling beside his hammock.

"Nicholas, are you all right? It's Sal."

The lower deck was shadowy. Nicholas sat up, hoping Seagull Sal could not see the redness of his eyes. He told Sal the story.

"Captain Parker is a good man only when it helps him get something," Seagull Sal said with disgust.

"It was my fault," Nicholas said, determined that Captain Parker had not been at fault. "I should have told him."

"Wasn't your fault he drowned the cat!" Seagull Sal said. "Only evil people torture animals."

That night, Nicholas tried to sleep, but he kept finding himself in water. There was always someone or something drowning. They were always out of his reach and it was always his fault.

In the days that followed, Joaquin continued to shadow Nicholas, talking endlessly in both Spanish and English. He pointed to objects and said the Spanish words. He also taught Nicholas to dip his hardtack into the coffee served at every mess and to keep drinking it until the bitterness decreased. Although Nicholas had resented his shadow at first, he found himself intrigued as Joaquin taught him to speak and understand Spanish.

• •

It was December 24 when the *Valencia* pulled up to a large castle on a wooded shore of Cuba. The castle was built into the rocks, and at places it was hard to tell what was castle and what was cliff. No ship could go up the river into the town of Santiago without passing the castle with its guns. High stone walls were topped with battlements, cut like teeth with a high part, then a low part, then a high, then a low. A round tower stood at one corner. It reminded Nicholas of a painting he had seen of a castle in Europe. He had not known there were castles on this side of the Atlantic Ocean.

"San Pedro de la Roca," Joaquin said at his elbow. "The castle of Saint Peter the Rock!"

"Why are we here?" Nicholas asked him.

"We always come here," Joaquin said.

Christmas Eve. Nicholas could almost see Mother knitting warm clothes for Christmas presents. He could almost smell Father's apple cider warming in a copper kettle over the fire. He thought of Mary stirring and kneading and sprinkling and chasing children away with her wooden spoon. He could almost taste the sugared breads and cookies from the stone oven on a cold night when snow fell deep and slow. He could almost hear Elizabeth squealing and begging Mary for a taste, her little hands folded on the edge of the table under her eager eyes.

Nicholas remembered running through the cold darkness to Pine's house for a popcorn battle and a story. There, Pine would tell him about the warm and sticky and beautiful islands of the West Indies where the slaves picked sweet stalks of sugar all day. But if they tried to taste the sugar, they might get their hand chopped off.

Pine was here! Nicholas thought. Had he seen the castle? Had he seen these green forests and rocks that appeared to be perched precariously on the ocean? Had Pine been in chains when he arrived? Had he nearly starved?

Captain Parker called Nicholas to assist him with his sea chest. "Thank you," he said when they had wrestled it up the companionway steps.

Captain Parker had never thanked Nicholas before. Nicholas looked at him. Captain Parker had handed his sea chest to a group of men who were lowering it toward a small boat.

"The next time you think a ship is going west when it should be going north, let your captain know immediately," Captain Parker said. "If you watch where you are going, you can keep out of trouble. You are a smart boy though. Perhaps I will see you again."

"But, sir, where are you going?" Nicholas blurted. Captain Parker could not leave! Nicholas had already parted with Old Pete. He would not have come on the *Valencia* at all had Captain Parker not been on board.

"It is each for his own in times like these," Captain Parker said. "A man must bargain to the best of his ability."

18

The Clang of the Door

December 1713

The Englishmen found themselves escorted to the castle and shown to a room with no windows and a bare stone floor. Their escort handed them a single candle. Amid the odors of a stinking bucket, Nicholas smelled the hot breath of his shipmates and the vomit of a sick man. Another man's gums were swollen and bleeding, and everyone was afraid he had scurvy.

Nicholas lay down beside Seagull Sal.

"I've never been in prison before," Sal hissed, "but it must feel a little like this. Where is Captain Parker anyway?"

"I think he went to bargain with someone," Nicholas said. "Probably he will get us released in the morning."

That night, Nicholas dreamed he was sitting in a tree along the Fresh Kills.

Jonah dived for water birds in the tall grass. The night herons rested in the trees, waiting for dusk. Daniel and Seger came from the fields to go swimming, and Nicholas sighed with pleasure.

Seger and Nicholas followed Daniel through the tall cordgrass and cattails. Jonah ran, first ahead of them, and then behind. The mud sucked at their bare feet with every step. Rain began to fall.

Daniel was the first to dive in off the bank. A slow rain created dimples and ripples on the water's brown surface. Seger and Nicholas dived in and followed Daniel. They struck off across the wider part of the kill, and came up dripping on the shore of the island. Their feet squashed in the mud of the grassy meadow.

Geese, snipes, and sandpipers lifted out of the grasses. A shiny wet sandpiper with a fish still dangling from its mouth eyed them suspiciously and then flapped away. Daniel killed a heron with a carefully thrown rock, and robbed its nest of the eggs. Seger tried to get a blue butterfly to land on his hand.

Suddenly a giant log came toward them, the size of a ship. Nicholas tried to duck, and then he was running, running, running, as fast as he could. He slipped and slid up the bank toward home. He fell, and a stump gouged his shoulder. He ran into the house. He burst upon his father, who was still at his wooden desk, dipping a quill into an ink bottle.

"Maybe you should watch where you are going," Father chided.

"Maybe you should watch where you are going," Captain Parker said from the other side of the room.

Nicholas awoke wet with sweat. He lay still in the darkness, hoping he had not been shouting in his sleep. He wondered when Captain Parker would be back.

When the sun rose, a man in Spanish uniform brought a tray of wooden bowls filled with gray gruel. He told them Captain Parker had gone to Jamaica to board a ship returning to England. To bribe the Spaniards for his release, he had left them with fifteen English sailors and one English boy to do with as they pleased.

The bilingual Spaniard smiled broadly and shut the prison door with a clang.

The room began to babble, voices snapping and snarling in frustration, confusion, and fear.

Nicholas did not even hear the noise in the room. Inside his mind, the chaos was even worse.

When the door clanged shut, the door to the life Nicholas had known shut with it. The world of wonder and delight he had anticipated ever since Captain Parker had invited him to sea was forever cursed. The wonder he had felt at the Staten Island mill when he heard Captain Parker was looking for sailors turned to darkness. Nicholas saw now that his defense of Captain Parker's torture of the cat had not been based on courage and loyalty, but on stupidity and blindness. He had chosen Captain Parker over Old Pete because he thought it would give him a better chance to advance. His decision had cost him his freedom and might cost him his life.

Seagull Sal began a mournful chantey about the Fiddler's Green. Nicholas had listened to enough songs to know that the Fiddler's Green was the place sailors went after they died.

"Stop!" Nicholas protested. "Just stop!"

"Sing a carol, you croaking bird!" someone suggested with a bitter laugh.

Seagull Sal came over to Nicholas, holding his bowl of gruel.

"Do you think what the man said is true?" he asked.

Seagull Sal held the bowl up and slurped gruel from its rim. Ribbons of gray streamed from the corners of his mouth. He wiped his jaw with the back of his hand.

At one time, Nicholas would have burst with pride that an older sailor would ask the opinion of the cabin boy. Now, the question was just a bitter reminder of the trust Nicholas had once had in their captain.

"I hate him," Nicholas spat out. "If I ever see him again, I will kill him."

"I tried to tell you," Seagull Sal said. "But just because Captain Parker killed your cat doesn't mean that Spaniard is telling us the truth that he deserted us."

"It proves he is evil enough to do it," Nicholas snapped.

Nicholas tried to ignore the whining men, forcing himself to eat the slimy, tasteless porridge. He tried to coax the man with the bleeding gums to eat some too, but he could not.

That evening, Nicholas used his best Spanish to ask for his friend Joaquin.

Joaquin came up to see them within the hour.

"Ah, no, I think not," Joaquin said. "No, no, you are not prisoners, no! They are giving you a room to stay here until another English ship comes along! And if that English ship has Spanish passengers, perhaps they will do a trade."

"Can we go outside?" Nicholas asked.

"No, no," Joaquin said, brushing off the question as if nothing could be more absurd. "It is the *Navidad.*"

"I know it's Christmas!" Nicholas said. "That's why I want to go outside and get us some fresh air. Take us out, Joaquin!"

In the light of the lantern he held, Joaquin's stubby nose turned several shades paler.

Five minutes later, they were silently following Joaquin down a flight of stone steps. Every man of the fifteen had insisted on coming along.

They followed Joaquin through a number of archways. The white plaster ceilings most likely covered red bricks and stone. The castle was nearly a hundred years old, they had been told, and patches of red brick reinforced areas where the stonework had crumbled. They dropped into a curving stairway with a fine sheen of moisture across the bricks and then to a passageway with a dirt floor.

"You taking us out the back way, Joaquin?" Nicholas asked pleasantly.

"Shhhh!" Joaquin said. For once, he had no words.

I think we are prisoners, Nicholas thought. *That is, we were prisoners.*

Despite the danger, excitement bubbled inside him. This would make a great story! Pine and Father and Daniel—they would never believe this one. Escaping from a castle with stone steps and wet passageways. And on Christmas Eve!

Then, Nicholas remembered the warehouse of his childhood and how easy he thought it was to break in. They were not out of danger. He must not let down his guard. They could all be shot at a moment's notice.

Nicholas felt a light breeze on his face.

"So you are in the fresh air," Joaquin hissed. "No soldier will come to this place for half an hour if you wish to run. Farther down, there are fishering boats on the water. Perhaps you can take one to Jamaica? It is only thirty or forty leagues."[1]

"Only!" said Seagull Sal.

The men looked at each other in the dimness. They had no food or fresh water or navigational skill. They were out of the castle, but what now? Traveling one hundred miles in a small fishing boat didn't exactly sound like a Christmas game. One man was already ill.

"Perhaps you should stay in the castle," Joaquin said. "The captain will have an idea."

"Where can we get a little fresh water?" one of the men asked.

"Oh close, very close!" Joaquin said. "I will take you. Some of you go to coast and find boat. Some come with me. Too many people."

He plunged into the Cuban jungle, the lantern held high. Nicholas walked at the head of the line, beside Joaquin. Half the men had headed the other way to the shore. Nicholas felt something cool and thin brush his forehead.

"What's that?" Nicholas asked, hoping it was only a leaf or a vine. At the edge of the lantern light, a golden eye set in a red eyeball looked at them. Nicholas thought he could make out a ragged spiny back with a fringe of leathery triangles.

"Ah! He? *Es una iguana,*" Joaquin said, laughing. "Great big Cuban iguana. They eat only Englishmen, but not on Christmas."

The line of Englishmen laughed nervously.

Half an hour later, they were down by the shore. The other men had selected the largest boat for their escape. In it they found several nearly empty water casks. These they emptied and a party of men took them back to the spring that Joaquin had shown them. In the jungle, Joaquin had snagged several oranges.

"For that man," he said, pointing to the man with the bleeding gums. "Make better."

The moon was waxing gibbous and the sky was as clear as a Christmas painting. The men spoke softly as they splashed around the boat in preparation.

"Everyone is going to Christmas Mass," Joaquin said, "but still we should darken

---

[1] One league is about 3½ miles.

the lantern or they might shoot from the castle."

The dark shape of the castle loomed against the starry night sky. Nicholas didn't doubt that the guards on duty would be only too glad to put their guns to use. Finally, with a scraping sound, they pushed the boat out and climbed in. It was only about twenty feet long.

I'm stealing again, Nicholas thought dully. *But I don't care.*

"Thank you, Joaquin," Nicholas said he stood in the shallow water preparing to jump into the boat. "Thank you very much. You are a good friend."

"Get in, get in," Joaquin said. "And then I will get in."

"You . . . are coming? With us?" Nicholas faltered as he leaped into the boat. Telling Joaquin he was not welcome would be complicated when he had just told him that he was a good friend.

"Yes, yes, I will come with you. Then I will bring the boat back."

It was ridiculous to think that one man would bring a twenty-foot boat 100 miles back across the water, but Nicholas held his peace. Probably Joaquin would be punished if he stayed and it were discovered that he had been in the castle on the night the Englishmen escaped. Nicholas gave Joaquin a hand into the boat.

They shoved off with a splash, keeping to the shaded water under the trees until they could gain distance from the castle. Nicholas glanced up at the gibbous moon. He thought of Staten Island again, and how he was so, so far from the life he had once known.

Then, with the quiet churning of the oars through the water, Nicholas remembered his mother's voice coaching him from the book that King James had printed.

"If I take the wings of the morning, and dwell in the uttermost part of the sea, even there shall thy hand lead me and thy right hand shall hold me. If I say, surely the darkness shall cover me, even the night shall be light about me."

Could God see him now, trying to escape in the darkness?

The Royal

1720, Jamaica, seven years after the escape from the castle

A dark feminine hand reached for his pewter mug, and Nicholas heard the splash of liquid. The mug thumped onto the wooden table and the candles flickered. A violin played in a corner of the tavern, and the smell of roasting meat and fresh vegetable stew filled the air.

"You come back," the waitress coaxed, as she reached for the mugs around the table and continued to pour.

Nicholas looked up, and recognized the Jamaican girl smiling down at him. She was dressed in green with a red scarf wrapped around her head. When she was finished pouring drinks, she let her elbow fall on his shoulder and her hand tousled his hair.

The men around Nicholas laughed. Seagull Sal was one of them, the only man Nicholas still knew from his early days at sea. Joaquin had fallen in battle on the deck of a pirate ship not long after their escape from the castle. The merchant ship had won the battle, recovering its treasures, but the loss of Joaquin had affected Nicholas more deeply than he had thought possible. He wished Joaquin had died on their own ship, where he could have had a proper burial, rather than on a pirate's deck.

Seagull Sal held his cittern on his knee and lazily watched the violinist in the corner. Seven years had not changed his eating habits, and bread crumbs lay about him like an ever present shadow.

Nicholas shrugged and took a drink, then reached into his pocket and slipped a coin to the girl.

"Your name is Sunny, is it not?" he asked. "Buy a new scarf, different color. I do not like red."

"Yes," she said, slipping the coin into the head piece. "Yellow, maybe?"

"Yes, yellow," he said. "Like the moon." He regretted the mention of the moon as soon as it slipped out. It reminded him of his godly mother. She would not like to see what he had become.

Nicholas was nineteen years old and the second mate on the *Yorkshire Dame*, newly arrived from Portsmouth, England. After escaping from the Cuban castle seven years before, he had taken up passage on merchant ships traveling from England to Africa to the West Indies and back to England. Sometimes they went to the American colonies, but he had not been back to Staten Island.

In those seven years, Nicholas had studied navigation with anyone who would teach him. He took out Seger's old slate every day and wrote his latitude and longitude on it. He learned to use the back staff and cross staff, and to estimate the angle of the sun before he measured it. His attention to navigation had gained him the respect of his superiors, who steadily advanced him to higher-paying positions. He was now third in command of the *Yorkshire Dame*, and Seagull Sal's superior.

Nicholas spent time with the women in the Atlantic sea ports. He knew the girls personally and often brought them presents. He knew their lives were corrupt. Many of them worked in the dance houses and taverns only because they had to feed family members. Some were the wives of sailors whom they rarely saw. Nicholas promised himself that if he ever married, he would become a landsman. He would not leave his family to go to the sea. But these promises to his future self did not stop him from his pursuit of pleasure in the moment.

Nicholas swore deliberately and often. He found that wild words and explosive cursing, dispensed in just the right quantity, gained him respect from the sailors. He had started with mild language. Now, without a twinge of guilt, he used the names of God and words from Scripture in his oaths. The captains read the same words in Scripture on Sunday, but it no longer bothered Nicholas.

In his advances up the chain of command, Nicholas had not neglected his relationship with Seagull Sal and the other men before the mast. Because he played checkers, told jokes, and shared his beer, he had many friends. He stayed up all night in the port cities and stayed awake during the day for his shift on the ship. One never knew what dangers would befall a ship at sea. Why not have a good time in port between the grueling voyages?

Nicholas occasionally tried to pray, but only in terrible storms when death seemed near. There were many times a sailor was not sure he would be alive in the morning. But did the prayers make a difference? Nicholas had left God when the door had clanged shut in the Cuban prison. Perhaps, as many of the men said, the Bible was just an old book that people passed down from year to year because they liked to tell others what to do. Maybe God was just a legend.

Sometimes, he thought of his childhood with fondness. When he saw brown and white dogs, he thought of Jonah. When sailors around him fell sick and died of scurvy, he remembered Mary telling him to eat his vegetables. Climbing the highest masts, he thought of Pine calling up the kitchen chimney when the snow came down. Little girls on the streets of the port cities, or pouring water in the taverns, reminded him of Elizabeth. When he saw the moon, he thought of evenings with his mother. She had told him in her soft voice that he had a bright mind and could learn whole chapters of the Bible.

But Mother was no longer on Staten Island. From the few letters he received, months after they were written, he knew his father had remarried. Although he longed to see Elizabeth and his little brothers who were now teenagers, he wasn't sure if he wanted to see his father or a step-mother he did not know.

If he went home, would Father be proud of his achievements? His father would certainly not like his language. He would not like the man Nicholas had become. Nicholas could not endure the thought of his father turning him away, so he pushed the unpleasant thoughts into the darkest corners of his active mind.

He had not been able to push them from his subconscious mind, however. In his sleep, Nicholas continued to see churning water. Sometimes he was looking for the hand of a boy. Sometimes he was looking for the paw of a cat. Always, there was only water. Sometimes Captain Parker was standing there watching him, crumpling his red handkerchief. Sometimes, the man watching was his father. But the man, whichever one, always frowned at him and asked him why he hadn't done a better job.

When Nicholas awoke, sweating, he sometimes imagined throwing Captain Parker into the water. Then he would stand, smiling, on the deck of the ship and watch him go down, down, down.

Nicholas tried to forget the dreams by laughing harder and climbing higher. Only when alone with Seagull Sal did he talk about his obsession with throwing Captain Parker overboard if he ever saw him again.

"Would you really do it?" Seagull Sal asked.

"Without regret," Nicholas said. He could tell that Seagull Sal admired his courage.

A new batch of sailors entered the tavern, ducking through the low door. They stopped to look for a table, several nearly bumping their heads on the heavy beams.

Nicholas glanced at them and turned away, but he shook himself and looked again, eyes suddenly fixed. He pushed back his stool and jumped up.

"Pine!"

Nicholas stood before his old friend and realized that they were the same height. Pine was almost completely gray, which was a change from when he stood on the shore waving goodbye to Nicholas and the *Ella*.

"Pine! How did you come to be here?"

Pine looked at the tall young officer, not unpleasantly, but without comprehension. Then, as his eyes moved from the white vest and scarf to the face and eyes, a look of warmth and pleasure filled his face.

"Could this be our boy Nicholas?" he asked, his hand on Nicholas' elbow.

"That's Nic," someone said. "But he's a second mate, not a boy!"

"I see that," said Pine, and then he wound his one and a half skinny arms around Nicholas and squeezed him nearly breathless with a tight hug. "Ahoy, matey! You still have both of your arms!"

"And you're still missing one of yours!" Nicholas exclaimed. "Let's go outside. We won't be able to hear each other in here."

It was twilight, but Port Royal—the part that had not sunk in the tsunami—was still bustling. Lanterns flickered here and there. Great ships could be seen in the harbor. In the night breeze, the wide leaves of the banana trees rustled. People called to each other as they passed in the streets. The wooden sign of the tavern squeaked as it swung on an iron hinge. It was known simply as "The Royal," with a crown painted on the sign for the benefit of all who could not read. They walked toward the water and pointed out the ships on which they had arrived.

"Why are you here?" Nicholas asked again in bewilderment, holding Pine's elbow in his long fingers.

"Why, my boy," Pine said as if he were offended, "I been to sea a heap long time before you been able to walk on dry land!"

"How is Elizabeth? And Father? And Daniel and Lambert and Susannah and Catharine and Isaac and Jacob?"

Pine chuckled.

"I been to sea for ten month, but when I left, that Elizabeth, she was as pretty as a picture. Golden hair and blue eyes just like your mama. Only reason it makes me hurt every time I see her is she come up to me, come right up to old Pine, and she says, 'When will Nicholas come home?' "

"I just . . ." Nicholas faltered.

"Oh, your Pa's new wife Mary? She's fine. But when her and your father got married, they let my Mary go free. Well, 'Lizabeth, she wouldn't have it, so we stayed close by. But now that she's used to the other Mary, she do just fine. My Mary is nanny to your sister Catharine's children. And since she be doing that and we be needing a little extra money, I took up for cook on the *Silver Susan.*"

"And my brothers?"

"Good, good. 'Cepting . . ."

"What?"

"Daniel."

"Daniel?"

"Off the coast of Africa on a ship that went down. News came just before I left."

No sorrow flooded Nicholas at that moment. *I should feel sad,* he thought. But all he felt was relief. *No one can blame me for his death. I was a thousand miles away.*

"I saw Captain Parker in London," Pine said. "I asked about you and he said he didn't remember having a boy named Nicholas with him."

"Lucky for him I wasn't there," Nicholas said. "He'll remember a boy named Nicholas when I strangle him with his red handkerchief and throw him overboard."

"Nicholas, my boy, no!"

"I don't want to talk about it," Nicholas said. "Let me tell you about my friend Joaquin."

They talked news for awhile. In both England and the New World people spoke of the longitude prize offered by Queen Anne—10,000 pounds to anyone who could solve the problem of finding longitude to within one degree on a voyage from England to the West Indies. The prize increased to 15,000 pounds if the longitude were measured accurately to two-thirds of a degree, and 20,000 pounds if calculated to half a degree. There were no rules about the method, but everyone was counting on either the stars or a watch that could keep time at sea.

Finally, Pine spoke solemnly.

"Nicholas. You have not been home for seven years."

"No," Nicholas said. "But I will go sometime."

"The sea is not a place for *sometime,*" Pine said. "Go home."

20

The Jolly Roger

"Deck there! Sail ho! Vessel behind us to larboard at 45 degrees. Flag not determined."

"Keep us advised," the first mate replied through the speaking trumpet.

It was noon on the day of departure. On the quarterdeck Nicholas stood with legs spread wide, sighting the sun with his back staff. He recognized the voice of Seagull Sal on the lookout perch.

The *Yorkshire Dame* was heading north from Jamaica to deliver sugar to the Carolinas and pick up tobacco to take back to England. Also hidden in the hold was cargo pirated from Spain but not yet returned to England—gold valued at several thousand English pounds. The captain and first mate had personally stowed the valuable cargo, and no one else was to know it was on board.

In half an hour, the sails of a ship could be seen from the deck. The captain pulled out his telescope, but no flag could be seen.

"Masthead!" shouted the captain. "What colors?"

"Flying English colors, sir!" the lookout said. "But doesn't look like an English ship to me, sir."

"Nicholas, up with you," the captain said. "These rum-sodden lookouts can't tell a snow from a brig."

Nicholas was glad for the chance to climb the ropes, especially since his friend was at the top. In the lookout Seagull Sal handed him the spyglass. Nicholas steadied himself with his feet and elbows as the mast rolled from side to side in its normal rhythm on a mild sea. He studied the image behind the lens for a long time, moving the spyglass from place to place and re-aligning it when the roll of the ship disrupted his position. He studied each sail and noticed the poor patching on nearly all of the sails. An English flag was flying, as Seagull Sal had said.

"I agree with you," Nicholas said finally, lowering the glass and handing it back to Seagull Sal. "If they don't hoist a Jolly Roger[1] before this is done, I'll give you my rum at mess."

Nicholas shinnied back down the mainmast.

"As stated, sir," Nicholas said. "Three-masted brig flying the Union Jack. Sails are patched with poor work and mismatching canvas."

"You suspect pirates?" the captain asked.

"I do," Nicholas said, feeling his heart rate accelerate as he answered.

Pirates were not interested in negotiation. If they won a battle with a merchant vessel, they demanded that the victims join them or be killed. Everyone knew about the "Terrible Three," a pirate known as Calico Jack and two fierce women who prowled the Caribbean with him. The governor of Jamaica had put out a warrant for their arrest. Perhaps they were the ones heading toward them now.

Pine was right, Nicholas thought. *I've run out of chances, and here I will die on the Caribbean without getting to see my family again.*

If they were captured, he could join the pirate crew to save his life. But the punishment for piracy was death. What would his father think if he heard that his son was being hanged as a pirate? It would be better to hear that his son had died at the hands of pirates.

The tropical sun burned down on the ship. Nicholas went to the quarterdeck to finish his figures, melted tar sticking to the bottom of his shoe. The captain spread his chart and determined to turn north and attempt the safety of civilization. They were not far from San Salvador, the port of the Bahamas where Christopher Columbus had landed in 1492. The wind would be with them instead of abeam.

The *Yorkshire Dame* turned north. The mystery ship followed all afternoon, gaining on them but not getting close enough to hail. At night a heavy fog fell over the Caribbean. Absolutely nothing could be seen.

At 4 a.m. Nicholas came on duty with the starboard watch. A few hours later the darkness began to lift, but the fog remained.

"Masthead, there!" called the captain. "Anything in sight?"

"Nothing, sir!"

At eight bells, the watch ended. Nicholas' watch spread their oil cloth on the

---

[1] Jolly Roger refers to a flag depicting a skull and crossbones, flown by pirate ships about to attack.

weather deck for breakfast.

"Depressing fog, this," one man grumbled.

"I don't mind the fog as much as I mind eating bread again," another man grumbled. The vegetables and meat of Jamaica had given them a fresh longing for something other than brick-like biscuit.

Nicholas drank his coffee and ate the small pile of salt pork that tasted of wooden barrel. He realized too late that his coffee was gone and his bread was not. He thought of throwing the bread overboard, but he was too hungry for that. He held the hard morsel between his fingers, and then popped it into his mouth before he could think a minute longer of what might now be living in the bread.

"Deck there! Ship astern! Jolly Roger flying, sir. We can see men on deck."

Nicholas felt a strange sense of calm. All night he had been worrying about the mystery ship and now all doubt was removed. They were about to be attacked by pirates.

"Fresh eyes," one of the men mumbled.

"The fog is lifting too," Nicholas noted.

As the fog lifted, everyone on deck saw the ship take shape, only a mile away. Oars protruded from portholes. Pirate ships were often re-purposed merchant ships designed to turn on a dime. The oars enabled them to move by muscle even when there was no wind. As he watched, the oars moved in tandem. The ship was ready to run them down.

The *Yorkshire Dame* was not equipped to fight. She had only two small guns on each side. She was not a warship.

However, she was fast. Perhaps they could outrun the pirates.

The wind did not cooperate. It blew in light puffs that pushed the *Yorkshire Dame* forward for a bit, and then left her tossing, becalmed, in the green water. The pirate ship continued to pull toward them foot by foot, by the power of the long oars. The men on both ships could see each other.

"Prepare the guns," Captain Parker said. "Helmsman, when I give the word, turn hard starboard. Back the main topsail!"

"Ahoy mates! Let's make this easy," one of the pirates called, a Spanish voice speaking English. "We need your box of Spanish gold. It is not England's gold, it is Spain's. Hand that over and no one gets hurt and you are on your way. We know how much, so whoever tries to trick us will be torn to pieces."

In reply, the *Yorkshire Dame* swung to the right at the captain's word.

Nicholas stood beside the captain, his hand gripping his cutlass.

"Fire!" cried the captain, and the men at the guns lit the fuses. With a boom, both guns went off and leaped backwards. The *Yorkshire Dame* heeled to the larboard side. Smoke filled the air.

"Hard to larboard," the captain said, swinging the ship about to allow the larboard guns to be used while the starboard side reloaded.

"Fire!"

This time, the pirate ship fired seconds before the *Yorkshire.* A fountain of water shot up from the sea past the *Yorkshire,* showing that the pirates had overshot with one gun. But above his head, Nicholas heard the splintering of one of the yards where a cannon ball had made a direct hit. Through the smoke, splinters of wood showered, and then a large piece of the yard split off and plunged over the side with a splash.

The guns of the *Yorkshire* tore new holes into the sails of the pirate ship, but the masts stayed strong.

Nicholas heard a whizzing noise and saw a grappling hook fasten itself in the mizzen topsail. The pirates intended to board the *Yorkshire Dame.* The cable grew taut, then slackened as the pirate ship came closer. Nicholas saw pirates crouched near the bulwarks, ready to spring.

"Fire!" the captain said to the men at the swivel gun. With a boom and a cloud of smoke, one of the pirates disappeared.

The others, however, leaped across the bulwarks onto the *Yorkshire Dame.* Metal flashed and the men began to fight hand to hand. Pistols banged and men fell to the deck.

Nicholas ran to the edge of the ship where the men were leaping across. He swung his cutlass with one arm and grabbed the foot of one of the pirates with the other. The man toppled backward against the man behind him. They collided in midair, and both fell into the water. They would probably reappear soon unless sharks got them, but at least he had delayed them.

The captain of the pirate ship had boarded the *Yorkshire Dame* with his men. Through the smoke, Nicholas saw a pistol ball knock off his battered three-cornered hat. This captain was not Calico Jack or one of the savage pirate queens— it was his old friend, Joaquin.

"Joaquin!" Nicholas screamed. "Hold your fire!"

Nicholas knew he could be demoted for giving commands. He was not in charge. But this was his friend, the boy who had rescued them from a cold Cuban castle on Christmas Day. This was his friend who he thought had been killed in a battle with pirates.

Joaquin turned and recognized Nicholas. But as he turned, one of Nicholas' shipmates thrust his cutlass into Joaquin's side.

"Hold your fire!" Joaquin shouted to his men. Then he stumbled and collapsed.

Nicholas ran to him, bending over him so it would be clear that they were friends. "Joaquin, what is this?" he asked. "Are you all right, my man?"

"Dying on a deck, as I always hoped I would," Joaquin gasped. "Nicholas, carry me back to my ship and I'll tell my men to back off, for your sake."

Nicholas stared in disbelief. How could a boy who had once annoyed him so thoroughly be saving his life for the second time?

"But . . . you fell years ago . . . in the battle!" Nicholas stammered out.

"Fell, but I did not die," Joaquin said. "Carry me back to my ship. I am going now. I will call off my men."

"We are old friends," Nicholas said to the captain of the *Yorkshire Dame*. "He tells me to carry him back to his ship and he will bid us goodbye."

Nicholas secured his cutlass on his belt and lifted Joaquin in his arms, alone. Joaquin was still a small man, though he must have been at least twenty-five by now.

The pirates who were left on board the *Yorkshire* retreated sulkily to their own ship, clearly furious at the interruption of battle. The captain of the *Yorkshire* ordered the grappling hook cut. As the crew cut the lines with their knives, the captain watched soberly, his bloody hand still clutching his cutlass.

"Nicholas, this is madness," Seagull Sal said from the group of men watching. "Let one of their own men take him back."

"I will take him," Nicholas said. "You don't have to wait for me. I won't abandon him this time."

Men from both sides steadied Nicholas as he made the delicate transfer from ship to ship with a grown man in his arms. The pirate ship pitched up just as he reached his foot forward. He almost slipped, but the momentum of his leap and two brawny pirate hands pulled him across.

Nicholas didn't know how many men had been killed or injured on each side, but he could see that Joaquin was going to be among the mortally wounded. His color was gray and his breath was coming in short gasps. Bright red blood dyed Nicholas' white uniform from the deep wound in his side, the wound that Nicholas had caused by calling for Joaquin's attention and so allowing a man to strike him.

"Puedes orar?" Joaquin asked. "Can you pray?"

21

The Pirate Ship

Nicholas stared at his dying friend.

"Joaquin! I haven't prayed . . . in a very long time."

Joaquin's eyes were fixed. His breaths were the merest puffs of air. Did it hurt to try?

"God, have mercy on this man's soul," Nicholas said in Joaquin's ear.

Nicholas felt the pirate ship moving. He had no doubt that the oars were backing them away from the *Yorkshire Dame* in an effort to kidnap him.

"He's gone," one of the pirates above him said. "He always wanted to be thrown overboard immediately, no formalities. You, sea-dog, will stay with us or join him at the bottom of the sea. We need men."

Nicholas merely nodded at the death threat. There in the morning mist with shrouds of fog still hanging above the water, it was exactly what he was expecting. *Join us, or die.* No doubt Joaquin had met the same situation and worked himself up to the position of captain.

Despite his grief for his friend, Nicholas couldn't help but be surprised that Joaquin had become a captain. In the days of the *Valencia,* Joaquin couldn't even tie knots. The pirates must be desperate for men.

Nicholas felt his cutlass being pulled from his belt and its point edged against his back.

"As you say, mates," Nicholas said, "I will join you. But let me bury my old friend. He wanted to be dropped into the sea immediately, you say. Bring some cannon balls and a piece of canvas."

Nicholas had been at sea long enough to know the proper preparation of dead bodies. A piece of sail cloth was wrapped around them and something heavy was tucked inside the grave clothes to keep the corpse from floating.

"Nay, we don't have spares like that on this ship," one of the men snapped. "He just goes over."

"Aye. Then we will use his cutlass."

The men grumbled audibly. Obviously they wanted to keep the knife, but Nicholas didn't care. It wouldn't weigh down the body sufficiently to keep it from floating. Still, it was the only choice.

He ignored the men as he carried Joaquin's body to the edge of the ship. They had lost their captain, and had not chosen a new one. They were treating him with a certain respectful hope that he, in his fine officer's clothes, might be a lucky break for them.

Nicholas lifted the dead man to his shoulder and with effort stepped onto the shrouds of the foremast. He stopped for a moment of silence, then dropped his friend into the water.

Splash!

Another loved one, gone under the water. And now Nicholas was a captive again. He had not had time to get his personal belongings, left on the other ship. Not even Seger's slate.

He stepped onto the deck. His hands were sticky with blood.

"Your pump?" he asked. The men pointed him to the water pump.

That night, the pirate ship cast anchor off one of the smaller Bahama Islands. The sailors carefully guided the ship into the shadows of overhanging trees.

"British warships prowling," one of the men said shortly to Nicholas. "Got to lie low."

Nicholas nodded. He had agreed to join the men. There was nothing else to do if he wished to live.

Maybe I'll get richer faster this way. It was no secret that pirates sometimes made much more money than legal seamen. But just the year before a crew of pirates had been hung on Providence Island in the center of the Bahamas. Nicholas might not have long to live. *I'll never see Father again either way,* Nicholas thought.

The moon was rising splendidly when Nicholas came on deck for his watch. His throat tightened as he heard his mother's voice coaching him with those same old words. *Even there shall thy hand lead me, and thy right hand shall hold me. If I say, surely the darkness shall cover me . . .*

"Ship ho!" hissed the man in the rigging. "Not a noise!"

Like a deer stepping across a field at night, the ship slid through the water about a mile away. It appeared to be heading straight for the island hiding the pirate ship. Would it come right past, or would it turn and cut west into the sound? The moon was bright enough that they could see it was a merchant ship, not a huge warship.

"Shall we attack her?" Nicholas asked.

"Go alert the acting captain," the man on the rigging said.

The pirate ship was in a state of disorder, since they had not yet finalized their choice of captain. They had been planning to vote in the morning, with one of the veteran sailors acting as captain in the meantime.

Since the approaching ship was not a warship, the watching men were no longer afraid of it.

"Aye, aye, sir," Nicholas said.

He hurried down the ladder to the lower deck. He stepped past the sleeping men in their bunks, including the acting captain. In the stern, he climbed the companionway steps to the quarterdeck. No one was there. The men on the rigging were turned the other direction while watching the approaching ship. Nicholas swiped a length of thin rope and tied one end fast to the bulwarks. Like a monkey, he climbed over the side and shinnied down the rope. He slid into the water without a splash, and struck off at a right angle to the approaching ship. He would have to make a wide arc around the pirate ship or the pirates would shoot him easily. Could he swim fast enough to make it to the merchant ship before it was past?

Nicholas struck off underwater away from the pirate ship. He surfaced for air and immediately went down again. The pirates would begin shooting as soon as they spotted him. He swam straight ahead, knowing he would have to turn at just the right time to catch his new ride. He came up twice more and wiped saltwater and seaweed from his eyes. His direction had been excellent. The merchant ship was still several hundred yards away, but he was far enough from the pirate ship to begin the turn.

But as he congratulated himself, a fountain of water shot into the air five feet in front of him. A musket ball, still within range. The pirates were shooting at him. He dove and swam for his life, stopping only for quick breaths. He thought of how often he had seen sharks in these waters, but he didn't dwell on that.

Nicholas came up for air, happy to be alive and confident he was out of range of the guns. However, the shots had alerted the merchant ship to the presence of the pirates, and the ship had taken a hard turn starboard. It would increase the distance Nicholas would need to swim.

Exhaustion filled his body like a dye, leaking into every muscle. *I don't know if I can make it.*

Had the lookout on the merchant ship spotted him and realized the musket balls were intended for him? The moon cast sufficient light, but it was hard to pick out an object in the ever-shifting canvas of the waves. Was the pirate ship intending to pursue him or attack the merchant ship? Would the merchant ship take him aboard if they did see him?

But I don't want to die, Nicholas reminded himself. *I will not give up.*

He slowed his strokes. He had started off at a frantic pace which he could not maintain. The ship was nearly even with him now. It would soon cross his path, and he would be chasing it, a dismal state of affairs. Nicholas turned left, heading for a point that was still ahead of the ship, knowing it would quickly close the gap. They would not want to slow down to pick him up while a pirate ship lurked in the darkness. Also, he had no way of knowing the nationality of the ship.

He swam on and on, ignoring the burning pain in each limb. He stopped to look again. The merchant ship had met him and was passing him. With a desperate dive, Nicholas swam for his life and resurfaced in the wake of the ship. He forced himself onward, circling around to the wooden hull.

Never in his life had Nicholas seen anything so wonderful as what he saw next—a piece of chain was dangling over the side of the ship. With a burst of adrenaline, he forced his way through the turbulence around the ship and grasped the chain. Then, his body collapsed into a mass of quivering muscle. Only his hand remained clasped around the chain, as tightly as if it were one of the links.

Nicholas floated, pulled by the ship. He gulped great breaths of sweet Caribbean air, the familiar lapping of water the only sound he heard. His ears were full of water, but he was sure he would still hear if guns were fired.

Lie low, Nicholas told himself.

He would not be spotted by the pirate ship as long as he stayed in the water. But would the pirate ship pursue? Had he aroused their anger enough to make them come after him? Nicholas hoped the gunmen would swear they had shot him dead. He dared not endanger the ship on which he sought refuge.

For some time, Nicholas let himself be towed. Finally, when the fear of sharks grew greater than the fear of discovery, Nicholas planted his feet on the slippery hull and hailed the crew.

"Ahoy there!" he called. "Man overboard! I am an English merchant sailor recently captured by pirates. I have just escaped! Will you take me aboard?"

He said as much as he could, hoping to make his case clear. They would shoot instantly if there was any doubt.

He heard the expected round of oaths above him—English oaths.

"I have hold of your chain," he called. "May I come up?"

A lantern burst over the edge of the ship. Although he was not able to see the hand holding it, Nicholas took the lantern as a welcome. His feet slipped on the slime coating the hull, but he made it to the top. Half a dozen arms hauled him over the side.

He slid to the deck. Now safe, he was so tired he wasn't sure that he could talk to the men bending over him.

"Pirates?"

"Just yesterday," Nicholas wheezed. "I was on the *Yorkshire Dame.* What ship is this?"

"The *Handel,* bound for Philadelphia. We lost a man to dysentery two days ago, so the captain will take ye on if you can climb."

"Blast you," another man interrupted. "Didn't he just swim across this here ocean and climb the side of this here ship?"

"I can climb," Nicholas said, "if you can get me to Philadelphia."

22

The Return of the Prodigal

In all his years at sea, the sky had been his constant friend. It was never quite the same as it had been the day before. He had seen it fierce with soupy gray clouds; calm, blue, and cloudless as a backdrop to flocks of shrieking water birds; busy with puffy white clouds, silver bottoms and tops glistening in the light of the invisible sun; and splendid with sunsets of pink and green and purple and orange and blue, each hue bleeding into the next.

But he could not remember a sky so glorious as the one that greeted him now above Staten Island. The ship slid through the channel and into the New York harbor. The sun was dropping behind Staten Island into the Arthur Kill. Ribbons of radiant coral shot across a darkening purple sky, as if the atmosphere itself were welcoming him back to New York.

He had thought he might travel from Philadelphia to New York by land, but the *Handel* had encountered a New York bound vessel, and he had made the switch.

At the Watering Place where the ferries huddled, Nicholas heard a rooster crowing him home. A ferry bumped against the dock, reminding him of the times he had taken the ferry across the bay. Sea gulls screamed a welcome, wheeling and diving in the glowing coral sky.

As they neared Manhattan, he saw there were more ships and taller buildings than before. The fort was still there, its English flag waving Nicholas in. The warehouses near the wharf reminded him of the cook who had drowned at the Cape Verde islands while the *Ella* broke into pieces.

At the ferry dock in Manhattan he paid the ferryman from his cloth bag of earnings. The bay seemed like a puddle compared to the ocean. At the Watering Place on Staten Island, he puzzled over how to get home. Seven years had passed. A three-mile journey on foot after dark did not entice him.

"Garrison's son, aye?" the ferryman said. It was no longer the same ferry operator, but he knew Lambert Garrison well. "I believe he'll want to see his son coming from the sea. Especially after . . . aye, but I mustn't speak of bad news for fear the boy hasn't heard it."

"My brother Daniel?" Nicholas asked. "I heard."

The man nodded. "Take one of our horses. Your father can bring it back tomorrow."

Nicholas mounted stiffly. He had scarcely ridden in the last seven years. He was nervous about riding a strange horse, but the ferryman had picked a well-mannered one. He gave Nicholas specific directions—reminders, really—about the turns and landmarks on the path over Iron Hill. He loaned him a lantern as well.

Before meeting Pine in Jamaica, Nicholas had been filled with misgivings. Would his father welcome him home? Would his father's new wife make him leave?

Now, Nicholas did not care. If his father rejected him, he would live with a neighbor. He could still see his brothers and sisters.

When he came to the fence around the old stone house, it was almost as if he had never left. The stone fence base, topped with split logs, opened its arms wide to greet him. A quarter moon smiled down. The trees rubbed their drying leaves together in happiness.

The only thing missing was Jonah, but he could not expect the dog to still be here after seven years. A few cats slinked into the shadows as Nicholas rode in, but no dogs barked.

Nicholas stabled the horse and was greeted by the lowing of cows and the whinnying of horses. More than likely, that noise would alert his father of an intruder. *Hopefully I won't get shot*, he thought. He grinned wryly, realizing it was probably an irrational thought. His nerves were on edge.

At the house, he stopped on the threshold. He had ruined his smart white outfit when he escaped from the pirate ship, and he no longer had his distinguished hat. *But I'm not in the bottom of the Caribbean*, Nicholas thought. *I'm not a pirate about to be hanged. I'm home!*

He gritted his teeth and knocked.

There was a soft rustle inside. Then he heard his father's familiar voice.

"Who's there?"

"Nicholas."

"Children!" his father shouted as he threw open the door. "Nicholas is home!"

Nicholas heard pounding footsteps. Elizabeth scrambled down the dark stairs and threw herself into his arms. "I knew you would come home! I knew you would come home!" she said.

The boys tumbled down the stairs, gawking. Elizabeth hopped around the kitchen in ecstasy. From under the stairs, a frail brown and white bundle limped toward him.

"Jonah!" Nicholas cried, dropping to the floor. He took the old dog in his arms and Jonah licked his face. "I didn't think you were still alive!"

"He's barely alive," Father said. "But I wonder if he doesn't know you!"

Nicholas said hello to Mary, his father's wife. She was pleasant enough. "Your father has worried about you so much," she said.

The next morning, after a hearty breakfast of bread and cheese and eggs and bacon, Nicholas hurried to Catharine's house. Elizabeth insisted on going with him, since, she said, he wouldn't know the way.

He pounded on the door.

A dark face with piercing black eyes appeared in the upper window of the door. Mary had not aged one day.

"Nicholas!" she gasped. "Catharine! Catharine! Cath-ar-ine! Do come see who's at the door!" Mary burst into tears, applying her apron to her face just as she had in the old days.

"Are you going to let me in?" Nicholas asked with a grin.

"Are I going to let you in!" Mary exclaimed, swinging the bottom part of the door wide. "Are I going to let you in, he says, he does. And how would I leave my boy what's been gone seven years standing out in the grass! Catharine, Catharine, *do* you know who this is?"

Catharine stood behind her, holding a baby girl who wailed in her arms. Two small boys stood on either side of her.

"Boys, look!" Catharine said. "It's your uncle Nicholas come home from the sea! You never even met him before!"

The baby wailed louder, and Nicholas patted her soft head.

Mary was already at the fireplace. She grabbed the kettles, throwing them onto their iron hooks with a clang. After stirring up the fire, she moved hot coals into the big Dutch oven.

"Now if I don't have a fine jug of apple cider just waiting to be drunk!" she cried. "We is all going to sit down and drink cider and the children are going to get a little bit of that candy I brought back from Manhattan, and it's going to be just like Christmas in this house, even if it is October. Oh yes, we are! If only

Pine would be here to pop some corn! And do tell us, Nicholas, do tell us what your father did when you came home!"

"First," Nicholas said, "I saw Pine in Jamaica!"

"You saw Pine! Now did you really! Praise be to Jesus, you should have told him to come home!"

"He told *me* to come home," Nicholas said.

"And you met your pa's new wife, Mary?"

"Yes, she is nice. She said father has been worrying about me for a long time and that she is glad to see me."

Catharine had managed to quiet the baby, and deposit her in the next room for a nap. She came back and poured Nicholas some tea while they waited for the cider to warm.

"You heard about Daniel."

"Yes. Pine told me."

"Ah, of course."

After a short time at home, Nicholas took a job as a surveyor. Plotting angles and distances still interested him. The position had been recommended by Mr. Van Woogelum, who was still as kind as he had been when he washed Nicholas' face after the Manhattan break-in. Nicholas helped his father on the farm whenever he could, Jonah limping along. He spent time with his sisters and brothers. When Jonah died, Nicholas buried him down by the Fresh Kills where he had loved to play and swim.

On a trip to Manhattan for surveying tools, Nicholas heard that the *Yorkshire Dame* was in port. He headed straight to the wharf for a visit. Perhaps Seagull Sal would be on board.

23

The Silver Locket

"Nicholas!" shouted Seagull Sal when they met at the bottom of the stairs leading to the forecastle bunks. "Never thought I'd see you again—'ceptin' maybe in Port Royal swinging from Gallows Point! Sit down, sit down, and tell us what happened! We are just sharing a drink and some fresh peaches!"

Nicholas settled himself on a bunk. He felt right at home even though Sal was the only face he recognized. Sal munched on a peach, juice dripping, as Nicholas told the story of his swim. It really was a great story, and he made it as graphic as he could. Seagull Sal and the other men in their bunks listened with wide eyes as Nicholas described the fountain of water shooting up within five feet of him.

"You coming back to sea?" Seagull Sal asked hopefully when story time was over.

"No," Nicholas said. "I need to be home for awhile."

"Oh, a girl," Seagull Sal said.

"Nope," Nicholas said. "I just need to be a land man for awhile. But it sure is good to see you again, my friend!"

"I almost forgot," Seagull Sal said. "Let me find the cabin boy."

They walked on deck. Seagull Sal returned with a large cloth bag.

"Cap'n kept it in his wine locker in case we would ever see you again," Seagull Sal said, slapping the bag against Nicholas' chest with a thump.

Was Seger's butterfly slate inside?

It was.

Nicholas left the ship, shaking his head. He had never expected to see the slate again. He wished he had the courage to show it to his father, but he did not. The two of them were getting along okay. If Father still blamed him for what had happened in the past, Nicholas did not wish to remind him. He put the slate in the loft beside his bed.

The next two years passed calmly. Then Father fell ill. As Nicholas entered his father's room, he wanted to run from the memories of the day his mother had died.

Father was sitting up in bed, writing.

"How are you, Father?"

"Weak," Father said. "My head is clear but my body feels very weak. I must get this will finished. Nicholas, I am going to put you down as one of the executors of my estate if you will agree."

Nicholas found a chair, relief and fear twisting inside his chest. Relief, because his father was naming him an executor and must actually trust him. Fear, because his father was preparing to leave this earth.

"I can do that, Father. But you may live for a long time yet."

"I think not."

The ink pen scratched across the paper lying on a thin slab of wood propped on his father's legs.

As clear as if the voice had come from the next room, Nicholas remembered his father's words. *"Perhaps if you start watching where you are going you will be able to avoid danger."*

Has Father forgiven me for what happened? Nicholas wondered.

Still, he could not ask. He could not bear to hear his father say, "If you would have been watching, your brother might not have died."

Out of respect for his father, Nicholas attended the Church of England every Sunday. In the small stone church near the mill, the charter from Queen Anne was proudly displayed, along with a large King James Bible and a gold communion cup. His father's name, Lambert Garrison, was listed on the charter as one of the founders. Queen Anne had died of a stroke in 1714, shortly after sending the charter to Staten Island and promising the longitude prize to any of her subjects.

Nicholas accompanied Elizabeth to social events and to church when Father was not able to go. Sometimes they escorted her friend Christina, the daughter of Mr. Van Woogelum.

"Are you going to bring us another cherry pie?" Nicholas asked Christina when he first met her after his return. And whenever he saw her after that, Nicholas mentioned cherry pie. Finally, one day when he and Elizabeth stopped for Christina, she climbed into the cart clutching a paper package. She placed it in his hands.

"What is this?" Nicholas asked.

Christina looked at him keenly.

"I guess you won't know until you open it," she replied.

Nicholas thought that cherry pie was the best thing he had ever tasted. When a young man named Matthys Inyard began calling for Elizabeth, Nicholas found he still wanted to escort Christina. She reminded him so much of his mother. She even loved to draw.

Nicholas visited Mr. Van Woogelum one day. The older man was sitting in his barn, sharpening his scythe on a whetstone. Chickens walked about, their heads moving in jerky motions as if they could not keep up with their feet. Handsome reddish-brown feathers slid in perfect rhythm with their steps.

"How is your father?"

"He is in bed again," Nicholas said. "He says he is not long for this world, but we thought that a few years ago."

"Ach, that is bad news. Such a good friend he has been to me."

They both fell silent. The hiss of metal against stone filled the air.

"So, Nicholas," Mr. Van Woogelum said, looking up at the young man. "When are you going back to sea?"

Nicholas cleared his throat.

"I am not planning to go back to sea," he said. "I enjoy being with your daughter too much."

"Ah! I see," Mr. Van Woogelum smiled. "My daughter enjoys the Dutch church and you go to St. Andrew's. How would that work for a family?"

"I am not partial, sir," said Nicholas. "My family attended the Dutch church before St. Andrew's came to Richmond, and I guess I can speak Dutch as well as any man."

A few days later, Nicholas and Christina climbed Iron Hill. Nicholas sought a spot where they could look out to the sea. It was spring time, so the leaves had not yet obscured the view. Nicholas gave Christina a hand and she sprang over a fallen log to sit beside him on a rock. Below them, the farms and fields of Staten Island spread wide. Much of the land was now cleared, and roads cut through the hills. Far off on the silver water, a ship moved toward the Narrows.

"Are you going back to sea?" Christina asked as she opened the basket she had brought. Nicholas followed her fingers with his eyes while she lifted a thick piece of cherry pie from the cloth napkin.

Christina's eyes were not on the pie. She was watching the gray line of water. Several strands of golden hair had escaped from her Dutch cap and were dancing around her face, but Nicholas could see fear in her eyes. He remembered the riotous nightlife in the port cities of the Atlantic, where he had taken advantage of the wives of other men gone to sea. A deep determination rose within him.

"No," Nicholas said. "I went against my mother's wishes to begin with."

Christina turned to him and let her hand fall briefly on his. His heart leaped at the gentle gesture. Then she looked back out to sea.

"I went to sea because I wanted to prove to my father that I could succeed at something. I felt like he blamed me for . . . something that happened when I was young. But that is all in the past. Land life is good enough for me," Nicholas went on. "At least if I have you!"

Christina turned toward him and smiled, her whole face lighting up. Nicholas felt his heart melt, and he took a small packet from his pocket. From it, he lifted a silver locket. He took Christina's hand and laid the locket in her palm, its fine silver chain falling around the oval case. Etched into the front of the locket were two ribbons, twined together into one. Above and below the ribbon, small flowers had been etched with leaves on either side.

"If I were a rich man I would get you a ring or diamond earrings," Nicholas said. "But I thought you would like this. You can open it and put little treasures inside."

"I do like it," she said, stroking the locket with awe and admiration.

She gazed up into his eyes, then blushed and looked down again.

"Will you marry me, Christina?"

24

The Surveyor

1725

Christina stood with Nicholas at the grave of his father. The simple stones that marked the graves of his mother and brother Seger were sinking into the earth close by.

I need to come straighten those stones, Nicholas told himself.

Then he thought, *Father named me as an executor of his will. Father named me as an executor of his will!*

It was the best way possible to part with his father. Nicholas shed tears of relief along with tears of sadness. Perhaps his nightmares would end now that he knew his father trusted him. He hadn't had many nightmares recently. If he thought of Captain Parker, he discarded the thought as soon as possible.

Although Christina's mother was still alive, Mary insisted on baking up a storm of Dutch cookies for Nicholas' wedding. She descended on the Garrison property to do just that. Nicholas' stepmother had moved in with her son since Father's death, leaving Mary with free use of the kitchen. Nicholas and Christina would be living in the old Garrison house after the wedding.

"Mary," Nicholas said one day when he found her white with flour, "Christina is grateful for the cookies, but she said you don't need to make so many! She and her mother can make some too."

"Now don't you say one word," Mary said with a shake that sent a cloud of flour across the floor boards. "Not one word, I tell you! It makes me feel as if your dear mother were here if I can help with your wedding just as she helped me with mine."

"Well—"

"But I do say, if that Pine doesn't make it back for your wedding, I'm going to beat him with this," she added, waving her wooden rolling pin at Nicholas.

"I hope for everyone's sake that he does," Nicholas said, laughing.

Despite having laid Father in the grave only a few months before, the August wedding was the happiest day Nicholas could remember. Christina was stunningly beautiful. Elizabeth alternated between laughter and tears.

Mr. Van Woogelum shed a few tears himself as he gave Nicholas a warm hug. "There's no one I'd rather see her go home with, Nicholas," he said. "You've really turned into a fine Christian man."

Nicholas was glad Mr. Van Woogelum did not know the truth about his past. Nicholas still felt like the boy Mr. Van Woogelum had met running from the warehouse with blood on his face.

But I'm different now, Nicholas promised himself. *I'm getting married and it will be easier to live right.*

Nicholas' stepmother Mary was in attendance and Nicholas was surprised to find he felt comforted by her presence. It wasn't the same as a parent, but still he was glad she was there.

Best of all, Pine's ship had sailed into harbor two days before the wedding. Mary was in a positive tizzy, expressing her delight to anyone in her path. Even though she scolded Pine for being gone so long and ordered him here and there with baskets of cookies, everyone knew she was as happy to see him again as she was to see Nicholas marry the lovely Christina. Pine, leaving trails of sugar and raisins in his tracks, complained of being made a beast of burden when he had only one arm, all the while grinning as wide as the Atlantic Ocean.

The next summer, Christina gave birth to a son. Nicholas thought they should name the baby Lambert after his grandfather, but Christina wanted to name him Nicholas, so they did. Sitting beside his wife, holding the tiny red-faced baby in his arms, Nicholas felt both elation and the weight of responsibility.

He was a father!

"And I do believe he's as healthy as they come!" Mary exclaimed, having spent the entire night with Christina.

"Thank you so much," Nicholas said. "You need to get some sleep, Mary."

"Christina is the one who needs to get some sleep!" Mary said, stifling a yawn. "Nicholas, don't you be letting her get out of bed now. I'll stop by and send Elizabeth if she's able to come."

Elizabeth was married and lived close by but she had no children yet.

Before little Nicholas turned two, his sister Susanna was born. A year and a half later, a brother Jan was born. Nicholas and Christina baptized all three children in the Dutch Reformed Church.

On a hot August night after little Nicholas' sixth birthday, Christina went into labor again, and things were not going well. Nicholas paced the floor late into the night. He had hired a neighbor girl to watch the children, but that only gave him too much time to worry that Christina was going to die this time. He walked to the barn.

The animals were sleeping, and he decided to take a quick nap. Mary would call him if there was anything he could do.

"There is nothing you can do," he heard someone say inside the world of sleep. *"You should learn to watch for danger."*

It was Captain Parker, taunting him, waving the red handkerchief from the quarterdeck of the *Ella.*

"You let your brother die. You knew he couldn't swim well." And Captain Parker laughed.

Then he heard a scream and saw his brother Seger falling from aloft, falling into the ocean. The sea swallowed him and Nicholas dived in after him, swimming as hard as he could.

But he only got as far as a wool blanket in front of a hearth where a small fire burned. Mother's face was above him, pale. She was telling him to be quiet, as if she was listening for the horses' hoofs to return from the Fresh Kills.

Father's chair was beside the fire, lying on its back where it had fallen when he leaped to his feet. Nicholas meant to go back down to the Fresh Kills with Father, but somehow he didn't have enough energy. Mother was probing the splinter in his arm and telling him to lie still. Jonah was nestled on the blanket beside him.

"Was Daniel fine?" Mother asked.

"He went into the kill to look for Seger," Nicholas replied.

He heard a voice calling him. "Nicholas. Nicholas!"

Nicholas jerked awake and found that he was a grown man in a barn, not a boy on a blanket near the hearth. Mary was standing in the dark barn doorway, calling his name.

"Nicholas, have you fallen ill? Where be you, when your old Mary is a-trying to tell you about your new son?"

"I'm here, Mary." He leaped to his feet. "Is Christina all right?"

"Christina is weak but doing just fine, and so is her strappin' new son what looks just like his father," said Mary, as pleased as if she had given birth to the child herself. "And here I can't even get his father to wake up!"

Nicholas rushed past Mary, through the Dutch doorway of the house and on into the bedroom.

Christina was exhausted and pale.

"Christina!" He kissed her forehead, and his tears fell onto the baby's damp head.

"Shall we call him Seger?" Christina asked.

"No!" Nicholas snapped.

Christina looked at him, surprised even in her weakness.

"I mean—" Nicholas faltered. "Remember, we were going to name a boy Lambert. After my father!"

"Lambert," Christina said. Her puzzled expression faded as she pressed her cheek against the new baby's head. "Lambert, my son. Perhaps you will be an important man like your Grandpa Garrison."

Mary had come panting in, and decreed that Nicholas should leave the bedroom sooner rather than later. She and Miss Christina had some things to attend to and Miss Christina needed some sleep.

As Christina grew busy with the four children, the farm work was left entirely to Nicholas. Crops were essential to providing food and income, but Nicholas found himself less available to do the surveying work he loved.

Richmond, just over the hill from the Garrison place, was home to the county jail and the courthouse, which was around the corner from the Church of St. Andrew. The county clerk appreciated Nicholas' precise and detailed surveying reports. No longer were land plots described by their location relative to a large oak, or the corner of a back field. Nicholas was scrupulous in his use of latitude and longitude, using the stars and planets and sun as his clock. Some days he took Nicholas Jr. with him.

Then, in late winter of 1733, just after Susanna's fifth birthday, the county hired a full-time surveyor from Manhattan. Nicholas was informed that his position had been eliminated.

"Christina, I don't see how we will make it," Nicholas said that night after the children had gone to bed. He paced in front of the fireplace, holding the cold poker. He tossed it from hand to hand, clenching his fists around it rhythmically. "In today's world, a man needs a job besides just farming."

Christina was putting small stitches into the torn hem of Susanna's little birthday dress.

"Do you suppose you could do survey work across the Arthur Kill in New Jersey? Or in Manhattan? Maybe there will be enough work for both of you."

"I just don't understand why they would hire that man without even asking me if I wanted the job," Nicholas fumed, still pacing. "I guess because they want a sponge-spined peacock from Manhattan who will lick their feet."

"Nicholas, dear, you are talking like a sailor!"

Nicholas spun around to face her.

"Maybe that's because I am a sailor," he snapped. "And maybe it's because I need to go back to sea to keep my family eating."

Even by the unsteady light of the fire, Nicholas saw the color drain from his wife's face. She was expecting a baby again, although not until late summer. Nicholas turned away.

"Surely you don't mean that!" Christina finally said softly. She got up from her rocker and let the little dress fall to the rocking chair arm. She walked to her husband, who stood beneath her painting of the Garrison property. She placed her hands on his folded arms.

"I don't know," he sighed, relaxing and taking her into his arms. "I might. We didn't get paid much at sea, but with my experience I could be a mate, maybe a captain soon. And that pays better."

"It pays better if you're alive to receive it," Christina said quietly, pressing her lips together and lowering her eyes.

"My dear, I was at sea for seven years, back when there were pirates and wars, and I still made it home. Of course there are still shipwrecks and storms, but people focus on those and think of nothing else. They forget that countless ships sail the ocean unharmed."

"Back when there were pirates and wars? Are there no pirates now, nor wars at the whim of any lord or lady?"

"Well, all right." Nicholas allowed himself to laugh. "But the British crown has really cracked down on pirates, and the merchant ships sail with a great deal more safety than before."

"You told me you would stay on land," Christina sighed. "I don't mind being poor! We don't need sugar and cinnamon from Manhattan and all those rich man's things. Will you at least talk to my father about it?"

"No," said Nicholas, releasing his wife with a frown. "He'll think I'm asking for help."

"No, he won't!" she protested. "He knows you're much too proud for that. And besides, what if you go to sea and never come back? Then my father will be forced to take us in. How much better to have his support at least."

Nicholas let his wrist fall back onto his wife's shoulder. He remembered the sea widows he had met, countless women of all ages forced to prostitution and grimy waitressing.

"Fine," he said. "I'll talk to him."

Silence fell over the kitchen. Nicholas rubbed his wife's neck, watching her eyes.

"Would you at least wait until the baby is born?"

"My dear, I haven't even said I am going."

"No," she answered. "But your eyes have said it."

25

The Golden Swan

1733

In August Christina gave birth to a baby boy, but his skin was blue and despite Mary's efforts, the little bundle never took a breath. They named him Benjamin, and buried him beside Seger and Father and Mother.

A few weeks later, Nicholas left for the sea. He had persuaded Mary to move back into the old house where she and Pine had lived in his childhood. Pine was still at sea as a cook. Nicholas felt much better about leaving his family with Mary close by. Christina was still grieving the loss of little Benjamin, though her arms were filled with Susanna, Jan, and Lambert. Nicholas Jr. was seven years old now and attending school when he wasn't needed at home.

"I'm not anxious to see you go, Nicholas," Mr. Van Woogelum had said. "I know it will be hard for Christina." The older man massaged his left shoulder with his right hand, and said nothing for a moment. Nicholas remained silent as well.

"But if you feel you must, check with Thomas Noble. He's a friend of mine from Manhattan with a very nice store. He has a steady trade with Jamaica, Eustatius, and St. Thomas. I wouldn't wonder that he would be happy for an honest man on his ship."

Several weeks later, Mr. Van Woogelum took Christina and the children to see Nicholas off. Nicholas had been hired as second mate on one of Thomas Noble's ships, the *Golden Swan*. He was happy to refresh his skills. The brass buttons shone on his new blue uniform. He wore black leather shoes with brass buckles and a three-cornered hat trimmed with gold braid. He had declined the tailor's offer to sell him gold buttons and buckles. His efforts to improve his circumstances financially would be in vain if he spent too much money on his uniform.

"You do look very fine, my dear," Christina said when they reached the wharf where the *Golden Swan* was at anchor.

"Not as fine as you," Nicholas said. "There is more color in your face today than there has been the last few weeks."

The two oldest boys crowded around their father. Nicholas picked up Susanna, who squealed and put her arms around his neck. She had barely recognized him in his hat and coat. She touched the gold braid of his hat and giggled. Lambert was just over a year old, and had no idea what was going on other than that he was not at home. He fussed and tossed in his mother's arms.

"I'll see if I can find you something pretty in the West Indies," Nicholas told Susanna as he set her back on her feet.

Nicholas held his head high and waved grandly as he stepped onto the ship, but inside he ached. He had not thought it would be so hard to leave his family.

The *Golden Swan* was a fine boat painted blue and gold. Nicholas met Captain Jenkins, who showed him around the ship. The captain pointed out the berths where the officers slept, below the quarterdeck close to the captain's cabin. The captain then took him around to the spare rigging, blocks, and sails, and the tools used to work them. As a second mate, Nicholas would be responsible to maintain and care for these spare sails and to call for them at a moment's notice. No sail maker was on board since this was a short voyage to the West Indies and back. Nicholas would be required to make any necessary repairs to the sails.

The captain introduced him to the first mate, and the two looked over the list of men. They would divide the men into equal watches, of which they would each be a leader. The first mate had worked with many of the men before, so he was able to divide the men much better than Nicholas could have alone.

Nicholas was surprised how quickly the routines and tasks aboard ship came back to him. A few knots made his fingers falter the first day, but soon they flew without a thought. Running up the ratlines made Nicholas gasp for breath. He determined to do it every day to build up the stamina he had thirteen years before.

As the *Golden Swan* sailed down the coastline, Nicholas felt justified for his claims of safety on the sea. Life aboard such a ship was utter boredom. Danger seemed impossible.

Every week, Nicholas wrote a letter to Christina, telling her where they were on the Atlantic coast. He wanted to write that all was well, but he decided that receiving a letter from him would be reassuring of itself. Then, if he ever felt that all was not well, he would not feel obligated to state the case.

Captain Jenkins and the first mate showed Nicholas a new instrument called an octant. The octant used two mirrors to measure angles in the sky. Now, instead of being able to measure only the angle between the ship and a celestial body, mariners could measure the angle between two bodies, such as the moon and a certain star. Nicholas used the device with awe and excitement. With the captain's star charts, it was even possible to determine longitude. The moon, Nicholas knew, retraces its path every eighteen years. It had taken astronomers eighteen years to track and record all the possible positions of the moon relative to the stars. It would only be a matter of time until all the charts were complete and cross-checked.

On clear nights when Nicholas was on deck, he measured angles between the moon and stars over and over, just for practice. Of course, any experienced seaman could tell stories of many cloudy days and nights when neither stars nor moon could be seen. It was on these cloudy days that knowing the longitude would be most helpful, but it could not be determined from the sky.

By the time they reached Jamaica, Nicholas felt confident and comfortable. It felt good to be down in the splendid green sea again. It felt good to hold onto the ropes at the top of the world, to sing songs with the men, to hear the salty sailor expressions and orders bawled from the quarterdeck and repeated across the ship. It felt good to use strong words again and watch the obedience they produced.

When they landed at Port Royal, the larboard watch poured off the ship first, heading for the taverns. They came back full of fresh food and drunk with rum. The next day, the starboard watch took their turn. Nicholas smiled as his feet landed on solid ground and he felt the tossing sensation beneath his feet. He had almost forgotten that feeling.

"You need a place to stay for the night?" a feminine voice broke into his thoughts.

Nicholas glanced at the beautiful dark-skinned girl, then looked again. She reminded him of Sunny.

"Yes," he said. "But I need to get something to eat first."

"I will be waiting," she said.

Nicholas walked into the tavern and asked for a bowl of stew. He sat at the table where the most rowdy seamen had gathered. The louder the stories, the more daring the oaths, the better he would be able to keep from thinking about what he had just agreed to.

26

The Captain

Nicholas paced the quarterdeck behind the helmsman. It was night, and Captain Jenkins wished to leave Port Royal on the morning tide. They would have just enough time to reach New York before Christmas if the voyage went well.

The moon, full and swollen, was rising out of the sea to the east and reflecting on the dark water. It would be time to do lunar measurements soon. Even though they were in port, Nicholas always took measurements when the sky was clear, usually lying on his back on the deck to achieve the steadiest hand.

"If I take the wings of the morning, and dwell in the uttermost parts of the sea, even there shall thy hand lead me, and thy right hand shall hold me. If I say, Surely the darkness shall cover me; even the night shall be light about me."

The words came to his mind unbidden, and Nicholas jumped. He looked at the dark shapes around him and reminded himself that he was at home on the *Golden Swan*. His mother was not at his side, and it was good she was not. What would she think? What would she say if she knew he had spent the night with a woman who was not his wife?

All the men do it, Nicholas comforted himself. Inside, however, he was sick with disappointment. He had been sure he would be strong enough to resist the follies he had committed as a younger man.

I won't think about it, Nicholas told himself.

Better to act bravely and take measurements and play and laugh and sing and eat noisily and swear loudly. Then, at least, the men around him would not know that he had come to sea intending to be decent, hoping to make his wife proud.

The next morning, before they cast off, Nicholas received permission from the captain to run ashore to a small shop in Port Royal. Nicholas remembered the wrinkled old woman who had run it years earlier.

"You want present?" a thin voice squeaked.

She was still there, more like a raisin than she had been thirteen years before.

"You have wife?"

"Yes," Nicholas said. "How much is that necklace? How about this pin?"

They bartered for a bit, and then Nicholas parted with his shillings and the woman dropped the items in his hand.

"Make peace with wife," she said.

Nicholas turned away angrily, forgetting to duck in the doorway and striking the top of his head on the jamb. How dare she assume he was trying to make up for something?

He arrived in Staten Island a few days before Christmas, loaded with presents for Christina and the children.

Thomas Noble met them at the dock minutes after the ship rolled in. The captain had the men bring up samples of the coffee and sugar that filled most of the hold. They also had brought several exotic birds and crates of citrus fruits and pineapples.

"Just in time for Christmas!" said Thomas Noble, quite pleased. "You know, gentlemen, I'm thinking of starting a coffee house here. They are quite the rage in London. A bit more elegant than your standard tavern. A place where a man can read a newspaper, meet interesting and intelligent people, discuss politics, and drink a coffee. What do you think, captain?"

"Well, as long as Governor Cosby isn't one of your regulars, I would patronize it," Captain Jenkins said with a laugh.

Governor William Cosby was not a favorite with the colonists. He was selfish and dull, according to those who dealt with him. Yet, as the representative of the British crown, he had considerable power to enforce taxes and by-laws on the New York merchants, captains, and pirates.

"I'm afraid you misunderstood me," Thomas Noble said. "I said my patrons would be interesting and intelligent people."

At this, they all laughed.

"I have heard, sir," Nicholas offered, "that members of the royal family who are so unpleasant that they cannot be tolerated by the royalty in London are sent to govern in distant places."

Everyone laughed again. They were drunk with the relief of arriving on shore and the camaraderie of a common enemy. Captain Jenkins slapped his knee with delight.

"I do believe you are right, Nicholas," Mr. Noble said. "I wonder if our colonies will ever think of being an independent state?"

"England would never let that happen," the captain said wryly.

"You are right," Thomas Noble said. "They will just send their refuse to govern us. But let's stop this chatter and talk of the future. Nicholas, our good Captain Jenkins here writes glowing reports of your seamanship and ability to navigate."

"Thank you, sir," Nicholas said. "I enjoy placing myself properly on a map."

"Excellent! Well, gentlemen, since I have no coffee house yet, do me the honor of coming down to my store this evening for a drink."

Nicholas received his payment in Thomas Noble's crowded store, where each shipman took a seat on a barrel of lard. Mr. Noble's slave poured them tall glasses of wine from Madeira and brought them a bowl of cashews from Brazil.

Then, Thomas Noble got right to the point. Captain Jenkins would take charge of his newest ship, just ready to slide into the ocean for the first time. He asked Nicholas to captain the *Golden Swan* on the next voyage.

"I would be honored," Nicholas said, shaking hands with the merchant.

"Will you go home yet tonight, or can I offer you a bed?" Mr. Noble asked. "My beds don't move in storms," he added, "but I'm sure you're anxious to get home to your wife and family."

"Maybe I will take you up," Nicholas said. "I'll leave on the morning ferry."

In the morning, Nicholas paid the ferryman's hired hand to take him across the hills in a cart so he would not need to carry his sea chest and presents on horseback. When they got close to the house, Nicholas unwrapped the necklace and laid it in the palm of his hand. It seemed necessary to distract Christina's eyes so she would not look too deeply into his.

"I'm going to be master on the next run!" Nicholas told Christina as soon as he leaped out of the cart. He took her into his arms. "Look what I brought you, my dear."

"You brought yourself," she said. "That is what means the most to me. But this necklace is beautiful. Will you be home for a bit?"

"Several months," he said. "But I will be responsible for collecting the crew and arranging the paperwork before departure. So I will be working from Manhattan quite a bit as well."

"You have done well, my dear," Christina said. "And we are so glad to have you back."

Nicholas could not force himself to meet his wife's gaze. He turned away and picked up the children one after the next and tossed them into the air.

"Let me unpack my sea chest so you can see what I brought you," he told them.

Nicholas was meticulous about preparing for his first run as captain, or more properly, since this was a merchant ship, as master. He met with the former captain at a tavern in Manhattan and went over the folder of paperwork from the previous voyage.

"Have a drink on me, Captain Garrison," Captain Jenkins said. "And congratulations on your promotion! I gave Mr. Noble my recommendations. I do believe you were more studious in your lunar measurements than either the first mate or I, and undoubtedly quicker on the ropes. Have you purchased an octant for yourself yet, sir? And don't forget to take your own wine and beer, or your men may not appreciate you very much."

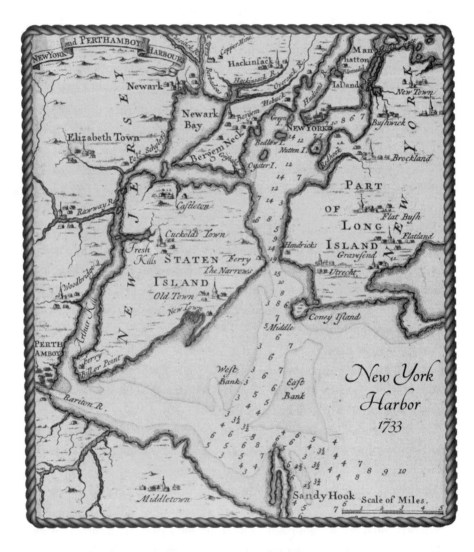

The numbers around Sandy Hook, between the West Bank and the East Bank and going north to Manhattan, indicate the depth of the water in fathoms. Pilots needed to guide ships through this narrow channel, avoiding the shallow water over the Banks.

Captain Jenkins spread the chart of New York Harbor across the wooden table. Nicholas had looked at a chart like this before, but it had never been solely his responsibility to keep a ship safe.

"The pilot will take you," the captain said. "But you still want to know this map."

Nicholas studied the small numbers on the map. Amazing, what had been discovered in the bay he had called home for so many years. To an onlooker standing on the shore of Staten Island, the bay appeared to be level ocean water. But if the water were drained out of the bay, treacherous banks that could run a ship aground would be visible. Only by staying in the narrow channel could a large ship be safe. The numbers on the chart showed how many fathoms deep the water had been measured at that point. The worst point was a spot close to Sandy Hook where the channel made the turn under the East Bank. Only three and a half fathoms!

The pilots who escorted the big ships in and out of the bay knew the underwater depths by memory. They knew the tides and the winds better than anyone else. They would be the best insurance against catastrophe in the bay.

"They need to update this map!" Nicholas laughed, pointing to the center of Staten Island where the old name "Cuckold's Town" was still printed. "It's Richmond now."

Nicholas spent long hours at the wharf and in the city, preparing the ship. He got specific instructions from Thomas Noble about the goods the merchant preferred for his New York store. He talked to men at the docks, and hired them as able seamen and mates.

His best find was his old friend, Seagull Sal.

"Sal!" he cried when he saw him from across the wharf. "Seagull Sal! Are you committed to a voyage?"

"In between, old friend, in between," Seagull Sal said. "Could this outfit mean you are a captain now?"

"I am, and I'm looking for someone who can steer a ship!" Nicholas replied. "What I wouldn't give to sign you on!"

"Just find me a paper to draw an X on," Seagull Sal laughed, his golden hair bouncing. Like many sailors, Seagull Sal could neither read nor write, so he signed with an X.

Seeing Seagull Sal reminded Nicholas of food. Nicholas was determined to keep his men as healthy as they could be. In consultation with Thomas Noble, Nicholas decided to take sauerkraut along as the best defense against scurvy. No official cure for scurvy had been identified yet, but anecdotes abounded of men on death's door being saved by eating fresh fruits and vegetables. Should they be at sea for a long time, the fresh fruits and vegetables would be gone. But sauerkraut was almost indestructible. Nicholas also purchased coffee, a good alternative to both water and strong drink. Nicholas had enjoyed coffee ever since his time on the Spanish ship where he had met Joaquin.

Thomas Noble asked if he would prefer to have a full-time sail maker on this voyage. Nicholas deliberated. He himself had managed the sails on the first trip of the *Golden Swan*, and although they had not encountered ravaging winds, it had been easily managed in addition to his other duties. He had selected a second mate who was competent with a sailmaker's needle and palm.

"I would prefer to have a surgeon on board if the roles are comparable," he said.

"Done," Thomas Noble said. "You have the funds if you can find one you wish to hire."

As captain, Nicholas would have an entire cabin to himself. Triple-pane stern windows formed the back wall. He would have the luxury of daylight to look over his charts. Under the windows, a bench seat opened on hinges to reveal locker space where Nicholas would store wine and beer for himself and the mates. There was a heavy wooden table and a high-backed chair and hooks in the ceiling for lanterns. On the table stood a brass candle holder for three candles.

The table was small, so if Nicholas invited any of the men in to eat with him, it would be cramped. But that was fine. Everything was cramped on a merchant ship. Nicholas had heard of the huge spaces on warships, but a large warship could hold 400 men.

Nicholas purchased his octant, his drinks, and a globe on a wooden stand. Having a globe gave Nicholas a feeling of importance. He liked to be able to look at the earth as a whole when visualizing his location relative to known land. He also bought a larger sea chest and a second suit of clothes. He upgraded his hat to a shinier one with a golden cockade. Like all English captains, he was expected to read aloud to the sailors on Sundays, and he bought a copy of the *Book of Common Prayer*.

Now that he was a captain, surely it would be easier to live a life above reproach. He would read the Scriptures on Sunday from a sincerity of heart that none of the vile sailors could criticize. He had wonderful accommodations in his cabin, so he need not be tempted to take up the offers to "spend the night." He would clean up his act before his wife and family could suspect that he was anything less than the righteous, respectable man he longed to be.

The Dreams

Easter 1736

Nicholas cleared his throat and picked up the *Book of Common Prayer* from the cloth-covered barrel on the quarterdeck. Below him in the waist of the *Golden Swan,* the crew was assembled on boxes and benches. It was April 1, 1736, Easter Sunday. The sky was a glorious blue, scattered full of cotton-white clouds. The sea stretched under the sky, relaxed and flat. The ship rocked gently back and forth. Nicholas stood behind the barrel with his feet planted solidly on the planks, his body instinctively adjusting to the gentle motion.

He found the section of the book devoted to special services. "O God, who for our redemption didst give thine only-begotten Son to the death of the cross," Nicholas began.

And then Nicholas was back on the haystack beside his mother, remembering her face by the light of the full moon, hearing her soft voice telling him he did not have to do wrong just because his brother did.

Nicholas continued reading mechanically, barely seeing the next words. He tried not to think of his mother much, but when he did he felt guilty. Guilty— his progression into sin had been faster this time. Guilty—as a ship captain, gratification of the flesh came more easily, not less easily. Guilty—despite his promises to himself to do better at the next port.

". . . and by His glorious resurrection hast delivered us from the power of our enemy."

He saw his mother's dying face as he had in so many recent dreams, asking him to stay home. He continued to read, but his throat grew tight.

"Grant us so to die daily to sin, that we may evermore live with Him in the joy of His resurrection; through thy Son Christ our Lord, who liveth and reigneth with thee and the Holy Spirit, one God, now and for ever. Amen."

He closed the book with a snap that caused several of the crew to jerk their heads up to look at him. After attending to the formalities of the rest of the service, he dismissed the men to their duties. High above, Seagull Sal had remained on duty during the service.

"Captain, if you please," the cook said.

"What do you need?"

"Sir, since it's Easter Sunday, I thought maybe we could have fresh mutton for supper."

"No."

"Aye, aye, sir."

The cook turned away. Probably he had been put to the question by the crew.

Nicholas glanced at the first mate, who was watching him. Nicholas tightened his mouth into a straight line.

"I'll be in my cabin if you need me," he said, and hurried down the companionway. He ducked into his cabin, and shut the door. His chart of the Caribbean Sea lay open on the table. He picked up his divider and fiddled with it, spreading the two pointers to measure the distance they had traveled yesterday. Then swinging one pointer ahead, he estimated how far their travels would take them today.

Even the map and divider seemed to be staring at him. He tossed the divider onto the map, gouging the paper. He strode across the cabin and yanked open the door.

"Charles!" He heard the name repeated by the helmsman, and the ship's boy hurried to him. He was a Negro boy they had picked up in St. Thomas a few voyages past. "Go tell the cook to slaughter a sheep for the evening meal."

"Aye, sir!"

"And if he argues with you, tell him I changed my mind."

"Aye, aye, sir!"

Nicholas slammed the door and sat in his chair, elbows resting on the map. He threw off his captain's hat, loosened the white lace around his throat, and let his head fall into his hands.

There were two sheep on board, and they were on the homeward voyage. It was reasonable to have fresh meat for Easter.

I will not be like Captain Parker, Nicholas thought, as he had numerous times a week for many years. But if only the dreams would stop!

There was a knock on the door. "Who is it?" Nicholas snapped.

"Charles, sir, and the cook."

Nicholas swore with sufficient force to be heard through the wood, using the very names of God he had read in the prayer minutes before.

"Come in, then!"

"Sir," the cook said, "this boy says I'm to cook a sheep for supper. Never can trust these little . . ."

"He carried exactly the message I sent, you onion-eye!" Nicholas said. "Now leave me in peace before I change my mind again."

"Aye, aye, sir," the cook and the boy chorused in unison, backing hastily out and pulling the door behind them.

No doubt Charles was unnecessarily proud of himself and would want a favor later. Nicholas put his head in his hands again. It was beginning to ache.

If only the dreams would stop, he could get some sleep at night and be sane by day.

But the dreams would not stop.

As a master of the ship, Nicholas alone had a chance to sleep for an entire night. As long as the weather was calm, he did not have to be present in the midnight watches.

Yet, when he lay in his cabin, the most spacious room he had ever had aboard ship, he encountered a zone of terror between sleeping and waking. He had the old dreams of the Fresh Kills, high with muddy water.

He heard Daniel's voice from farther up the creek bank. "Nicholas, where's Seger? You were with him."

Daniel ran toward the creek, rushing past him. Nicholas joined the chase, eyes searching the ripples for his brother's brown hair. Daniel slipped on a rock and fell headlong into the bushes, but he was up almost before he was down, even before Nicholas could fall on top of him. They slipped and slid the whole way to the mouth of the creek and stood helplessly searching the brown water.

"I'm going in," Daniel said, ripping his shirt off over his head in one motion.

"No!" Nicholas screamed.

But Daniel was already in Arthur Kill, swimming in the salt water around the mouth of the creek, lifting his head to scan the water. Nicholas too searched the water until his eyes stung, willing some sign of his brother to appear, a hand, a foot, anything. But not even his imagination could make a boy out of the pair of geese that floated past, or the eddies of white foam, or the branches collecting in a bush along the shore as the flotsam increased.

He screamed at Daniel that another log was coming, but Daniel just told him to run home. He ran, slipping, sliding, falling, with Jonah alongside. He landed on a rough tree stump once and a sliver of wood buried itself in his shoulder.

The dreams were different each time, and sometimes he was in the water, searching for Seger that way. Sometimes a white and orange cat was drowning, not a boy. But always, there was a man's frowning face staring back at Nicholas, telling him that if he were smarter or better or faster, this would not have happened.

Lately in the dreams, Nicholas too was drowning. He would wake just as hell was about to swallow him, just as the face of his mother in heaven was about to disappear. He would jerk angrily awake and sit up, sweating. He would push away his blanket and reach for the lantern swinging from the low ceiling beams.

Light. Light would remind him that these nightmares were foolish fantasies. By day, he made up for the pain of the dreams by indulging in nearly every form of debauchery he could invent or attain.

The letters he received occasionally from Christina began to show the strain of a lonely sea captain's wife. Nicholas didn't think she knew what he indulged in when he went to the West Indies, but just her busy life was enough to exhaust her.

After losing Benjamin, they had lost another baby in 1734 while Nicholas was at sea. Christina had still been grieving when he came home. Then, in 1735, she had given birth to another son. She waited to name him until Nicholas arrived, but she really wanted to name him Benjamin. It was common among the Dutch to reuse the name of a child who had died, and Nicholas agreed with her wish. The baby had been baptized and Nicholas stayed home for the summer.

A little girl, Catharine, who they called Katie, had been born just before he left on his current voyage. Little Benjamin was beginning to toddle around the wooden floor like a landlubber on deck for the first time. Nicholas was fond of all six of his living children: Nicholas Jr., Susanna, Jan, Lambert, Benjamin, and baby Katie. He could hardly fathom that Nicholas Jr., nearly ten, was nearing the age he had been when he first went to sea.

Christina had plenty of money to pay Mary for her help and to buy nice clothes for herself and the children. Having the means to buy art supplies, she picked up her drawing pencils again and was teaching the children a few tips she had learned on her own. As the wife of a sea captain, she had status and respect on Staten Island.

But Nicholas was not sure that she cared much for status. Sometimes he wondered if she was hiding a secret sorrow she would not tell him, and he avoided her eyes as much as possible when he was home. He brought presents every time—beautiful fabrics and jewelry, drawing pens, fruits, and a parrot for Nicholas Jr. He played with the children and read them prayers from his book, trying in his own way to teach them right from wrong.

But was it possible to teach them to be good, something he could not do himself?

The Unhappy Man

August 1736

"Nicholas."

Christina's voice was soft but determined. She was in her rocker, holding Benjamin who had fallen asleep. Nicholas was at his desk beside their bed. He was making plans to add a parlor to the house so he and Christina could receive guests in a special room rather than in the main kitchen area. This would make Christina happy, to have a room just for guests, he thought.

A candle burned on his desk, giving him just enough light to dip his quill in ink and jot down his ideas.

"Yes, my dear?"

"The boys so love having you home."

Nicholas tightened his grip on the quill and deliberately finished several words before answering.

"What are you wanting to say, Christina? Just tell me, instead of hinting."

"We have plenty of money. What if you would get a job closer to home? Perhaps even something on the water where you could be home several times a month?"

"We have money because I'm master of a ship that travels the Atlantic seaboard," Nicholas said.

"We could do with less though. The children need *you* more than they need trinkets and candy. And I need you, more than I need a parlor or fancy clothes."

Nicholas felt anger choking him. He bit his lip, but the emotion rose. He jammed the quill into the ink, causing a small wave of the black liquid to swell over the lip of the jar and pool on his paper, irritating him further.

He pushed back his chair and looked at Christina, who was looking at Benjamin's silent face pressed against her. Even in his anger, he was struck by her beauty. But how dare she imply that they didn't need his salary?

He swore, and Benjamin jumped in his sleep. Katie, asleep in her cradle, let out a brief cry.

"I appreciate your gratitude for my months of bitterly cold nights and hot days and mosquito bites and danger and sickness," he said.

A tear slid down her face, but she kept her composure.

"I *am* grateful for your work, Nicholas, and so proud of you. Mary told me that the men at the mill were talking about how the other captains speak of your navigational ability. They said you are almost always closer with your measurements than the others. Really, I am proud. But what if you didn't have to face the dangers and threats of death? And with six children, I miss their father even more."

Her praise surprised and softened him, and Nicholas berated himself. He had fed her anxiety by suggesting his life was dangerous.

"Perhaps you are right," he said. "But I am committed for the voyage I'm preparing for right now. Maybe I can check around for a job here on the island one of these times."

Christina turned the toddler into his trundle bed. Lambert was four now and old enough to sleep in the loft with his brothers. Nicholas and Christina were soon sleeping too.

Nicholas found himself standing on sharp black rocks. He felt tired from swimming, but it wasn't a long swim to the other side. Then they would have the hard job of walking home through the mud.

Daniel moved into the water on foot.

"Current is not too bad," he shouted before diving in. Jonah dived in after Daniel, his white fur turning brown.

Seger walked out after them, the brown creek washing around him. He stood for a moment, as if he wished it were shallow enough to walk across the whole way. As Nicholas watched, a ray of sunlight broke through the heavy clouds in the western sky. Light and mist enveloped the world, turning the budding trees a brilliant green. The sunlight fell on Seger's back.

"Look!" Seger cried. "Blue butterflies! Remember how we saw them last year!"

Seger leaped forward, and the sunlight caught again in the thousand water drops that sprang up behind his splash. The air was filled with diamonds, and then empty again. Seger moved ahead, and Nicholas saw him grab a huge breath before ducking under water and making for the opposite shore.

The sun disappeared. Nicholas shivered, and moved to the rocks. He jumped into the water, swam forward, and then veered left for the opposite shore.

Just as he moved into the deep part of the creek, he saw a large log coming toward him. It was coming at an angle, and he was surprised at how fast it was moving. Nicholas dove straight down. He felt something scrape across his back, but when he came up, the log was past, leaving only a swirl of foam.

Then Nicholas was on the shore, spitting, but he couldn't see Seger. He must have come to shore farther downstream. He had to be hiding in the bushes. Maybe he had gone home without Nicholas and Jonah. But no, that could not be. Nicholas dove into the churning waters and swam, yelling. He was sinking, about to die, but still he called for his brother.

"Seger!" Nicholas screamed. "Seger!"

"Nicholas! Nicholas!"

Nicholas felt his wife's hands on his arms. He shook himself and realized he was sitting up in bed, blankets strewn around him. Baby Katie in her cradle whimpered and began to wail. Christina got out of bed and patted Katie's back and she soon settled down.

Nicholas felt his neck. It was wet with sweat.

Christina came back to bed.

"Are you all right?"

"Yes," he said. "I'm sorry. It was just a dream."

"A nightmare, I guess," she said. "Is this the first one you've had or do you have them when you are out at s—"

"No," Nicholas snapped.

He fell back to the pillow, exhausted. Christina said nothing, but he was sure she knew he was lying.

• •

A few days before his next voyage, Nicholas met Mary at the well, drawing water for herself and Pine. Both Jack and Sarah were married. Pine no longer traveled as a sea cook.

"About to be fully cooked myself," he would say when he complained about getting old. "One of these days I will hear the Savior say, 'Well done.' "

"Master Nicholas," Mary said, resting her empty wooden bucket on the side of the well with a clatter. "Are you happy with the life you live?"

Nicholas yanked his bucket off the well rope hook.

"Have you been talking with Christina or what? She wants me to get a job on the island."

Mary shot him a withering glance, the whites of her eyes flashing.

"Did I say anything about your job?" she asked. "Or the island or the sea or occupations of any kind? Oh no, I do not believe I did."

"Then what do you mean?"

"I asked, 'Are you happy?' "

"I guess I am about as happy as a man has a right to be," he said. "I have six beautiful children and a beautiful wife and a good job—and an obnoxious hired woman."

"Nicholas, don't you be sassy and funny, oh no, do you not! I is asking this minute about your soul, just like your mama used to care about!"

Nicholas picked up the bucket and turned toward the house.

"Christina's waiting for water," he said, walking away.

Inside the house, Nicholas Jr. came across the kitchen with a secretive expression and a folded paper. Nicholas saw Christina watching from the corner.

"I made this for you, Father," Nicholas Jr. said, holding out the paper.

Nicholas took the paper and unfolded it. He caught his breath.

It was a ship at anchor. It was obviously done by a child, yet the detail, even the perspective, was astounding. A small boat was in the water beside the ship, and a stick figure was handing a barrel to someone in the ship. On the back of the ship, standing on the quarterdeck, was a man with an elaborate hat and the words *Captain Garrison*.

"You made this, son? You drew this by yourself?"

"Yes, I did, but Mother helped me with the figurehead and the captain's hat," he said.

Sure enough, the ship had a carving of a curving swan's neck at the bow, just as the *Golden Swan* had.

"This is excellent!" Nicholas said. "Good job, my son. May I take it with me? Although I almost want to keep it safe at home."

"It's for your cabin," Nicholas Jr. said. "Since you are there more than you are here."

Nicholas ignored the sting in his heart at those last words, and he helped Nicholas Jr. make a plan for framing the drawing with thin strips of wood.

"Pine will help me," Nicholas Jr. said.

Nicholas felt the sting increase.

29

The Peaceful Stranger

October 1736

Over a month later, the *Golden Swan* was at anchor with several other ships on the island of St. Eustatius. Nicholas made a few trades, replenished the ship with fresh water, and took on several passengers who wanted to go north. One, he was told, was a clergyman who had fallen sick on St. Thomas, one of the Virgin Islands. Nicholas had no objection to taking on passengers as long as they paid for their passage and stayed out of the way of the crew.

After spending the evening at a dance under the palm trees, Nicholas arrived back at the ship. The crew saluted as he climbed through the entry port. Nicholas noticed the clergyman, standing on the far side of the ship. Nicholas looked away because the man was watching him closely. He walked around giving orders for plans to sail in the morning.

Finally, he made his way to the clergyman, still standing along the bulwark. The man was thin and pale and wore a brown coat that was too big for him, suggesting he had lost weight. He had been looking out over the sea, but he turned at the sound of Nicholas' footsteps. Nicholas saw he had a long nose that came to a sudden point and calm, inviting eyes.

"Ah, Captain Garrison," the man said with warmth. "It's a pleasure to make your acquaintance. Thank you for allowing me passage on your ship. My name is Josef Spangenberg. I go by Brother Josef."

"What brings you to these parts?"

"I am delighted to tell you, sir," the man said. "My brothers—in our community,

Brother Josef Spangenberg
Artist: Johann Gothard von Müller

we address each other as brothers and sisters—have come to St. Thomas to bring the Gospel of Jesus Christ to the slaves. We call ourselves 'the Brethren' or the 'Unity of the Brothers.' Others call us Moravians, since many of our people came from that location in Europe. We all wish to have the knowledge of the Savior spread to those who have never heard."

"I see," Nicholas said. It was the safest comment he could think of, even though he swore in his thoughts. *Why would educated Europeans spend their lives on a mosquito-laden island in an effort to educate slaves?*

"I wanted to be of assistance to them," Brother Josef said with a sigh, as if reading Nicholas' mind. "And I pray that I benefited them somewhat. But, alas, my health simply will not tolerate this climate. I have been in bed nearly the entire year with some complaint or another. I believe I was made for a temperate climate, Captain."

"Ah, yes. I have been quite fortunate myself to be able to enjoy the pleasures of the tropics," Nicholas said, and instantly regretted his choice of words. "But I know that many people find it hard to adjust," he added hastily. "Do let me know if I can help make your stay more comfortable aboard the *Golden Swan*. Your berth may lack comfort for a man who is ill."

"I feel better than I have, sir," Brother Josef said. "And I believe I will ride just fine. By the mercy of God, I am not prone to seasickness."

"I will have my surgeon check in with you daily," Nicholas promised. "Charles!" The ship's boy was at his elbow instantly.

"Show this man where the water pump is and check on him every day to see if he needs anything."

"Aye, aye, sir!"

The next day they weighed anchor and headed for New York. That evening in the second dogwatch, the sailors were in fine form, dancing, singing, and playing games. Nicholas had eaten in his cabin alone. He had not slept well, as usual.

Now, he stood on the quarterdeck, looking up at the sky and the sails catching puffs of wind. He looked down at the reveling men.

Then he saw the visitor climbing out of the main hatch. He moved awkwardly, probably either from not being accustomed to ladders or from his sickness. But he was also carrying a book in his hand.

Once he got on deck, he swayed a bit, found his footing, and sat a little apart from the checkers game. Seagull Sal was squatting nearby, strumming a tune on his cittern.

The visitor took out his book and a pencil and began to write.

"Are you a preacher?" Seagull Sal asked him.

The men playing checkers laughed.

Brother Josef looked at the questioner with kindness.

"Thank you for asking," he said. "I guess you could call me that. But really, I like to think of myself as a servant of our Savior."

He paused. No one laughed this time. Everyone had gone quiet.

"My own sins are so great, but He has forgiven them, and I rejoice every day at His great mercy. That is why I am His servant and will be until I die."

"You! Sin?" Seagull Sal exclaimed.

"My brother!" cried Brother Josef. "Each of us has a heart of sin that separates us from God. I am no different than anyone else. It is no use for us to judge ourselves or to try to be better on our own, because we all merit death for our sin. But Jesus redeemed us back to God!"

"What are you writing in that book?" another asked.

Nicholas cringed. The man obviously had education and class. The sailors were treating him like an equal, asking him nosy questions. But the man did not seem to mind. In fact, he welcomed the men, not just with his words, but with his eyes.

"I am writing a hymn," he said. "Perhaps I can sing it for you after I finish."

Throughout the voyage, Brother Josef spoke to the men of the Savior. Some of them laughed at him, but most had a quiet respect. Nicholas learned that Brother Josef was thirty-two years old, just a few years younger than he.

But unlike Nicholas, this man glowed with inner peace. He sang hymns as he walked the deck. He helped the men with little tasks when he could, even though he still required long naps. He grew stronger each day and wherever he was, that spot seemed just a little more peaceful than it had before he arrived.

Nicholas invited Brother Josef to dinner in his cabin one night. The clergyman told how he had become an orphan, just a year after Nicholas had lost his mother. Educated at the University of Jena, he had received his degree in 1726. He had been a professor of theology at the University of Halle until he was expelled in 1733 for associating with Count Zinzendorf. The count led a community of believers in Herrnhut, Germany, and Josef had joined the community.

"My full name is August Gottlieb Spangenberg," he said with a smile. "But I have come to be known as Brother Josef, which I much prefer. In Christ, we are brothers and sisters."

Brother Josef had come to the West Indies the year before to help with the new mission outreach to the slaves on St. Thomas. In March, Friedrich Martin had come to assist the mission, which was good because Brother Josef had been forced to keep to his bed.

Nicholas listened as Brother Josef shared his story.

Brother Josef asked a few questions about Nicholas' life, which Nicholas answered as briefly as possible. Brother Josef looked at Nicholas with a searching eye.

"Have you been sleeping well, Captain?"

Nicholas took an unnecessary bite and chewed slowly. "No," he finally said.

He was shocked that Brother Josef had sensed his unrest and more shocked that he had answered honestly. Sea captains were supposed to be above weakness.

Instead of prying, Brother Josef spoke about Christ's death and how His blood can cleanse the sin of any man who calls on Him. He shared about the hope and peace that can be experienced when one claims that blood and turns his life over to the service of the Lamb of God.

"May I share a bit about the background of the Moravian Brethren?' Brother Josef asked. At Nicholas' nod, he continued. "Most of the Brethren fled persecution in a Catholic land. Count Zinzendorf allowed them to settle on his estate and a motley village sprang up. The refugees called it *Herrnhut,* meaning 'the Lord's care.'

"Count Zinzendorf devoted himself to prayer for hours each day. He and his wife moved to the refugee camp. The Count dreamed of starting a Christian community based on the Bible. The refugees were dreaming of a safe community where they could live out their beliefs. It was a perfect match.

"But there were a lot of arguments about theology. Count Zinzendorf suggested that instead of arguing about religion, they focus on Jesus Christ and His sufferings. They met for Bible studies and prayer meetings.

"In 1727 a turning point came during a communion service. The Spirit of God descended on the Moravian believers as they worshiped the suffering Savior. The refugee camp was never the same. A few weeks later after a night-long prayer meeting, they decided to keep prayer going continuously. One man and one woman were assigned to pray each hour, every day."

Nicholas listened with astonishment, the rest of his supper uneaten.

Brother Josef continued. "They came up with a daily schedule, gathering every morning at 5 a.m. for devotions in the large meeting room known as the *Saal.* After breakfast there was prayer and the reading of the Watchword. The Watchwords are daily Scriptures that follow a yearly schedule. In the evenings they held prayer services or song services.

"Count Zinzendorf met with two leaders who had escaped persecution. The three men took turns examining the lives of the others. They pointed out the blemishes that still marred the image of Christ in their lives. This complete openness and accountability spread, producing a loving and trusting community."

Nicholas listened respectfully. Brother Josef's words were awakening hope and longing in his heart. Could he too find the peace this man had?

• •

A week later, almost into New York Bay, a terrible wind threatened to crush them on the rocks. Nicholas ran onto the deck, shouting and cursing as the ship tilted and several of the crew staggered. After yelling at the first mate to have the men get the sails in, he descended to the lower deck to check on their visitor.

"Brother Josef!" he shouted, banging on the door of the closet-like room the man occupied.

"Come in," Brother Josef answered. "It must be a bit breezy outside?"

His bed was built into the side of the ship, and he was thrown against the side as he finished the question. Nicholas saw in his hand a small book.

"A terrible gale," Nicholas snapped, "that threatens to break the boat in pieces any minute, and us just outside of New York."

"Captain Garrison, sit down if you can spare a moment."

"I certainly cannot! My men could be going overboard at this moment!"

"Then I will continue alone my prayers for you and the other men," Brother Josef said.

Frustrated with himself for being more anxious than an ill passenger, Nicholas climbed the ladder two rungs at a time. From his post on the quarterdeck, he watched the men put the final knots on the sails, watched the waves pick up and the boat roll. He felt irritable and dissatisfied.

"They've got the sails in, sir," the first mate said.

"We need to heave to," Nicholas said curtly.

"Aye, aye, sir," the first mate and Seagull Sal said together. Seagull Sal began to maneuver the rudder to turn the ship into the wind.

Nicholas tried to forget his embarrassment in front of Brother Josef, but there was a question he could not stop asking.

How can that man be so calm when his life is in danger?

30

The Blood of the Lamb

The port of New York was abuzz with the usual activity when the *Golden Swan* arrived.

"I am very glad to see you," Thomas Noble said. "I couldn't stop thinking about you in that wind yesterday."

"You had reason to worry," Nicholas said.

Nicholas introduced Brother Josef to Thomas Noble, the merchant. In his hospitable manner, Thomas invited the church man to spend the night at his house.

"I'm a Presbyterian," Mr. Noble said. "If you can handle staying at the house of a Presbyterian, you are more than welcome!"

"I am learning in whatever state I am in to be content!" Brother Josef said with a smile. "I thank you for your kind offer and I will take you up on it."

"Captain Garrison!" Mr. Noble continued, "perhaps your days of struggling to measure longitude are coming to an end. Did you hear the story of the *Centurion?*"

"I don't believe so," Nicholas said. "Is this about John Harrison? I heard he had invented a clock that was supposed to keep time at sea."

"Oh, but it proved itself!" Mr. Noble said. "It hasn't gone all the way to the West Indies though, which was the queen's original condition for the prize. They only let him take it to Lisbon, Portugal, and back to England. But it lost only a few seconds a day!"

"Only a few seconds per day?" Nicholas repeated.

"A seaman told me that on the return voyage the captain thought they were near Dartmouth," Mr. Noble went on. "This Mr. Harrison insisted that by his measurements they were sixty miles west and the point of land was the Lizard. He was right!"

"Fascinating!" Nicholas said. "How big was the clock?"

"Well, that's just it. The clock is as wide as a *kast* and took up half the captain's cabin. So it's not practical yet."

"But it worked," Nicholas mused. "I wonder how?"

"Well, springs and levers and weighted arms. And Harrison is just an ordinary seaman!"

"I have long hoped to see the day when the longitude problem is solved," Nicholas said. "Perhaps I shall. Any other news here in New York?"

"The journalist who Governor Cosby accused of libel has been acquitted!" Thomas Noble chuckled. "The jury decided that what he said about the governor was true!"

"That's almost as exciting," Nicholas said. "The less the heavy arm of England can oppress us here, the better."

There was nothing like arriving at Manhattan. News. Drama. Payment for the voyage. Fresh water and fresh food. A dozen languages being spoken on the streets. Always a new building that hadn't been there when they left.

Mr. Noble's coffee house was up and running, and they went there directly for a fresh cup and a look over the accounts from the voyage. The woman tending the large copper pots brightened when the owner, Mr. Noble, walked in. She dipped mugs of coffee for the men.

"Captain, I'd like you to go to Antigua on your next run," Mr. Noble said. "It's a new settlement, only been colonized since '32. But I heard of several plantations there producing indigo, ginger, and tobacco. I intend to write to see if they would be open to trading, but it looks positive."

"Certainly," Nicholas said. "I enjoy new ventures. I'll study the charts."

Suddenly he thought about his wife's plea for him to be at home more. "When are you thinking of that voyage?" he asked.

"Oh, let me see if I can correspond with them. I'll let you know, but probably in a few months."

Nicholas excused himself when the accounts were settled. He bid farewell to Mr. Noble and to his kindly passenger.

He wondered again how Brother Josef had deduced that he was not sleeping well.

Brother Josef had prayed for him the night of their dinner. He had prayed for him personally, as if he was talking to Jesus as a brother and friend. He had prayed for the men on the ship, too, as if he considered them brothers as well. Nicholas determined to be more like Brother Josef in his dealings with others.

He went to the ferry, where his sea chest was supposed to have been delivered. Not finding it, he retraced his steps to the wharf.

"Charles!" he shouted when he saw the black boy. "Where is my sea chest? I asked to have it delivered to the ferry two hours ago!"

Charles looked up at his captain. Then his head fell. "It's still here, sir."

Nicholas swore. "Sal! Why is my chest still here?"

Seagull Sal looked up from the box he was stacking onto a cart. His forehead was beaded with sweat on the cool fall day.

"I'm sorry, sir," Seagull Sal said. "Mr. Noble's manager was after us to get the tobacco carted over. But we will take the chest immediately."

Nicholas turned to head back to the ferry and nearly bumped into Brother Josef, standing as if he had heard the entire conversation. Nicholas mumbled an apology.

"No need to apologize to me," his passenger said gently. "I'm just here to find something I left as well."

Nicholas kept walking, filled with regret for his angry words. Before he turned down Dock Street toward Whitehall, he looked back at the dock.

Brother Josef was helping Seagull Sal load Nicholas' sea chest into a cart.

Nicholas swallowed and turned away.

At home the five oldest children crowded around Nicholas, trying to be the first to look into the sea chest. Little Benjamin, who was quite steady on his legs by now, squawked as the older ones pushed him aside. Little Katie stared at her father with wide eyes since she did not remember him. Christina greeted him happily, but Nicholas could see she was exhausted.

"Mr. Noble wants me to go to Antigua," he told his wife. "But I don't think it will be until spring. I'll be here for the worst of the winter, certainly."

"That's good," she said.

Nicholas saw disappointment cloud her eyes, and he knew she had been hoping he would not agree to another voyage so soon.

"I need to tell you about a passenger I picked up in Eustatius," Nicholas said. "A good Christian man who is part of a missionary effort to the black slaves of St. Thomas! Isn't that amazing?"

"And why would that be so amazing?" Mary demanded from her spot near the oven. "I guess black people need a Savior as well as white ones!" Mary did not seem to age. Perhaps she moved a little more slowly than she had thirty years before. But that was all.

"I think you would get along splendidly with Brother Josef," Nicholas said.

"Perhaps we could have him here as a guest if he is staying in New York,"

Christina said.

"Pine isn't doing well," Mary said. "You need to go visit him."

* *

Before Nicholas left for Antigua in the spring of 1737, Pine died of fever. He had been weak all winter, and then had rallied and gone to Manhattan one day. But a few days later he was in bed and he never got out.

"Don't you let the children come see him," Mary said, wiping tears when she reported his illness to Nicholas and Christina. "It might be con-gag-ious."

"I'm a-going, Nicholas," Pine whispered when Nicholas came to see him.

Nicholas thought of arguing but decided against it. "I will miss you, my friend," he said.

"Popcorn," Pine said. Nicholas thought he was delirious, but he went on. "When we had popcorn battles. You usually missed me then too."

And so Nicholas and Pine parted for the last time with laughter, as they always had.

* *

Nicholas had been on the *Golden Swan* only a few days when he grew dizzy. Earlier he had noticed a sore throat, but he now felt weak. He would have fallen on the quarterdeck had not Seagull Sal grabbed a barrel for him to sit on.

"I believe you are sick, sir," he said.

Seagull Sal called for a couple of able seamen who were winding cable.

"I think I will be all right," Nicholas insisted, but they helped him to his cabin and called the surgeon.

The surgeon held a lantern high and asked Nicholas to open his mouth. "Have you been around anyone ill lately?" he asked.

"No," Nicholas said.

"I'm afraid you have diphtheria, sir, from the appearance of the gray tissue in your throat. Although I find it surprising that you would catch it at your age."

"Oh," Nicholas said. "My hired hand. He died a week before we left and I did go visit him. Pine was even older than I am."

"Ah. My advice, Captain Garrison, is that you appoint one of your men to navigate. I would be remiss if I didn't tell you that this disease progresses quickly and can be fatal. In addition, it is highly contagious, and I recommend you remain in your cabin for the sake of the men."

"I understand, sir. Thank you."

"I will attend to you myself," the surgeon went on. "I'll find a bell for you to ring and I will sleep close by. I have cared for diphtheria cases many times and am not worried about getting it myself."

The surgeon went to find the bell. Per Nicholas' instructions, he directed the first mate to take command of the ship until the captain could recover.

Alone in his bed, Nicholas felt a wave of terror wash over him. Diphtheria was a child's disease. How could he be sick with it?

God is punishing me for my sins, he thought. *And I have no right to argue.* He remembered Brother Josef speaking to the sailors on the last voyage. *The penalty for sin is death.*

"Here is your bell, sir. Ring as needed."

I am going to die, Nicholas thought. *I'm going to hell, and that's where I deserve to be. I have sinned in every way that I promised I never would. I never confessed my wrongs to the cook. I hate Captain Parker so much I could kill him. I have left my family alone. I have exploited the women in the port cities of the tropics. I am worse than a sinner, because I'm a hypocrite too, keeping the truth from my wife. I'm a liar, just like Captain Parker.*

At this thought, Nicholas felt even greater terror. Never before had he seen himself similar to Captain Parker in any way. The thought filled him with grief and pain and despair.

He slept, and the surgeon laid cloths on his forehead.

"Not long until we reach the West Indies," the surgeon said. "Just hold on a bit longer, sir."

"Ask the first mate to take me to St. Thomas," Nicholas said.

"St. Thomas? Aye, aye, sir, I will tell him St. Thomas."

As thirst burned Nicholas' throat and his breath came faster and heavier, he saw faces and heard words. Joaquin. Mother. Christina. Brother Josef. Nicholas Jr. Old Pete. The cook. Captain Parker. Seger. The orange and white cat.

"Captain Garrison, Captain Garrison! Do take a drink. Careful, sir, very carefully or you will choke. But you must have water. You have been lying here already for three days."

But Nicholas was not able to drink. He saw the surgeon's face above him wince with disappointment, and Nicholas knew he was dying.

The surgeon's face mingled with other faces. Everyone began talking to each other in a low-ceilinged smoky tavern. Christina was there, talking to the prostitutes who were pointing to him. Brother Josef was telling Joaquin about the Savior. Seger was playing checkers with Joaquin. But none of them seemed to notice that Nicholas was pounding on the window, trying to get in—except for Captain Parker—and he was laughing.

Then the tavern moved away and Nicholas saw it was a three-masted vessel sailing toward a golden city. Nicholas ran along the shore, cutting himself on the rocks, trying to get the attention of the ship to stop and pick him up. *Ahoy! Heave to! I'm your captain! Avast!* But on the quarterdeck he saw a man with a red hand-kerchief laughing at him. Captain Parker had taken his ship and marooned him on the island. He was on the edge of a volcanic hill covered with ash and belching smoke. The ground close to him collapsed and he saw red hot lava below. The rocks and black dirt and ash fell into the hell below, and the ash came toward Nicholas. Soon he would be falling into the fire of hell. He turned back to the ship, waving his arms and screaming.

"Help!" he croaked, but the tightness of his throat choked the words.

"Rest, Captain Garrison, rest."

Nicholas opened his eyes.

Rest, said the blocks of pink sunset light let in by the stern windows. On a haystack under the stars, perhaps. With Mother's beautiful face looking down on him, coaxing him to say his verses. *Rest,* said the lantern, throwing an ever brighter circle in the darkening room.

"If I take the wings of the morning, and dwell in the uttermost parts of the sea, even there shall thy hand lead me, and thy right hand shall hold me. If I say, Surely the darkness shall cover me; even the night shall be light about me. Yea, the darkness hideth not from thee; but the night shineth as the day: the darkness and the light are both alike to thee."[1]

If these verses were true, God had seen every sin he had ever committed, every indulgence, every dishonest deed. God, like Captain Parker, knew that Nicholas was not smart enough to escape, not good enough to go to heaven. God, like his father, knew that he was to blame. There would be no rest for him. He was a sinner, and deserved to die. His attempts to be good had all fallen to the ground around him, and he was bare and naked before God, with nowhere to hide.

Dy-ing, dy-ing, each breath seemed to rasp. *Dying,* the dark bedpost beside him echoed. *Dying, so another man can sleep in this bed. Dying, dying* the ceiling beams repeated into the dark corners of the room. *You are going to die and another man will take this cabin while you burn in hell. Another man will plot voyages on this globe and on these charts. Dying. Another man will marry your wife and be a father to your children and he will do a much better job than you have done.*

---

[1] Psalm 139:9–12

Dying. Nicholas had hated Captain Parker so much that he had wanted him to die. Captain Parker with his red handkerchief—red as blood.

Blood. *"Jesus can redeem us. Like a Lamb to the slaughter, so he opened not his mouth."* Even in his weakness, Nicholas was startled that he remembered Brother Josef's words to the sailors, and a verse from his childhood.

My sins are too great! he thought, and again, he heard the chorus begging him to die.

But maybe Brother Josef was right. Maybe the blood of Jesus did count in God's eyes. It was his only hope, and he wrestled his cracked lips to whisper a message to the ceiling beams.

"Father God! Save me! I believe that Jesus shed His blood for me! Give me one more chance!"

31

The Happy Man

May 1737

"Captain. Captain Garrison. Sir!"

Nicholas awoke. He heard fire crackling. He saw red coals.

"Am I in hell?"

His breath was even and deep, not rapid and raspy as it had been on the ship. He saw the thin face of a dark-haired man looking down at him.

"No sir, you are not in hell," the man said. "You are in the home of Mr. Carstens, the plantation owner."

Nicholas had not realized he had said the words out loud, but he was too relieved to be embarrassed. Of course, this must be earth. He could feel a bed beneath him.

"You are recovering and doing better each day, sir. My name is Friedrich Martin. I was told you asked for me."

Nicholas vaguely recalled the end of the voyage. He remembered the surgeon speaking, although the memories were so foggy they might have been dreams.

"Captain, we are at St. Thomas. Is there someone we can send for? Someone who might be expecting you?"

"Friedrich Martin, I believe. I will go to him," Nicholas remembered answering.

"Ah, sir, you are very weak! I am very surprised you did not die last night! I must insist—"

"Take me to him!"

At least, Nicholas thought he remembered such a conversation, but it had a dream-like quality.

Mr. Martin now explained to Captain Garrison that the men of the *Golden Swan* had done just that. They had carried their captain on a makeshift bed of planks, past the cacti and palm trees of St. Thomas to the house of Friedrich Martin.

"My home is just a hut," Mr. Martin said. "So I asked Mr. Carstens for the privilege of lodging my sick friend in his house. May I ask, Captain Garrison, how you know me?"

Nicholas felt too weak to speak, yet at the same time he wanted to burst into song. He was alive! God had spared his life and given him a second chance through the blood of Jesus, just as Brother Josef had said.

"Brother Josef," Nicholas said simply.

"Ah! Could you be the captain who picked him up here last year?" Friedrich Martin's serious eyes lit up with joy at the mention of his friend.

"Yes," Nicholas said. "Water."

"Ah, certainly, my good man," Mr. Martin said, reaching for a glass goblet at the bedside.

He supported Nicholas' head and let the water trickle between his lips. Nicholas found that swallowing hurt, but he could do it.

He leaned back on the pillow, and felt feathers under his head. Nicholas saw silk hangings around the bed and windows. A section of palm leaf bobbed outside the window against a blue tropical sky.

"No, Mr. Martin," Nicholas said. "I am not a good man."

Mr. Martin had been arranging the glass on the bedside table. He turned a searching look at the weak figure in the bed, then seated himself on a stool at the bedside.

"I would like to hear more of what you mean when you say that," he said. "But I fear you are too weak. And, call me Brother Friedrich."

"Brother Friedrich, I am a sinner. I begged God to spare my life by the blood of the Lamb, like Brother Josef told me. And he did!"

Nicholas stopped to breathe. He wanted to talk more. He wanted to voice his amazement. He wanted to try to explain the joy that was building inside him. But he could not.

Brother Friedrich sat perfectly still for a moment. He glanced out the window toward the palm tree, an expression of deep joy and affection on his face. It was almost as if he communicated with the Savior Himself in that brief moment. Then Brother Friedrich turned toward Nicholas, a smile splitting his thin face.

"Praise God, my friend! I live for the joy of watching men turn to the Lamb of God. And, although I used the phrase as an expression, there was only ever one Good Man to walk this earth. And He was the Savior who was chosen to suffer horribly because all the rest of us are not good! What a blessing it is indeed to know Him!"

"Yes," Nicholas said, tears filling his eyes. "I must get back to New York and tell my wife . . ."

Here, Nicholas found he could not go on as the tears overwhelmed him.

"Captain." Brother Friedrich placed a hand on his arm. "Rest now. Rest so we can get you back to New York to your family."

"Can you call me Brother Nicholas?" the captain asked a moment later. "Or is that a special . . ."

"It is a term we use for members of our church," Brother Friedrich said. "But, my friend, when a man has experienced the mercy and grace of God our Savior, I am more than honored to call him Brother."

He squeezed Nicholas' hand. "Now rest, Brother Nicholas."

The next day, Nicholas sat up in bed and fed himself broth. Mr. Carstens came to the sickroom and introduced himself.

"Thank you for your kind hospitality," Nicholas said. "This is a wonderful room."

"More than happy to help you, Captain," Mr. Carstens said. "Mr. Martin and his community have some strange ways, but I respect them. I am happy to give you my assistance. I am also glad to see that you are recovering. I will send Edward in to help you wash up."

Edward was a black slave, about fifteen years old. He addressed Nicholas as "Massa" as he assisted him with a basin of warm water, a towel, and a change of clothes.

"Do you know Friedrich Martin?" Nicholas asked.

"Yes, Massa, I do," the boy said, his face lighting up. "He speaks to us about the Savior dying on the cross for our sins. On the other plantations, no one is allowed to meet to hear him speak, or they will be whipped or burned or hanged or have their feet cut off! But here, Massa Carstens lets us meet. Massa Carstens is a good man."

Nicholas wanted to ask more about how slaves were treated on the plantations, but he found that the work of washing and dressing was exhausting.

"Massa Captain," Edward said as he helped him with his shirt. "Did you get whipped?"

"Yes, my boy, I did," Nicholas said with a smile. "It was many years ago when I was about your age."

Edward dressed him with tenderness, as though the twenty-four-year-old scars were still throbbing with pain.

As Nicholas recovered, he spent time with Friedrich Martin. He followed him around the island of St. Thomas, watching him serve the Lamb, as Friedrich called Jesus.

Brother Friedrich told him how so many of the slaves were horribly treated by their white masters who called themselves Christians. As Edward had mentioned, punishments included branding, flogging, cutting off arms or legs or ears, and hanging. No legal marriages between slaves were allowed, but rampant immorality was all but enforced.

Brother Friedrich explained the strategy of the Moravians for reaching the slaves. The brothers determined to support themselves to set an example of hard work and humility. They had met great difficulties and many of the missionaries had died from tropical diseases. But more missionaries arrived from Europe to replace the ones who died.

Brother Friedrich wanted to meet every slave on every plantation on St. Thomas. He and a friend began to take in abandoned children. They hired a former slave woman, Rebecca, to care for the children.

"In our time here, we have encountered things that we have no idea how to deal with. As I said, we have discovered that church-going, white plantation owners can be much more wicked than the black slaves who have never heard of the blood of the Lamb."

"Aye!" Nicholas said. "So much cruelty."

"Many situations threaten to defeat us," Brother Friedrich said with a shake of the head. "But we present everything to the Savior in prayer, pleading for His mercy and direction. And He is so good to us!"

Brother Friedrich's face lit up with confidence in the Lamb. Then he looked back at Nicholas, as if he had forgotten that someone was there.

"Remember this, my friend. At any time, you can cry to the Savior for help. He will always hear you."

"Aye, as I did when I was dying on the ship," Nicholas said. It still seemed like a dream. *God met me! He met me and redeemed me by the blood of the Lamb and gave me a second chance!*

It was late summer before Nicholas was strong enough to arrange his crew and load the *Golden Swan* for the return to New York. He thought of Christina and how he would tell her what had happened. He had written her one letter, saying only that he had been delayed by sickness. He wanted to tell her the other details in person.

What if they were captured by pirates and never got home? What if he succumbed to sickness and Christina would never hear his story nor yet his confessions? What if a storm took the ship down before it reached New York?

As a precaution, Nicholas wrote a letter to Christina, telling her the details of his conversion. He wrote of his sins of unfaithfulness and how sorry he was for them. He sealed it and wrote "Mrs. Nicholas Garrison, Staten Island" on the front. He put the letter in his sea chest.

Then he fell to his knees beside the chest and begged God to let him make it back to New York.

32

The Answered Prayers

August 1737

On a muggy August morning, Nicholas stood on the quarterdeck. He took a last look at the striking beauty of St. Thomas. He had not noticed the details of that beauty before. Green hills checkered with cultivated plots stood out against a blue sky. The red roofs of the town of Charlotte Amalie reflected the sunlight. Palm trees and cactus dotted the land. Patches of orange hibiscus and brilliant pink bougainvillea waved in the sea breeze as if bidding farewell to the *Golden Swan*. Even the beach glittered with crystals.

The bougainvillea plants had caught Nicholas' eye one day as he had been walking about. He asked his men to dig several and plant them in pots. He was hoping at least one would survive for Christina.

"All right then, men, let's weigh anchor!" Nicholas called.

"Aye, aye, captain!" the first mate called. "Weigh anchor, men!"

"Weighing anchor!" the men of the larboard watch chorused back, and one of them started a capstan song.

> Haul away, and up she rises.
> Haul away, and up she rises.
> Haul away, and up she rises.
> Early in the morning.

Nicholas watched the men moving up the rigging and loosening the sails. They called to each other with the energy of a new voyage ahead. Their stomachs were full with fresh fruit and meat. He wished Seagull Sal were with him, but he could not blame him for not waiting. Only a few men from the *Golden Swan* had waited for its captain to recover.

Nicholas had stood on the quarterdeck many times before, yes. But this time he was a different man. His eyes filled with sudden tears as he thought of the years wasted on pleasures that had never made him happy. The desperate eagerness to be reunited with Christina and the children filled him like wind in a sail. Oh, to tell them of God's amazing mercy to him, a wretched man. How, for all these years, could he have missed what the blood of Jesus really meant?

As they sailed, Nicholas noticed how ordinary scenes overflowed with beauty when a man's heart was right before God. Dolphins leaped and plunged, in pairs and in larger pods. Sharks trailed the ship for miles in hopes of a stray scrap or a man overboard. Pilot fish swam with the sharks, directing them. Sucking fish clung to the backs and bellies of the sharks. Just below the surface, the blue, green, and gold rainbow of the dorado fish flashed, reminding him of Christina's art pencils. When the waves were high, they peppered the ship's deck with scuttle fish, flying fish, and small crabs clinging to seaweed. Pods of whales appeared and disappeared across the water. Far in the distance, waterspouts rose against the dawn. At night, the phosphorescent algae glowed as the ship cut a path through it.

How could I not have seen, Nicholas wondered, *that these creatures praise their Creator just by living?*

Above the ship, magnificent frigatebirds wheeled in wide circles, their eight-foot wingspans far exceeding the width of their bodies. Nicholas watched them pestering smaller birds, trying to get part of their latest meal. Sometimes the frigatebirds feasted on the regurgitated food of other birds, snatching it as it fell. Red-billed tropicbirds also danced and circled through the air, two long tail feathers streaming behind each white body.

Higher still, Nicholas' favorite part of creation continued to run like a well-oiled watch that never lost time. The stars. The moon. The sun. What splendor! What design!

One night, as he gazed at the stars from the quarterdeck, he thought of his attempts to ignore the God of this amazing creation. He had resented God because He had not saved Seger. God had not saved Mother. God had not stopped Captain Parker's cruelty. Now, Nicholas realized, it was not in a man to understand the ways of God. His anger at God had sprung from his desire to be his own god. But God's plans soared above man's highest imagination. Only with the love and grace of Christ could Nicholas be a different man than Captain Parker.

And only with my grace can you forgive Captain Parker. Nicholas jumped. He did not hear the voice, but he felt it. The words broke into his thoughts like a whisper that could not be ignored.

Forgive Captain Parker? Nicholas asked himself. *Could I?*

Nicholas had overestimated his physical strength. Long before they reached New York, he was forced to take to his bed. He came on deck only at noon and at night to take measurements, but these efforts exhausted him. Rather than sit at his desk to review the logbook entries of the first mate, he had the second mate read them to him. He only went to the table if a correction had to be entered.

He did read his Bible every day. One night he read the parable of a man who had been forgiven a huge debt. As soon as he had been pardoned, he imprisoned another man who owed him only a small amount of money.

Tears sprang into Nicholas' eyes as he thought of the great love of God that he had experienced on what could have been his deathbed. Through the blood of Jesus, God had forgiven his huge debt. Looking at the ceiling above his bed, he whispered the words he had thought he could never say. "In your strength, Lamb of God, I forgive Captain Parker! Give me the grace to treat him right if I ever meet him!"

Joy filled his soul. It was as if the door that had clanged shut in the Cuban prison had been opened again by the mercy of God.

The *Golden Swan* arrived in New York in September. Nicholas was able to walk off the ship, but he was very weak. A coach was called, and Nicholas with his sea chest and the bougainvillea plants were loaded. From the coach, he boarded the ferry to Staten Island. At Darby Doyle's tavern, he hired a wagon for the journey up Iron Hill to the Garrison home.

As the horses plodded up the hill through the oranges, greens, and yellows of early fall, Nicholas felt a twinge of nervousness. What would Christina do when he confessed his sins to her? What if she would not believe he had changed?

She had every right to be angry and spiteful when she found out that he had been unfaithful, but he must tell her. The only way to win back her trust was to prove trustworthy over the next months and years. He determined with the help of God to make the changes necessary to regain his wife's trust. He would find a surveying job close to home, and spend time with her and their children.

A cold autumn rain was beginning to fall. The driver had seen Nicholas' weakness and helped him carry the sea chest into the house. Christina let them in. The kitchen was quiet and the children were in bed.

"I hope you can make it over the ridge before it gets slippery," Nicholas said to the coachman. He dropped an extra shilling into his hand.

"Thank you, Captain! I appreciate it!"

The coachman had a booming voice and failed to consider that there might be children sleeping. As he turned to go, the loft erupted with shouts. Nicholas did not have even a word with his wife, before Nicholas Jr., Jan, Lambert, and Benjamin had tumbled down the ladder and were crowding around him.

"Boys, Father is still sick," Christina said. "Jan, get him a chair."

Susanna appeared sleepily from her mother's bedroom where she slept when Father was gone. Baby Katie began to cry at the commotion, and soon everyone was talking and laughing and digging in the sea chest. A sealed letter slipped to the floor.

"That has Mother's name on it!" Nicholas Jr. said.

"Yes, it does," Nicholas said as he picked it up. "I will keep it for her."

His heart swelled with gratitude. The letter was not necessary, because he was home in person. *Thank you, God! Thank you for letting me see my family again!*

"I'm sorry, children," Nicholas said after he had kissed them all. "I didn't bring as many presents this time. But I did bring a bag of rocks from the beach in St. Thomas. If you hold them to the light, they sparkle."

Christina was preparing to send the children back to bed when there was a knock on the door and Mary walked in. "I do apologize," she said, "but I heard this big commotion and I had to come see that my boy Nicholas was fine. "Nicholas," she sobbed, "Missus Christina told me you were sick and I says to myself, I says, he got Pine's sickness, I did! And I was like to break my heart. Oh, I'm so glad, glad, glad, you're all right! But he do look a bit pale, do he not, Missus?"

"He does, Mary," Christina said, her own face wet with tears. "But I think a good cup of tea and some of those raisin biscuits you made today might put him on the road to recovery."

"I think you are right, my dear!" Nicholas said with a smile. "Ah, if that doesn't sound good to a weary traveler."

Christina banished the children to their bedrooms and put the baby back to sleep. Mary brewed tea and warmed the biscuits, but as soon as Christina returned, she poured two cups of tea and said she had to go home.

"Oh, Mary, you can stay!" Christina said.

"And that I shall *not* do," Mary said. "It's time for just the two of you, as I always wanted when Pine came home."

As soon as Mary left, fear returned to Nicholas. But he remembered Brother Friedrich's words about calling on the Savior at any time.

God, please help me talk to my wife, he prayed as he took a sip of the tea.

"You look so tired, Nicholas," Christina said, standing beside him with her hand on his shoulder. "I think I should help you to bed as soon as you have a bite."

"I am tired," he agreed. "But I want to tell you . . . some things."

Christina insisted on first making him comfortable in bed. It was a great relief to lie down. She placed his cup of tea at the bedside, and hung the lantern on a hook below the picture she had painted of the Garrison homestead.

In the lantern light, they could just see each other's faces. With an effort, Nicholas raised himself on one elbow and kissed her. He fell back onto the pillow, and his tears began to flow. He could not speak.

Christina sat beside him and put her hand in his. "Perhaps you should sleep first and we should talk later," she said.

"No," he insisted, swallowing and taking a deep breath. "I must tell you. Even if you cannot forgive me, I must be honest with you. The Lord has had mercy on me, and I must try to make these things right. I wrote them in that letter just in case I would die on the journey."

"I am so glad you made it back," Christina said.

"I've done you so much wrong, Christina. All these years I tried to pretend I was a good man, but every time I went to sea or got into the wrong company, I did whatever I wanted. I was a hypocrite. I cheated myself and I cheated you."

Nicholas told her everything he could think of that he had hidden from her. He told her how the terror of death had been building in him for some time and how he had nearly died on the last voyage. He told her how he cried out to the Lord, realizing that the blood of Jesus was his only hope of salvation from hell. He told her about Brother Friedrich. He clung to her hand as he talked but he could not bring himself to look at her face in the silence that followed.

"Nicholas."

His heart leaped at her soft voice. She had the most beautiful way of pronouncing his name. Her tone did not suggest anger, but he could not identify the emotions that were present. He looked into her eyes, and saw that her face was wet with tears.

"Did you think I did not know all that you have confessed?"

Nicholas blinked with surprise.

"I . . . no, I didn't. How could you know?"

"Oh, I didn't know the details you have told me. But . . . it felt like you were distant even when you *were* here."

She shook her head and began to sob. She put her head in her hands and wept like Nicholas had never before seen her weep, not even after the babies had died. Again, he raised himself up and took her in his arms. His whole being burned with the shame of inflicting so much pain on his lovely wife.

"Do you know why I'm crying?" she asked, collecting her voice. "I'm so happy,

Nicholas. I'm so happy. I feel like my husband has actually come home to me."

Nicholas sighed with relief and decided, not for the first time, that there was no use trying to guess what a woman was thinking.

33

The Scars

Fall 1737

After her initial relief, Christina seemed nervous about Nicholas and his new faith. Nicholas prayed for the strength to be faithful. He prayed for the chance to regain her trust. He prayed that she could be awakened to the power of the blood of Jesus.

Nicholas visited each of his brothers and sisters and his father-in-law. With each of them, he spoke about the Lamb of God. He went first to visit Elizabeth and her husband Matthys Inyard and three children. Elizabeth made tea for her big brother and listened with wide eyes to his story of redemption.

"What a wonderful ending!" she said. "I always liked you, Nicholas, but I was beginning to worry that you were turning into one of those hardened seamen. So what did you call Brother Josef's people? Moravians?"

"Yes," Nicholas said. "They started as a refugee community in Germany on the land of a count named Zinzendorf. They live in community where they can attend church services together every day."

Nicholas told Elizabeth about the Moravians. He spoke of their focus on Jesus Christ and His sufferings, their love feasts, their continual prayers, and the hymns they composed. The Moravians dressed in quiet colors, lived simply, and served the poor.

"I would like to meet some of them," Elizabeth said.

"I could never say no to my little sister," Nicholas said. "I will be sure to introduce you. I intend to keep in contact with them."

Nicholas enjoyed several surveying jobs he picked up with the county clerk. He worked on the farm with his brother Lambert and at the mill his brother-in-law Abraham Cocheron owned. He threshed grain with Mr. Van Woogelum. He told his family of his past sins and hypocrisy, and how God had spared his life in mercy and had granted him another chance.

"I am so happy to hear your story," his father-in-law said. "The people you speak of sound a bit eccentric, but Christina is much happier now. She suffered much during your absences."

Nicholas played and worked with his children. Nicholas Jr. had gotten into the habit of treating his mother with disrespect, and his attitude was spreading to his younger brothers. Nicholas knew he had not done well in setting a good example himself. He also had not been present when Nicholas Jr. began to display these attitudes. He attempted to right that wrong by setting a good example now. He helped his wife with household chores and treated her with courtesy. But still Nicholas Jr. snapped at her. Nicholas treated his son kindly in an effort to reach his heart, but he was confused about how he should address his attitude.

Finally, one day, Christina came to Nicholas. "Why can't you deal with your son?" she asked, frustration tinging her voice.

Nicholas looked at her. "What happened?"

"I asked him to draw a bucket of water. He took the bucket out, dropped it on the ground, and walked away. This happens all the time, Nicholas, and you just ignore it. Must you leave the role of father to me even when you are at home?"

Nicholas' confusion suddenly vanished. "I will take care of it."

The boy was twelve years old. Nicholas did not want to use physical punishment, but he could think of no other solution. Furthermore, he knew only too well how much worse punishment awaited a young man who did not respect his elders. He went to the barn where a bundle of willow whips was drying and selected one. Then, he fell to the straw-covered barn floor and cried out for wisdom, begging the Lamb to give him the words to reach his son.

"Nicholas," he called from the barn. "Come here."

The boy sauntered across the lot. His defiant posture confirmed Nicholas' resolve.

"Nicholas, sit down. I want to talk to you."

The boy looked startled but obeyed.

"I have been gone a lot while you were growing up, Nicholas. So it is my fault that I let this go so long. But I notice you are not respecting nor yet obeying your mother. She has been taking care of you your entire life, and you must respect her. I am going to punish you for disobeying her instructions to draw water."

"But I was going to do it later," Nicholas said nervously.

"No," his father said. "That is not good enough. Men on ships have been flogged half to death for not obeying immediately. I will let you keep your shirt on, but I am going to whip you. I don't want you to get in trouble later in life because you won't respect your elders."

"Fine," Nicholas Jr. said with a sneer, defiance flaming in his eyes. Nicholas knew that the whipping was long overdue. Still, he was sick with his task.

He made Nicholas kneel on the floor with his hands on a small dusty barrel. He winced every time he struck his son. After twelve lashes he dropped the whip and put his arm around his son's shoulders. Nicholas Jr. sobbed on his father's shoulder. Nicholas suspected that his tears were more from emotional release than from pain. Nicholas cried too, for the same reason.

"Let me see your back," Nicholas said after a bit. "I want to make sure I didn't break any skin."

He had not.

"I don't want you to grow up with a back like mine."

Nicholas Jr. looked up at him, startled. "Like *what?*"

Nicholas loosened his shirt. "Look."

Nicholas lifted his father's shirt and stared for a moment. Then he looked at his father with big eyes.

"I was your age when I received these," Nicholas said. He sent up a prayer of thanksgiving. Never, in all his thoughts about the flogging, had he imagined that his scars would ever help someone else.

"What did you do?" Nicholas Jr. asked, curious.

Nicholas considered how to answer. The actual flogging had been unjust. But the accusation had sprung from his attempted theft.

"I broke into a warehouse and tried to steal some money," he said. "Later, the owner had me flogged aboard ship."

"With your shirt off?"

"Yes. That is how it is done at sea. And with a whip much worse than willow."

They were silent for a moment. Nicholas wasn't sure what to say next, and again he cried out to the Lamb. Almost instantly, the answer came.

"All right, son. What do you need to do now?"

"Draw the water, sir."

Nicholas clapped a hand on his son's shoulder and smiled encouragingly.

Nicholas realized that evening at supper that he had gained the respect, not only of Nicholas Jr., but also of his wife and his entire family. Everyone had noticed the boy's attitude. From that day, Christina trusted Nicholas without reservation.

One day, Nicholas walked alone to the family graveyard to visit his brother

Seger's grave. For the first time since the dark day Seger had gone missing in the Fresh Kills, he could freely think of his brother's death. And he could cry! The tears falling on Seger's stone felt like the cooling salve on his lacerated back years before. Tears—not only for the brother he had loved more than anyone else, the brother with whom he had planned to go to sea—but also tears of sadness for the years of fear and guilt, and tears of joy for his salvation. For the first time, peace about that night flooded his soul.

Nicholas had imagined his father blamed him for Seger's death. He, the stronger swimmer, had been right beside his brother when the log swept past. But looking back now, Nicholas was not convinced. It was Daniel who had asked, "Why didn't you look to see if the log hit Seger? You could have rescued him."

Daniel had said that—not their father.

In October, Nicholas and his family were eating the evening meal when Nicholas heard a horse outside and a rider saying, "Whoa!" He went to the door.

"Brother Josef!"

34

The Uncle's Namesake

"Captain Garrison!" Brother Josef leaped off the horse. "It's been months."

"It is so good to see you! But do call me Brother."

"Thomas Noble told me earlier where I could find you, but that was while you were gone on your last voyage. What a blessing this little ride over the hills has been. You live in God's country, my friend."

Nicholas called to his son. "Nicholas! Come put this man's horse in the barn. Do come in, Brother Josef, and have a seat. My wife, Christina."

"Pleased to meet you, madam," Brother Josef said. "Your husband gave me passage last year about this time when I was ill in the West Indies."

"He told me about you," Christina said. "Will you eat with us?"

Brother Josef joined them for the meal. He had been traveling, he said. He had gone to Georgia to check on a Moravian settlement there. The Brethren had met with opposition because they would not take part in military service. They were considering a move to Pennsylvania.

"But how have you been, my friend?" Josef asked, turning toward Nicholas.

"I want to tell you the whole story," Nicholas said. "Join me in the parlor."

"I am not a seaman anymore," Nicholas said, when they were settled. Brother Josef listened spellbound as Nicholas relived the terrifying but wonderful voyage.

"Brother Nicholas," Brother Josef said. "God bless you! God be praised! What does your wife say?"

"Christina!" Nicholas called.

She came to the door, a puzzled look on her face. "Do you need something, my dear?"

"Brother Josef wonders what you say about my awakening to the mercy of God and the blood of Jesus," he said, reaching out his hand to invite her into the conversation.

"Sir," Christina said, coming to Nicholas' side. "I have only one thing to say. Thanks to you, I have my husband back."

"Ah, Madam, not so," said Brother Josef. "It is to the praise and honor of God and the gift of His Son on the cross that you have your husband back. And I venture to guess you have him in a better state than ever before."

"Yes," she said.

"So you have given up the sea altogether?" Brother Josef asked.

"Yes," said Nicholas. "It was a source of temptation for me, and I need to be with my wife and children."

"Ah, yes. You need to follow the directions of the Savior on that. I think, though, that some captains take their wives with them on voyages, do they not? Or perhaps a son?"

Nicholas and Christina looked at each other.

"I have never been on a ship," Christina said weakly.

"Never mind, never mind," Brother Josef said. "It's just something to think about."

"Would you like some wine?" Christina asked.

"Tea is fine for me," Brother Josef said. "As a community, we have chosen to avoid alcoholic beverages, except as medicine for sickness."

"Is that so?" Nicholas asked, intrigued. "Does the Bible speak on this matter?"

"Perhaps you should study that yourself," said Brother Josef with a smile. "But I will give you a summary. The Bible is quite specific about drunkenness and excess of wine. But as a group, we feel it is safer, especially for those with a drinking problem, to abstain when possible."

"What about at sea?" Nicholas asked. He was trying to imagine drinking only worm-spawning water for an entire voyage. It was not a pleasant thought. Alcoholic beverages were not prone to contamination because the fermentation process sterilized the drink.

"Ask the Savior," Brother Josef suggested. "My personal opinion—though I doubt a sea captain would agree—is that being at sea is similar to sickness."

Nicholas laughed heartily.

"You are right. I would hate to be on a voyage without any alcoholic beverages," said Nicholas, "since plain water can be a source of sickness."

"Ah, yes," said Brother Josef. "Nicholas, are you truly interested in joining the Brethren?"

"I am. I have never encountered in either the Dutch Reformed Church or the Church of England such a commitment to living out the teachings of the Bible. I also had not known about accepting the blood of Christ as a personal gift to each sinner. I had read the Bible quite a bit in my life, but I concluded it was a history book rather than a life manual because even the church leaders didn't follow it."

"Then I will keep in touch with you, Brother. Thomas Noble seems interested as well, and perhaps a group of you will form here in New York. If not, we are moving toward a settlement in Pennsylvania with whom you could associate. Let me caution you on one thing, Brother Nicholas."

"What's that?"

Christina returned with the tea and seated herself beside her husband after pouring it.

"Following Christ is not always easy. Perhaps I should rephrase that: it is seldom easy. Sometimes, new believers live in a bubble of joy when they first experience the mercy and grace of God. And rightly so!

"But I have seen a few who got discouraged when difficulties came their way, because they expected life to be easy. In my experience, when a person follows Christ with diligence, life becomes more difficult, not less so. The enemy of our souls cares little for a sinful person who is living to please himself. He knows the end of that life is destruction. But the enemy delights in tormenting those who follow Christ, to try to persuade them from the faith."

Nicholas was silent for a moment.

"Thank you, Brother. I have a feeling I will have many opportunities to be grateful for your warning. One other thing. My sister Elizabeth would like to hear about your people. Could you stop and visit her family as well?"

• •

The next August, Christina gave birth to a son.

"I want to call him Seger," Nicholas said to Christina.

"You do?" Christina asked, surprised.

"Yes." He touched the baby's arm. The baby, a perfect miracle, opened his small eyes and stared at his father.

"I used to think my father blamed me for my brother Seger's death," Nicholas said simply. "I have peace about that now, even if it was true. And I'm not sure that it was."

Christina looked at him sympathetically. "Would you blame your son if another son died in an accident?" she said gently. "I don't think so. Perhaps your father's sadness was so great he said hurtful things that sounded like he was accusing you."

Nicholas nodded and swallowed, blinking to keep back tears. "You can say it so beautifully, my dear. I should have talked to you about it before. Father was sitting right there—" Nicholas pointed to the corner where his father's desk had been— "when I came into the house to tell him Seger had disappeared while we were swimming."

"Ah, my dear!"

"Daniel stayed down at the Arthur Kill to look for him. I'm surprised he didn't drown too. I wanted to go back to the creek with Father, but Mother made me stay here by the fire. I had run the whole way through the mud, and I cut my shoulder. Half the neighborhood went out searching anyway. I would have done no good."

"And they never found him."

"Not until weeks later, washed ashore," Nicholas continued. "Later, the schoolmaster returned Seger's slate to me. I took it with me to sea. I even went down in a sinking ship to get it. I still have it in my sea chest. But I don't know why I am telling you all this."

"Because I never heard it before," Christina said. "I am more than happy to name the baby after his uncle Seger."

A few months after Seger's birth, Thomas Noble came calling.

"Nicholas, I know your desire to stay home with your family. Brother Josef has spoken to me, and I too am inclined to consider the Moravian faith and manner of life. My wife finds it attractive even more than I.

"However, would you consider going on one more run to the West Indies? You could visit St. Thomas and check on the people there. Brother Josef told me that Count Zinzendorf, the leader of the Moravians, is planning to visit St. Thomas soon. He thinks you would enjoy meeting him."

Nicholas first prayed about the offer, then spoke to Christina. "I don't know, dear," he said. "I didn't think I would go back to sea. Part of me considers the rough lives some of the men live and how much I would like to share my story with them. But I don't know if putting myself in that position again is the answer. And it would mean leaving you and the children again."

"It would be winter time," Christina said. "The boys all go to school in the winter, so they are a bit easier to manage. Did you pray about it? Do you not say that sometimes God directs you when you ask Him?"

"Well. The only answer He gives is . . ." Nicholas found it awkward to explain. "I keep seeing the faces of some of my old comrades. I just wish I could speak to them about the Savior. But—I thought you would object."

"I don't wish for you to be gone," she said. "But what pained me most was doubting your faithfulness and love. I don't doubt that now. And if you are going to St. Thomas—the temptations you faced were not so great there, were they?"

"No. Jamaica more than any other place."

"Could you avoid going to Jamaica?"

"I can make that a condition, I am sure. Mr. Noble is quite anxious to have me as captain. Perhaps I should speak to your father, my dear. He told me you did not do well when I was gone."

"You may speak to him," she said. "But you have my support if you wish to go."

"I guess you don't want to go with me." A smile flickered on Nicholas' lips.

Christina shook her head but smiled back.

"Maybe someday," she said, "when we don't have a small baby. But you could bring me another pink bougainvillea."

35

The Count

1739

Christina and the children went to the wharf to see Nicholas off shortly after the beginning of the new year, 1739. Nicholas felt almost nervous in his captain's uniform. He also wore a heavy brown overcoat due to the cold. But he smiled to cheer his family, who were wrapped in shawls and coats on this chilly morning.

"Nicholas, my son. Let's see how you do in school this winter, and with helping Mother while I'm gone. If I need to go to sea again, I am hoping to take you with me."

Nicholas' face lit up. "I will work hard, Father."

Susanna, Jan, Lambert, and Benjamin crowded around as well. This time four-year-old Benjamin held up a drawing for his father. It too was a ship, done with childish abandon. Katie kissed her Father gravely, scarcely recognizing him in his captain's uniform and hat. Little Seger babbled in his mother's arms. Nicholas kissed Christina and let the baby play with his finger, before tearing himself away and stepping onto the *Golden Swan* with a wave. He got to work, organizing the charts in his cabin and taking stock of the weather.

Seagull Sal was on board again. If he had been able to read and keep records, Nicholas would have made Sal a mate. But Seagull Sal was an excellent helmsman, and Nicholas had often called upon him to steer in bad weather.

"Are we ready, men?" he asked.

"Sir, the pilot isn't here yet," Seagull Sal said.

"Was he sent for?" asked Nicholas.

"He was, but Frederick, the sailor who was sent for him, is not back yet."

All the men looked at Nicholas.

"All right then. We are ready as soon as the pilot arrives."

At that moment, Frederick arrived through the entry port, holding a paper packet. He averted his eyes when he saw the waiting crew and captain. The crew fell silent.

"Frederick, a word please," Nicholas said.

"Sir?"

"Men's lives have been lost over much smaller delays," Nicholas said to him privately. "If I see one more failure to carry out orders in a timely fashion, you will be flogged or removed from your position. Do you understand?"

"Aye, aye, sir. Thank you, sir."

Nicholas knew that the unexpected gratitude sprang from the man's expectation of a much worse punishment. Perhaps he should have dealt more harshly with him.

Nicholas prayed for wisdom. Before he became a captain, he wondered why captains were always so tight-lipped and merciless. But after feeling the responsibility for dozens of lives, and cargo valued at hundreds of pounds, he had become everything he once criticized.

Now, he wasn't so sure. A captain had to be exacting to ensure the safety of all aboard. But could he not be demanding and still merciful?

"Frederick!"

The young man had been walking away, but came back nervously.

"Tell me why you delayed."

"Sir, my wife . . ." He looked at a paper parcel in his hand. It reminded Nicholas of the package of pastry Mary had handed to him before his first voyage as a boy. "I—we just got married three months ago. I went to the pilot's house—and they said he had just stepped out and would be back. So I ran home because I had forgotten the peach pie my wife made. I live close by, but I was delayed in the street. When I got back, the pilot—"

"Enough," Nicholas said. "I've decided to punish you after all—I order you to share a slice of that pie with your captain."

The man's face had turned from deadly pale to colorful relief between the ends of Nicholas' statements.

"Aye, aye, sir!" the man said, eyes twinkling. "She makes the best in Manhattan! I'll write and tell her the captain had some!"

Nicholas had intended the statement as a joke, but now he saw that the man was pleased by his request.

"Just give a very small slice to my cabin boy and he'll see to it that I get it. Save the rest for yourself, Frederick. It will be long enough before you get to taste it again. And remember, no more delays for any reason, peachy or otherwise."

"Aye, aye, sir!"

And so the voyage began with smiling rather than swearing.

At Sunday services, Nicholas continued to follow the prayer book schedule. But now he also led in prayer as he had heard Brother Friedrich and Brother Josef pray, from the heart.

Nicholas continued to demand much of his men, as he did of himself. He insisted upon accuracy and punctuality. He knew that being too familiar with the men could prevent them from taking him seriously. He had served under captains who would not crack a smile from the time the anchor was weighed until the time it was cast at their destination. But he wondered if, as a follower of Christ, there could not be some middle ground.

Nicholas began by asking the men brief questions about their homes and families. Following Brother Friedrich's example with the slaves on St. Thomas, he made a practice of talking to each man every day. This was unheard of among his contemporaries. But the men seemed to respect him more for it, not less.

He shared with his old friend Seagull Sal many details about his conversion. He did not need to tell Sal of his former life, as he had told Christina. Seagull Sal knew those sordid details.

"The mercy of God saved me when I called on His name by the blood of Jesus," Nicholas said. "I will serve Him from now on."

"I see," Seagull Sal said.

St. Thomas was as beautiful as Nicholas remembered it, when they arrived in early February. He hurried to the plantation of Mr. Carstens, hoping to find Brother Friedrich. To his surprise and pleasure, Edward answered the door.

"Ah, Edward! Do you remember me?"

"The massa with the stripes on his back!" the young man said.

"Indeed! I am Brother Garrison. Do you know where I can find Brother Friedrich?"

"He is still recovering from his illness, but he is here," Edward said, "with Mr. Carstens and Count Zinzendorf."

Moments later, Brother Friedrich appeared, leaning on a cane and much emaciated.

"Captain Garrison!" he cried. "Brother! How well you look."

"By the mercy of God," Nicholas replied. "I'm afraid you have been sick though. Am I interrupting something?"

"Ah, no, you must meet Count Zinzendorf," he said. "And I am feeling much better since the count has come to help us."

He introduced Nicholas to the count and the planter. Mr. Carstens remembered him well.

Count Zinzendorf, who appeared to be about the same age as Nicholas, greeted him with warmth. "I have heard of you, Brother Nicholas," he said, "and you have probably heard much of me. But I will also say something respecting myself. I love the Savior, and He loves me."

Nicholas found the man's warmth and peace captivating. He sat spellbound as the three talked.

"When we sailed into the harbor here at St. Thomas on January 29," the count said, "I asked, 'What if all of our Brethren are now deceased?' One of our party replied, 'So, we are here!' We came ashore, and found that, while they were not all deceased, they were in a dire situation."

"Do you remember how we were taking in children when you were here last?" Brother Friedrich asked.

Nicholas nodded.

Brother Friedrich reminded him of the details. He and Brother Matthaus Freundlich, both half-ill from the climate, had been unable to care for the children properly. They had hired Rebecca, a free black convert, to help them. Brother Friedrich had received a written ordination from London, allowing him to officially baptize slaves. To avoid suspicion, Brother Friedrich suggested that Matthaus should marry Rebecca since the three worked together so closely. Because he had been ordained, he performed the ceremony himself.

When the Danish authorities found out about the marriage between a white man and a black woman, they were livid. They said the marriage was not official because Brother Friedrich had not had his ordination orders signed by the Danish authorities. The three were falsely accused of a robbery attempt. When they were called in to testify, they refused to swear an oath, because the Bible prohibited it. They were all locked in the Danish castle.

In jail the men made buttons and Rebecca sewed. Many slaves risked their lives to come hear sermons preached through the bars of the castle. There were now 750 believing slaves scattered across 51 plantations.

By the time Zinzendorf arrived from Europe, Brother Friedrich had been released, due to his severe illness. The husband and wife team had been imprisoned for fifteen weeks and were nearly dead from poor treatment and insufficient food.

"I burst into the castle like thunder," the count said. "The governor apologized to me and released the two."

"That was the turning point for my sickness, as well," Brother Friedrich said.

"I almost forgot I was sick. I cannot describe to you my joy at seeing our prayers answered, Brother Nicholas."

"Answers to prayer are an amazing blessing, indeed," Nicholas agreed. "And you are the one who taught me to pray."

"We are organizing the island into quarters so the work of Christ can proceed in as orderly a fashion as possible," Count Zinzendorf said. "I also intend to teach the brothers and sisters to form into small groups or bands, and to assist with the hourly intercession. Then I will speak to them at a meeting before I leave. You are welcome to attend if you wish, Captain Garrison."

"You may call me Brother Garrison, if you please," Nicholas said. "Can you tell me what you mean by hourly intercession?"

"Brother Garrison," the count explained, "at our home base in Herrnhut, we maintain a continual prayer vigil, with people praying each of the twenty-four hours every day."

"Oh yes," Nicholas said. "I was told about that."

Nicholas stayed in the same lodging as the count for the few weeks of his visit. He was much encouraged by the count's joy in his relationship with Christ.

Nicholas attended the meeting with the slaves. He stood at the back of the packed room, awestruck as Count Zinzendorf instructed the slaves to think constantly of Jesus Christ, as if they could physically see Him on the cross. He asked them to be true to their husbands and wives. He led them in several Creole hymns that he had written.

Nicholas sailed toward home with a hold full of cargo and a refreshed spirit.

As he paced the quarterdeck one night, waiting for the clouds to move so he could get his measurement, Nicholas thought of Count Zinzendorf and Brother Friedrich and their work on St. Thomas. Both men had inspired him to serve the Lord with all of his being.

But what would that look like? Surely God did not want him to remain at sea!

36

The New Brother in Christ

"Sir."

Nicholas turned from the railing. The clouds still obscured the moon. "Seagull Sal," he said. "My oldest and best friend aboard ship. How goes it?"

Seagull Sal turned to look out at the ocean. "I-I-it goes well, sir," Sal faltered. Gazing at some distant spot, he asked, "What about those people on St. Thomas, sir?"

"You mean the missionaries?"

"Well, yes, sir. Why . . ."

Sal turned away from the water, toward Nicholas.

"I-could I-learn to know the Savior as you do, sir?"

"Sal!" Filled with emotion, Nicholas could barely choke out the word.

"I didn't believe you at first," Seagull Sal said. "But, Captain, you are not the same man you once were. What would you do if you met Captain Parker now, sir?"

Nicholas sighed and looked up at the clouds.

"I am not perfect," he told Sal, "but I know the perfect Lamb, and I would turn to Him for the strength to walk up to Captain Parker and say hello. Really, he taught me the first things I knew about navigation. I should thank him."

"That's what I thought," Seagull Sal said. "But, sir, I am full of wickedness, even more than you! Perhaps God—"

"No," Nicholas interrupted. "We are all unrighteous. 'There is none righteous, no not one.' This is why God sent His only son Jesus into the world to pay the penalty for our sin!"

Nicholas had hoped to lead an old friend to the Savior, and the experience was amazing. Now he understood Brother Friedrich's passion for souls.

Together, he and Sal prayed on the quarterdeck as the ship tossed. Nicholas completely missed his moon measurements that night.

As soon as the ship cast anchor in Manhattan, Nicholas headed for home. He told his family about his adventures—about the dedicated missionaries on St. Thomas and how Seagull Sal had come to the Savior.

From Benjamin to Nicholas, they sat open-mouthed, trying to picture the green island with the sparkling rocks, the pink and orange flowers, and the cackling birds. Suddenly Nicholas stared at his wife.

"I have a confession to make," he said.

"What is it?"

"I forgot your pink flower, the bougainvillea!"

Christina tried to look fierce, but she was too happy to have him home.

Nicholas and Christina spoke much about the Moravians. Christina had misgivings about them.

"Can't we just live a normal life and be good people?" she asked. "They seem extreme to me—going against the Dutch planters to teach their slaves. They know they might get sick and die, and yet they go to that island to live. They are throwing their lives away for the sake of those Africans who aren't their responsibility!"

It bothered Christina too, that the Moravians were so strict about clothing and lifestyle. She had grown up in a conservative Dutch home and had always covered her hair. But it seemed extreme to her to ban jewelry and certain colors of clothing and to ask each woman to wear the same style of tight-fitting cap. The Moravians were adamant about loving each other and greeting each other with a kiss, as if they were family. Thomas Noble's wife had told Christina that there were even restrictions on extravagant cooking and tailoring. And what about refusing to fight in wars or swear oaths? Christina found all of it shocking.

"They are living out what they believe," Nicholas said. "Because the Bible does talk about those things. It's just that most of the churches we know aren't following the Scripture so closely."

He tried to remember how Brother Josef had explained these things. Most of all, he tried to avoid pushing Christina. She had been the faithful one, not he, for most of their marriage. He hoped in the end that she would see the Moravians' single-minded focus on serving the Lamb.

Meanwhile, he spent time with the Savior every day, praying in the early morning as he walked along the Fresh Kills where Seger had drowned. He visited with the Moravians whenever one of them came through New York. Thomas and Mary

Noble and his sister Elizabeth met with them as well.

Seagull Sal came to visit every time he could. Nicholas introduced Sal to his family and to the Moravians. He read the Bible to Sal, because Sal could not read. But with his talent of poetry and song, Sal could memorize, and memorize he did. Soon, he was putting psalms to tunes on his cittern.

* *

A year later, Nicholas was back at the coffee shop. He took a sip of coffee from his mug and looked at the men across the table. They were friends of Thomas Noble.

"We really need a reliable captain to do this run," the older one said. "Mr. Noble commends your navigational skills and your character and we feel sure you are the man for the job. Mr. Noble has given us the use of the *Golden Swan* in return for a part in the cargo."

"Where do you want me to go?" Nicholas asked.

"Jamaica."

Nicholas was certain he would not do the Jamaica trip, and not just because of the destination. There were other things that bothered him.

Christina was expecting a baby in the summer and since the merchants wanted him to leave in May, he would likely not be back in time for the birth. It would not be the first time Christina had delivered a child in his absence, but he had hoped it would never happen again.

Furthermore, he had contracted dysentery during a quick trip north in the fall. The trip had been one of great suffering as he struggled to drink water to keep himself hydrated. He had pitied his cabin boy who was continuously called upon to empty his chamber pot. After arriving home, he had recovered, but he still grew exhausted easily. And there was news of war with Spain.

Besides all of those circumstances, Nicholas had a vague sense of uneasiness that he could not put to words. He could not pin the feeling to the war, or the baby, or his physical condition, or the merchants, or even Jamaica. Maybe it was just a combination of all of those issues.

He took the matter to the Savior and discussed it with Christina. Jamaica was the home of his wildest indulgences and worst nightmares. However, Christina had a good suggestion.

"I will do this one run for you," Nicholas told the men when they met again, "if you will approve me taking my oldest son. He's thirteen years old and I would like to train him to work with the men before the mast."

"Not a problem at all," the men said. "Here's to a successful voyage, Captain!"

37

The Old Friend

May 1740

With pleasure, Nicholas showed his son around the *Golden Swan* and introduced him to many of the men. He took him to the lowest deck where barrels of water would be stored. He showed him the hold filled with cargo and bags of corn, wheat, and rye. In the forecastle, they viewed the men's bunks. Nicholas pointed out the "outhouse," a seat with a hole, built onto the bowsprit extending ahead of the ship. Unlike an outhouse on land, it had no walls.

"You will sleep with the men," Nicholas said. "I will not give you special quarters. I want you to learn what it is really like to work at sea."

Nicholas Jr. agreed and looked at everything with eagerness. The two of them had already been working on knots at home, so Nicholas Jr. felt ready to attempt that task. But climbing the rigging or weighing anchor were mysteries to him.

After touring the ship, they returned home for the night and bid farewell to Christina and the other six children in the morning.

Nicholas broke down as he held his wife and children, kissing them repeatedly. There was always a chance, on any voyage, that a person would not come home. There was a chance that he would return and one of them would be gone. But he could not pinpoint why he felt even more nervous than usual.

He rested his hand on Christina's expanding waist, mostly disguised by yards of cloth. "God be with you and the new little one, my dear."

At the wharf, Nicholas turned Nicholas Jr. over to an able seaman. He instructed his son to address him as sir. "If you need me, you can come find me," Nicholas said. "But you must ask to speak to me as your captain. I want you to know how to address those in charge. If you have questions and I'm not around, ask Seagull Sal."

"Aye, aye, sir," said Nicholas Jr. He knew Seagull Sal well from Sal's visits with the family.

Nicholas gave the call to weigh anchor and turned the helm over to the pilot. He had journeyed in and out of the bay numerous times, but the channel was so treacherous that all captains called upon the pilots of Sandy Hook to guide them out to sea.

Nicholas was exhausted just from the effort of giving orders. He needed to talk to the crew as a whole, but he felt he did not have the strength. He went to his cabin to rest while the ship arrived at the Watering Place and the crew brought water on board.

When the ship was in open water, he called the crew to the waist of the ship while he stood on the quarterdeck and laid out the expectations for the voyage. Their destination was Jamaica, where they planned to deliver grain and root crops from the colonies. They expected to load indigo, sugar, and tropical fruits, and come back to New York with as few stops as possible.

When he finished these announcements, Nicholas looked at his first mate. "Can you think of anything I've missed? If not, you may confirm the members of each watch."

"Is it appropriate to discuss the war with Spain, sir?"

"Ah. Thank you. Men, we understand that the British army is present in the West Indies region with an eye for retaliation toward Spain for their savagery toward a British sea captain.[1] While a state of war poses a hazard, the presence of the British army may afford protection as well. I do not anticipate any problems, but as always, those on watch must maintain a strict devotion to reporting any unusual sights or sounds. Am I clear?"

"Aye, aye, sir," chorused the men.

The trip went well, and Nicholas watched his son climb the ratlines and haul ropes with the men. Nicholas Jr. worked hard, and in a few weeks was quite comfortable. As the *Golden Swan* passed the Bahamas, Nicholas recalled the fateful pirate battle and the death of his friend Joaquin. He thanked God for his escape from the pirate ship and for a successful voyage with his son.

"Around Cuba, men, and then we are on the final stretch to Jamaica!" Nicholas called.

---

[1] An English captain's ear had been cut off by a Spaniard. The British government saw it as an opportunity to punish the Spanish and gain more land in the West Indies.

"Hurrah!" shouted the men.

A soft tropical rain began to fall. It was the end of May and the rainy season was not quite over. The sails grew glossy with moisture and then began to drip. The planks of the *Golden Swan* grew slick. The sea remained calm, but Nicholas reminded the men to take care. "A little water has put many a man overboard."

Nicholas Jr. was playing checkers with an able seaman—and beating him, from the looks of the board. "Captain Garrison, call off your son, will you?" the man grumbled. "It's too wet to play, much less to get beaten." The onlookers standing in the drizzle burst into laughter. Nicholas smiled and walked on.

"Deck there!" called the lookout. "Sail to windward."

Nicholas felt his muscles tighten. Why did the announcement have to be here, where the pirates had attacked so many years before? *Savior in heaven, not here! Not here in the same waters where I watched Joaquin die in my arms,* he prayed. *Please protect us.*

Why did he feel such trepidation? Countless sails had appeared on countless horizons in his time at sea. He walked to the binnacle and selected his speaking trumpet. He pulled his telescope from his pocket. No sails were visible yet from the deck.

"Mast there! Keep me informed when you see colors!"

"Aye, sir!"

"Continue course," he said to Seagull Sal at the helm.

Just before darkness fell, Nicholas spotted the large ship on the western horizon. He suspected it was a warship. Perhaps it was the British.

Nicholas still felt weak and he needed his sleep. But he could not rest that night. When eight bells struck at midnight, he went on deck. The watches exchanged and he bid good night to Nicholas Jr. and the men who were going below. The second mate had seen no action in the darkness.

The first mate was now on deck and assured Nicholas that he would call him if anything was amiss. The rain had stopped, but the sky was still shrouded with clouds.

Nicholas returned to his cabin and dozed a few hours. At eight bells again at 4 a.m., he went on deck to watch the exchange. By the light of the lantern, he saw his son stumble sleepily to his post.

"Nicholas!" he called softly.

The boy turned.

"Stay awake!"

"Aye, aye, sir!"

At daybreak Nicholas was on deck again. The ship had gained on them during the night, moving directly with the wind. The *Golden Swan* was forced to move several points off the wind to round Cuba.

The cabin boy brought Nicholas his porridge. Nicholas set it on the binnacle wordlessly and paced the quarterdeck. The cabin boy watched him.

"Captain!"

"Yes, my boy."

"Sir, you said you needed to eat to keep up your strength and that I was to remind you if you forgot."

Nicholas was tempted to snap at him for interrupting his reverie, but he restrained himself. "That I did, my boy." Nicholas thanked God for the food, then ate it mechanically as he watched the vessel coming across the Caribbean Sea.

Nicholas turned to give his bowl to the cabin boy. "Prepare my towel, please," he said. It would not do to avoid washing up just because he was nervous.

As he returned from toweling himself at the ship's pump, the lookout called. "Deck there! Spanish colors flying."

Across the water, the blast of a cannon sounded a challenge.

"We are not a warship," Nicholas said. "Haul down the flags."

"We could shoot a few rounds," one of the men grumbled.

There were four guns on board used for saluting other ships or ports. It would be utter futility to use them against a warship full of weapons, even if Nicholas had wanted to.

"Quiet," Nicholas said. "I don't relish having an ear cut off, but we are not going to throw away our lives aimlessly. They will want the grain for their army but may let us go free."

An able seaman was already running down the flags, both of the merchant company and the British crown.

"Heave to," a voice shouted across the water through a speaking trumpet. The words were English but the voice reminded Nicholas of Joaquin.

"As he says," Nicholas said. "The rest of you, get your things together and prepare to be taken prisoner."

He found Nicholas Jr. "Put your clothes in a bag and meet me on deck. Stay with me no matter what happens."

Nicholas hurried to his cabin and assessed his belongings. He most valued his charts, but the Spanish would value them too. He packed his sea chest with his most important items, including his instruments and Seger's slate. He slipped his New Testament inside his belt. He doubted they would allow him to take the sea chest, but it wouldn't hurt to ask.

The Spanish might not even allow him to live.

He stood on deck and watched a small boat being lowered from the Spanish warship. A heavily armed band of men soon crawled up the side of the *Golden Swan*.

"Come with us," the leading officer said in English. Then he added, somewhat mockingly, "Captain." He grabbed Nicholas by the shoulder and yanked him forward. Two more men searched him for weapons and removed his coat and captain's hat. Nicholas breathed a sigh of relief as they passed over the New Testament.

"May I bring my sea chest?"

"No."

Nicholas looked back at his son. *"Mi hijo?"* he asked.

"Si," said the man, followed by a string of Spanish that Nicholas could not understand.

The loss of his tools and Seger's slate brought no sorrow. He had his son. They clambered down the rope ladder and into the small boat where he was put into irons. Nicholas Jr. was allowed to sit beside him unchained.

A few more seamen were added to the boat, including Seagull Sal. The boat pulled away to the warship, leaving some of the crew on the *Golden Swan*. He hoped he had not made a foolish decision to bring his son with him.

The climb down the ladder into the small boat had sapped his strength and now he had to climb up into the warship. He collapsed on its deck. He heard a chorus of Spanish voices mocking and jabbering. He staggered up, his vision patchy. Calloused brown hands pushed him into the foul-smelling lower deck of the warship. The sailors tossed him into a corner, and he lay there, exhausted, a few feet from the track of one of the big guns.

"I'm here, Father," he heard Nicholas Jr.'s quiet voice beside him. "Shall I go find a surgeon? They took Seagull Sal to another deck."

"Stay with me a few minutes, son," Nicholas said. "Let's pray."

Around them, the Spaniards off watch shouted and played and jeered. The deck planks dug into Nicholas' back. The air was thick and foul-smelling, and in his weakened state, Nicholas found himself close to vomiting.

For the first time since the sails had been spotted, Nicholas allowed himself to think of the possibilities for him personally. *I may never see the rest of my family again. And I brought my oldest son into this disaster with me.*

He turned his thoughts to the Savior, taking comfort in His sufferings. "Dear Savior, we thank you for sparing our lives in the capture of the ship. We ask for continued safety for the rest of the crew. Please comfort us with your presence and help us to find a friend. Bring us in safety to our home, if it is your will. We know that nothing will happen to us without your will. We beg for your mercy and direction. We thank you that you have suffered for us. Amen."

A few minutes after the prayer, a man approached, walking across the blocks of light falling through the hatch. He was an old man and carried a black bag and a pewter mug. Ship captains found surgeons wherever they could and often conscripted men who were not really doctors. Though Nicholas felt sorry for this man who had to serve at such an elderly age, he thanked God for sending the surgeon so quickly.

The man knelt beside him. "Are you the captain who just collapsed on deck?" he asked in perfect English.

"I am," Nicholas said, his heart leaping. "And you are not a Spaniard."

"Aye, you are right. I am not even a true surgeon, I'm afraid. I am being held here against my will, but I will do what I can. What is your name, Captain?"

"Nicholas Garrison," he replied. "And my son Nicholas Jr. is here with me."

Nicholas heard a thud and a splash. The man seemed to have dropped the pewter cup without considering where it landed. Did this old stranger need a surgeon more than he did?

Then, the man thrust open the porthole cover, and light flooded in.

"I," a gentle voice said, "am your friend, Old Pete."

38

The Island Journey

Nicholas opened his eyes. *Is it morning already? Has no one called me?*
Then, he saw the wooden walls around him and remembered that he was not on the *Golden Swan*. He was in the surgeon's room, and the surgeon was his friend, Old Pete.

Old Pete and Nicholas had talked as long as they dared, crouched beside the gun.

"A captain, Nicholas! I am not surprised at all! And a handsome son who looks much like his father did when I first met him!"

Nicholas felt as if he was once again that young boy who had just been flogged, being visited by a kind man who seemed like an angel. As he had so many years before, Old Pete gave Nicholas a drink of water.

"What ever are you doing here, Pete?" Nicholas had asked, wringing the man's hand with joy. "You are—forgive me—too old for this job!"

"Ah, I could not agree more," Old Pete said.

Old Pete had agreed to make a short run with an English ship in need of a surgeon. After brief instructions from the previous surgeon about the instruments and medicines in the ship's infirmary, away they went. Pete planned to be back in a few months to his job of tide surveyor in Liverpool. A tide surveyor, Old Pete explained to Nicholas Jr., met and inspected ships coming into harbor. However, war broke out, and his ship was taken by the Spanish, and that was the story so far.

"The vile life of a sailor is more stressful to me now than it once was," he said. "This crew is intolerably wicked and profane, although thank God I cannot understand much Spanish."

"You were never profane anyway, Pete. Why not? Feel free, my friend. I am a different man now. God in His mercy has spared me from death and changed my life. It is my goal to serve the Savior, though I can never repay the suffering He endured for my sins."

"I also am in His service," Pete said. "And I realize now how great a harm it was to be silent on the matter all these years. What a shame that I never encouraged you, a young boy, to give your life to Him! But God has been faithful all the same. I prayed for you, Nicholas, many, many times."

They talked about Captain Parker and the shipwreck of the *Ella* and the castle in Cuba. Nicholas Jr. listened with wide eyes.

"You will sleep in my bed, Captain," Old Pete said. "You are weak, and I will not have you sleeping on the floor. I wish I could offer you fresh fruits and vegetables but we have not loaded fresh provisions recently. We are still eating hardtack—and men are dying of scurvy and dysentery every day."

"What? So close to the islands?"

"I do not understand it," Pete said simply. "Although I believe they are eating better in the cabins."

Pete and Nicholas both looked at Nicholas Jr. "This is my son's first voyage with me," Nicholas said.

"Your father chose quite a voyage for you," Pete said with a gentle smile. "But I believe he had a rough initiation to sea life himself." Pete looked back at Nicholas. "Have you told him?"

"Yes, he knows."

"I felt the same for you then—three days at sea, and then that! Ah, that flogging was one of the most painful things I have ever watched. But young Nicholas, take heart. The water and bread will be full of worms—that is the worst. But try to eat it bravely to keep up your strength. Likely they will exchange you for Spanish prisoners before long."

Nicholas and Pete talked whenever they could over the next few days. They found Seagull Sal, and the three followers of the Lamb praised the Lord together. Old Pete could not read either, so Nicholas read to them both from the New Testament.

About a week after the capture, the prisoners were gathered to be put on shore and sent to Bayamo, Cuba.

"God bless you, my friend!" Nicholas said to Old Pete with a warm embrace. "Thank you for the use of your bed and your kind attention. Despite the worms in the water, my health seems to be improving."

"You have blessed me beyond what you can understand," Old Pete said with tears. "God has answered my prayers for a young boy I thought I would never see again. He may have allowed me to be captured just so I could see this day!"

"We will likely never meet again," Nicholas said. "May God repay your kindness and bring you safely back to Liverpool."

"Muevanse! Muevanse!"

Nicholas felt a hand wrenching his elbow. "I think that means 'get moving,' " Nicholas said to Pete with a wry smile. "God bless you, old friend!"

A dozen prisoners were dropped into a small boat. A few of them were sailors from the *Golden Swan,* including Seagull Sal. Six Spanish soldiers escorted them.

As the boat glided toward shore, Nicholas looked back at the great hulk. He was glad to be off the ship, but the green island ahead held no promise of comfort. The boat slid into the mud. The prisoners and soldiers jumped off, and the boat headed back to the ship.

They were alone, with no civilization in sight, accompanied by six men with loaded muskets.

"Vamos!"[1] one of the soldiers shouted. "Thirty miles!"

Nicholas' heart sank. The tropical sun was already beating down on them. The soldiers had small bags of provisions, but he did not expect them to share water or food with the prisoners. Could they walk through thirty miles of jungle with no water? Thirty miles was more than twice the length of Staten Island's longest side.

They set off on a trail that was little more than a footpath. The soldiers in the lead swung swords to cut through the banana and plantain leaves that had overgrown the path. Around them tall palm trees with bare stems grew in patches. Nicholas saw a bird with patches of red feathers and a beady black eye set in a florescent green head. A tiny hummingbird hovered beside something that looked like a bright red thistle. He heard calls and chirps and trills and cries. He smelled something that reminded him of his past days in the tropics—white ginger blooms that many girls wore in their hair. He had been told that messages written on small papers were sometimes concealed in the tube-shaped base of these flowers.

If only that would work to send a message to Christina now! Nicholas thought.

Although at sea Nicholas confirmed everything with instruments, he had grown adept at estimates in general. It was summer, and he reckoned there would be about thirteen hours of sunlight in this latitude. The sun had been up for three hours when they reached the shore. Over level ground with adequate water and food, thirty miles in ten hours would be easy.

But those were not the current conditions. Nicholas felt stronger than he had

---

[1] Let's go.

when they boarded the warship, but he knew he was not yet fully recovered. Nicholas Jr. had been perfectly well until their capture, but he looked pale now. Possibly his body was not reacting well to being sustained for the first time on maggot protein.

Seagull Sal was ill too, having contracted a stomach bug from the men in the warship. He had been forced to leave his cittern in the merchant ship, and this depressed him.

Nicholas tried to turn his troubled thoughts into prayers. He put one foot forward, then the other. Hour after hot hour, they walked. At first, sweat poured down their faces. Soon, their bodies were so low on moisture the sweat stopped, and they grew even hotter. The soldiers stopped several times to drink noisily from their packs. Nicholas ached more from the desperation in his son's eyes than from his own thirst. The boy was quite pale and could not go on much longer.

In late afternoon, they topped a small rise where they could see through the undergrowth. There was still no civilization in sight. Nicholas searched the hills for signs of cultivation or the square shape of a banana field, but he could see nothing other than palm trees, undergrowth, and blue sky.

The men from the *Golden Swan* looked at Nicholas as the soldiers stopped on the rise to drink again. Nicholas wished he could offer them something, but he could not. He was not sure that he could go on much farther himself, but at least most of his men still looked as if they could continue. Seagull Sal was slumped against a tree, panting.

Nicholas Jr. suddenly crumpled to the ground. Nicholas knelt beside him and rubbed his forehead with a broad green leaf until he opened his eyes.

"Puede tener . . . un poco de agua?" [2] Nicholas asked, looking at the soldiers. He picked the words slowly as he remembered them, hoping it amounted to something close to a request for water.

"No," the leader said with a smirk.

"I'll carry him," the tallest sailor of the *Golden Swan* offered.

Nicholas sensed that the man was being tactful so Nicholas would not have to ask for help. The men knew that Nicholas was ill, but since he was their captain, they tried to ignore his weakness.

Nicholas Jr. was a slender boy, and the sailor lifted him easily. But carrying the boy in the intense heat would not be possible for long if they could not rest and drink water soon.

They trudged on for several more hours. Nicholas concentrated on every step.

---

[2] Can we have . . . a little water?

Even the strongest men from the *Golden Swan* began to waver. They had taken turns carrying Nicholas Jr., but now, as the soldiers stopped, they set him on the ground and looked up at Nicholas.

"We can't," the tallest one said, his lips parched and cracking. "We'll all die if we don't get water. We're going to go ahead."

"I'll stay with you," Seagull Sal said.

"No," Nicholas said. "Perhaps you can save yourself. Leave us to the mercy of the Savior, Sal. He will receive us if we do not survive."

Nicholas watched the band of men move on down the trail. The soldiers were leaving them behind for obvious reasons. They were in no condition to survive, much less escape.

39

The Hunters

Nicholas felt his heart sink as the men disappeared. He looked down at Nicholas Jr. and saw that his eyes had fallen shut.

Hagar.

Nicholas remembered the Genesis Bible story from his childhood. He had never in his wildest imagination expected to be replaying Hagar's story on the island of Cuba, watching a dying son. But her example gave him an idea.

He stepped off the trail a little, away from Nicholas Jr., and fell to the jungle floor, caring nothing for the insects and spiders hurrying from him.

"Dear Savior," he cried, "you have shown yourself strong. I know you are with us! Please spare my son's life if it is your will! Show us where we can find water!"

Nicholas felt his surroundings retreat from his senses. He wondered if he was fainting. Perhaps he and young Nicholas would go to their heavenly home together, instead of their earthly one. But he soon realized he could still see the foliage around him, still hear the parakeets shrieking. He could still feel his cracked lips.

But a settled quietness had taken the place of the desperation he had felt. With a surge of strength, Nicholas knew it was the presence of Jesus, here. Here! In the madness of captivity in the Cuban wilderness, the Savior had heard, and He was with them. Jesus had endured horrible suffering Himself for forty days and nights in a wilderness.

"Emmanuel," Nicholas whispered. "God with us!" Never before had he grasped the full meaning of those words.

He went to Nicholas Jr. "Get up, Nicholas," he said, taking the boy's hand and helping raise him. "We'll walk together. It's not much farther."

In thirty minutes, they found the soldiers and sailors resting beside a creek. Nicholas' men brightened, and the tall sailor leaped up to help Nicholas Jr. to the water.

"Thank you, God!" Nicholas prayed as he dipped his head and arms into the water, and drank.

It was growing dark under the trees by the creek. A shaft of sunlight reached through a gap in the canopy and glowed on the water. Nicholas stepped into the light and washed his face and drank again. As he lifted his head, a butterfly danced into the sunbeam.

Its wings were a brilliant blue.

"Look, Nicholas!" He pointed to the butterfly. But by the time the boy looked up, it was gone.

The men looked at Nicholas as if he was going crazy, but he just shrugged and laughed and reveled in the joy of water and the unexpected remembrance of his brother Seger.

The soldiers waited until Nicholas and his son had replenished themselves in the water. *"Gracias,"* he said to the men.

"Vamos!" the leader snapped.

They went on. Nicholas Jr. was still pale, but he had responded to the nourishment and was walking independently. They walked only another half hour, when they saw a house before them.

"Praise God," Nicholas breathed again. "He is with us!"

A wrinkled old man welcomed them. Nicholas rejoiced to see his smile. The man pointed to himself. "Rodrigo," he said as he motioned for them to come in.

The prisoners entered a low, dark room beneath a thatched roof. A fire was burning low in a corner, and a cooking pot was over it. Nicholas realized the soldiers had left. Seagull Sal fell to the floor, holding his stomach. A low moan escaped from his mouth.

With some linguistic creativity and use of gestures, Nicholas and Rodrigo were able to communicate. The old man had chickens outside, and if one of the men would find and kill one, Rodrigo would cook it for them. It would be good for sickness, he said.

Nicholas sat beside Seagull Sal. "I'm so sorry, my friend," he said. "What can I get you?"

"Water," he whispered.

Nicholas sent the tall sailor for water. Rodrigo told him of a spring nearby.

Seagull Sal sat up and drank when the sailor returned.

In an hour, a delightful smell was coming from the cooking pot. The room was filled with smoke.

"*Ropa vieja,*" their host said, pointing at the pot.

Nicholas decided either his ears or his memory of Spanish were faulty. Had the man just said *old clothes?* But he was pointing to the food.

"*Ropa vieja?*" Nicholas asked, puzzled.

"*Si, si!*"[1] Rodrigo cried, chortling and pulling at his own threadbare, stained clothes, and then pointing to the pot.

Finally, Nicholas realized that the dish the man was making was actually called "old clothes" because of its appearance. Nicholas peered into the pot by the light of the fire. Long pieces of dried hot peppers and chunks of onions floated among jagged pieces of chicken. It was a motley stew certainly, but Nicholas did not think he would have ever called it "old clothes."

Regardless of its name, the men ate it with delight. Nicholas Jr. declared he had never before eaten anything so tasty. They scraped the pot clean, but it had been sufficient to give them strength. Seagull Sal ate, too exhausted even to create a mess of his food as he usually did.

As they ate, Nicholas asked Rodrigo if they could rest in his house for one day, before continuing their journey.

"*Si, si,*" their host agreed. Then he cocked his head.

Outside, there was a tramp of feet.

The soldiers had returned. With them were three men. One of the newcomers held a lantern high over the group of prisoners.

In his years at sea, Nicholas had seen sea cooks with missing limbs and sailors with missing teeth, ears, and noses. He had seen burn victims with disfigured faces and men with tumors and skin diseases. He had seen pirates with badly healed scars and broken and missing teeth.

But he had never before seen any human who filled him with more horror than the men with the soldiers. Perhaps it was the metal rings threaded through the leader's forehead or the dried blood caught in his machete-trimmed beard. Perhaps it was the conniving, sideways glances of all three hunters or their belts strapped full of machetes and broad hunting knives. More likely, it was the gleam in their eyes as they studied the captives, first Nicholas Jr. and then the rest of the men.

Nicholas inferred that the soldiers were giving the prisoners over to these men. "Hunters will take tomorrow," one of the soldiers said.

---

[1] Yes! Yes!

After the soldiers departed, the hunters came closer, holding the lantern over them. It was clear they had all been drinking. The hunter who held the lantern talked on and on in Spanish as he surveyed the prisoners. His comrades laughed.

The hunters left, and Rodrigo again assured Nicholas that they could rest one day at his house.

The men lay down, exhausted. Though alarmed by the visit of the hunters and their murderous machetes, they soon fell asleep.

Nicholas could not.

He replayed the hunter's words over and over in his mind. He was unsure of his Spanish, but he thought he had understood the joke that had set the men laughing.

That boy will taste much better than the old ones.

40

The Bayamo Prison

In the morning the shriveled old man fed them again. He cooked bananas into a mash and fried eggs in an iron skillet. In his large pot, which he had not cleaned, he boiled coffee. He set it before the men along with one cracked cup, and they drank and passed the cup to the next man.

"This coffee is alive," Seagull Sal muttered. It was the darkest coffee any of them had ever tasted, and before long they were shaky with the punch of the caffeine.

Old Rodrigo heaped mash and eggs into wooden bowls and passed them. *"Fufu, fufu,"* he said, pointing to the mash. *"Fufu de platano."* [1]

After breakfast, their host suggested that Nicholas visit a farm not far away where they could get sugarcane. They could take it with them on their journey through the forest.

Nicholas set off with one of the sailors to help carry the sugarcane, should they be successful. He left Seagull Sal, who was feeling somewhat healthier today, in charge of the others.

Only a quarter of a mile away, Nicholas finally saw cultivated fields and gardens. The farmer welcomed them. He seemed friendly and sensible, and Nicholas decided to confide in him. As well as his Spanish would allow, he described the hunters who would guide them to Bayamo.

---

[1] Fufu is a staple food in parts of Africa. It is made by boiling starchy vegetables such as plantains *(plantano)* and then pounding them into a dough-like consistency.

"Metal?" the farmer asked, pointing to his forehead.

"*Si,*" Nicholas said.

The farmer looked grave. Nicholas explained that he thought the men talked about killing them and possibly eating his son.

"*Si, si,*" the man said.

Nicholas asked again, to make sure they understood each other. He used the plainest Spanish he could muster. Would the hunters really kill and eat them?

"Oh yes, they will kill you," the man said in Spanish. "It is too bad. Maybe they were only joking about the eating. Say strange thing, make people laugh . . . but, yes, they will kill you."

Under less desperate circumstances, Nicholas would have burst out laughing himself at the calm manner in which the farmer assured him they would be killed. He could not even think of a fitting response in English or Dutch, and in Spanish he was utterly stranded.

The sailor received the sugarcane while Nicholas debated what to do and with what words to beseech help. Finally, with the transaction complete, he made his appeal. "Do these hunters know you?" he asked. "Could you go with us?"

The farmer considered. Nicholas wasn't sure what was going through his mind. Was he only inviting this man to join the feast? But he had to try.

"Yes, I will go."

"Tomorrow."

"Yes, tomorrow."

Great was Nicholas' relief at daybreak to find the farmer at Rodrigo's door. A gourd of drinking water, a small packet of sugarcane, and several pistols rode on his belt. Scarcely had he arrived, when the hunters appeared, machetes clinking in their belts. There were seven of them now, instead of three. Nicholas did not see any firearms on them. If they were to be killed, a musket would be less menacing than those awful knives.

When the hunters spotted the farmer, the leader with the metal forehead muttered, but then ignored him. While some of the hunters held their machetes high, others tied the men together at the waist, using a long rope—and bad technique. Nicholas wished he could show the men how to make efficient knots, although under the circumstances, their poor knots might be a benefit.

They set off through the forest in a replay of the previous trek. However, they had water and sugarcane this time. Despite their frightening escorts, Nicholas felt hopeful.

About the time the shadows shifted from west to east, the hunters stopped by a stream. Nicholas realized there were now fifteen or twenty of them. When had they multiplied? They pushed the line of prisoners to the ground and produced more rope.

The farmer, who was standing by the prisoners, asked the leader a question.

The metal-faced leader answered.

The farmer snapped an answer back that started with "No" and ended with two pistols being withdrawn from his belt.

The two shouted back and forth. Nicholas caught words here and there and realized the farmer was trying to save their lives. Nicholas feared it would be a needless loss of the farmer's life to have him with them.

"Sir, save yourself if you must! Why add your death to ours?" Nicholas called desperately. He had spoken in English, not Spanish. As he began the mental translation to Spanish, the leader called off the man with the rope.

The whole party drank at the creek and refilled their gourds and went on. Perhaps the farmer had merely delayed their deaths. Nicholas was afraid the farmer would leave them. They arrived that night at a plantation. Nicholas asked the farmer if he needed to go home in the morning.

"Your journey is not over."

"Will you go with us the whole way?"

"They are determined to kill you," the farmer said, "but they will have to kill me first. They are paid to take you, and the Spanish care nothing for the lives of prisoners. But if I would be killed, they would be punished. I will not leave you until you are handed over to the governor in Bayamo."

Nicholas grasped the man's hand in gratitude.

He joined his men who huddled around a fire. Seagull Sal moaned from the ground, but the others were sitting up. "Shouldn't we escape?" the sailors asked.

"Where would you go?" Nicholas asked. "This is not a country where you are likely to survive, and the coast is crawling with Spanish warships even if you would get there. And none of you speak Spanish." He explained what the farmer had told him, and the men relaxed a bit.

"Men, I wish to thank God for his protection," Nicholas said. "I also wish to thank Him for a friend of mine who died years ago, but whose influence I believe is saving our lives. That man's name was Joaquin, and he taught me to speak some Spanish aboard a Spanish ship. Let us pray."

Nicholas stood before the fire and poured out his heart in thanks to the Savior. He begged for guidance on the day ahead and for comfort and healing for Seagull Sal. The sailors were not surprised. Even if they did not share his faith, they knew and respected their captain.

In Bayamo three evenings later the prisoners were delivered safely to the governor.

The farmer who had saved their lives parted from them. The governor's men locked the prisoners in a closet-like room. It was so stuffy and hot they scarcely were able to sleep. Seagull Sal continued to moan.

In the morning Nicholas and his son and Seagull Sal were moved to a larger room which held other English sea captains. Nicholas thought he would feel relief, but he was not even through the door when he heard words and laughter that he remembered all too well.

Was I wrong, he wondered, *to ask God to spare my life? How can I take my son into this filth?*

He remembered the passage in the first chapter of Romans—a person who darkens his heart toward God sinks into depravity. The men described in those verses had walked off the pages into this prison.

Nicholas turned to the prison guard who was closing the door. Behind him stood a man in uniform.

"Señor," Nicholas entreated, "my helmsman and I are followers of Jesus Christ, and I do not wish to bring my son into a place filled with such sin. May we be placed in a different room?" It was an act of desperation, but to his surprise, the overseer promised to check.

The captains had stopped talking, and several of them understood Nicholas' halting Spanish. "Ah!" one cried, "we have a sea captain who is too good for us."

"No, men, I am not good," Nicholas said, "but I have given my life to the man who is good, and who gave His life for all of us."

"Ah, if He is so good, why are you here? Why have I been here for a year?" another man taunted. "Pretty rotten way to treat the humans that your god has created."

A shout of laughter filled the room. Nicholas decided that silence was the best approach. Thankfully, it was nearly night, and he found a corner to rest between Seagull Sal and Nicholas Jr. Seagull Sal fell asleep without moaning.

But Nicholas did not sleep. He was tormented by a terror worse than the fear of his son being eaten by the hunters. Now, he feared they would have to live with these wicked men, forgotten for years. He remained face down on the floor boards, spending the night in silent pleading before the Lord. The boards grew damp with tears.

The days were bitterly long. Enough light came through the windows to distinguish the various men. They taunted Nicholas for his faith and tried to strike up conversations with his son. Nicholas Jr. stayed with his father and remained silent.

"You will rot in here praying to your Jesus," one man mocked. "You'll die with your prayers just like Old Park died with his curses."

"Old Park? Who was that?" Nicholas asked cautiously.

"Captain Parker died in here last week," one man offered. "Used to sail out of New York."

"That's just what he said," another man mumbled. "Said he escaped from Cuba too, but I didn't believe either of his cock-sure stories about trading his own sailors for his freedom."

"He was mean enough to do it though," the first man replied.

A weight of sadness settled over Nicholas. He exchanged glances with Seagull Sal, whose eyes had opened wide.

"Did he leave his red handkerchief?" Nicholas asked.

Several men looked at him, startled. "How did you know about that blasted handkerchief?"

"No," another said. "All clothes of a dead person are thrown out with the body."

On the fourth night of prayers and tears, Nicholas felt the peace he had felt in the Cuban jungle when his son was near death.

The wooden floor was still his pillow, damp with tears. The iron bars in the windows still divided the sky into sections. The snoring of the men and the scurrying of the rats still disrupted his thoughts. His son still slept by his side and his helmsman on the other side.

But the room was suddenly a sanctuary, the place where Jesus was present. Again, Nicholas breathed, *"Emmanuel, God with us! Thank you, Jesus!"*

He closed his eyes, and he saw Christina at the old Dutch fireplace, little Seger running into her arms.

I want to rescue you and take you home. Nicholas had not heard the words, but he felt them deep in his spirit. The Savior had heard him and was weeping with him.

The rest of the night, Nicholas wept tears of love and gratitude for the amazing presence of Jesus Christ, the Lamb.

41

The Presence of the Lamb

"Captain Garrison looks like he's been praying all night to his *Savior*," one of the men taunted as bowls of *fufu* were handed into the cell.

The others howled with laughter.

Slurping noises filled the room as each man grabbed his bowl. Nicholas cleared his throat.

"Sir, you are right!" he said. "We are not alone in this prison. Last night as I prayed I received great comfort and joy as the Savior met me.

"Friends," he continued, "Jesus Christ has walked on this earth just as you and I do and He experienced every kind of hideous suffering. He understands pain and isolation and hunger. He understands death and weeping and rejection. His presence can penetrate the deepest darkness."

The men were silent, not meeting each other's eyes.

Nicholas went on, telling them of the gross sins he had lived with daily and how he had ignored the teaching of his parents. He told them how Captain Parker had drowned his pet cat and abandoned the men from the *Ella* in the Cuban castle. He confessed how he had hated Captain Parker. He told them how he had fallen ill and felt the very fires of hell around him, and how God in His mercy had saved him and given him hope. He quoted to them the verses of Psalm 139:7–12.

Whither shall I go from thy spirit? or whither shall I flee from thy presence? ⁸If I ascend up into heaven, thou art there: if I make my bed in hell, behold, thou art there. [9]If I take the wings of the morning, and dwell in the uttermost parts of the sea; [10]Even there shall thy hand lead me, and thy right hand shall hold me. [11]If I say, Surely the darkness shall cover me; even the night shall be light about me. [12]Yea, the darkness hideth not from thee; but the night shineth as the day: the darkness and the light are both alike to thee.

"Men of the sea, you have seen the power of God in the wind and the waves. That same God demands of us righteousness, and we can never be good enough on our own. Only through relying on the blood of His Son Jesus, who walked in our shoes, in our flesh, can we hope to be right before God. I have claimed this blood, my friends, and I have forgiven Captain Parker from my heart. No powers on earth can prevent the peace of God from filling me, even in this desolate place."

Nicholas turned and went to his corner. He picked up his New Testament and pressed it close between his hands.

Thank you, Jesus, he prayed silently. *Thank you for speaking through me. Oh, draw the hearts of these men to yourself.*

He sat beside Seagull Sal and put a hand on his son's knee. Nicholas Jr. had retreated to the corner after eating his breakfast. Nicholas grieved for the many uncomfortable and desperate circumstances the boy had been through.

"Are you all right, son?"

"Yes. They listened to you, Father."

"Yes, they did. Perhaps God will speak to the hearts of some of them."

Nicholas Jr. was looking over his shoulder. Nicholas heard a footstep and turned.

"Captain Toler," he said kindly, gesturing to the floor so the man would feel welcome. There wasn't much to offer by way of hospitality in prison, but there was space.

"Captain Garrison," the man said. "May I speak to you?"

"Please," Nicholas said.

"It might take awhile."

"What, and keep me from my daily schedule?" Nicholas asked with a twinkle in his eye.

Captain Toler laughed, the muscles of his face relaxing visibly as he seated himself.

"It's just that I-I have experienced the things you speak of—the peace of God."

"That's wonderful."

"It . . . was."

Captain Toler told Nicholas and Seagull Sal of his youth. He had heard of the salvation of Christ Jesus from John Bunyan's *Pilgrim's Progress* and the teaching of his grandparents. He described the relief of having his sins covered by the blood of Christ and how he loved to sing hymns which spoke of Him.

"But, then, I-I fell into bad company." The man put his head in his hands.

Nicholas put a hand on his shoulder. "Brother, did you hear my story? I have been there."

"But, listen," Captain Toler said, shaking his head. "I made fun of all those verses and songs I had once loved. It was as if the devil wanted to make an example out of me. I lied and swore and used the most vile words. I treated every woman in my life with deception and cruelty. Captain Garrison, I fear I have missed my chance for mercy!" The man dropped his head into his hands again and sobbed quietly.

"Brother," Nicholas said again. "You are wrong." He paused and prayed. He was not sure how to explain to Captain Toler that he was mistaken.

"There is a verse that says, 'If thou shalt confess with thy mouth the Lord Jesus, and shalt believe in thine heart that God hath raised him from the dead, thou shalt be saved.' Here, let me find it."

His childhood training helped Nicholas find his way around the Bible now. He managed to find Romans 10:9. "See? It doesn't say anything about how many times you've done wrong," Nicholas said. "And do you remember in the Gospels when Jesus told the disciples if someone offends seven times in a day, or seventy times seven, that we should forgive? Don't you think that if Jesus is asking this of us, He is more than ready to do the same when we offend Him that many times?"

Captain Toler considered. He squinted as if he were estimating the angle of the sun. "Four hundred and ninety sounds low for my sins," he said.

"Do you think it really is about a number?" Nicholas asked. "Captain, 490 sins is low for every man. If we were to be judged on the basis of a number, we would all be damned. Do you believe that Jesus Christ came to die for your sins and that God raised Him from the dead?"

"Yes," Captain Toler said with tears. "I do."

"Then, you are saved by His mercy, my brother!"

Nicholas, Seagull Sal, Nicholas Jr., and Captain Toler spent the day reading Scripture and praying together.

"I wonder if we could sing?" Captain Toler said. "I always liked that story about the two men singing in prison. Paul and . . ."

"Silas, I believe," Nicholas said. "Well, I do not consider music one of my natural giftings," Nicholas admitted, "but I do enjoy singing. And Seagull Sal here is a master at it, thank God!"

Nicholas and Seagull Sal had learned a few hymns from the Moravians, and Captain Toler remembered several from his childhood. They finally found one they both knew: "O God, Our Help in Ages Past." They managed to sing several verses, although they were uncertain of a few phrases. Seagull Sal, still weak with sickness, taught them some of the psalms he had put to music.

None of the other prisoners berated them. Captain Toler thanked Nicholas over and over, but Nicholas pointed up.

The days went by. Every morning and evening, the handful of believers read Scripture and sang together. One day, another man asked if he could join, and they welcomed him. Soon, there was a small group. "O God, Our Help in Ages Past" became their theme song, because it was a familiar English song that gave them hope.

The days, however, turned into weeks, and the weeks into months. The year of 1740 dragged on. In September, Seagull Sal died. His body remained for a day before the guards removed it. Nicholas mourned his friend, yet he envied Sal's release.

"I am weary of this suffering," Sal had said before he died. "I only wish to go to the Savior who I have learned to love. And you, Nicholas, are the reason that I know Him! Thank you, thank you for saving me!"

"My friend, it was not—"

"I know, Captain, but you were the one who told me I could be saved. I will die with willingness if I can only go to the Lamb of God!"

A young man from the town of Bayamo was seen standing at the prison windows in the evenings, listening to the Scripture and hymns. He finally received permission to visit. He asked who the hymn leader was, and the men pointed to Nicholas.

Nicholas chatted with the young man in Spanish. He said his name was Gabriel. The next evening he was back for another visit, this time with a bowl of *ropa vieja* made with beef. He gave it to Nicholas, who passed the delicacy around the room so everyone could have a bite. Almost every day Gabriel came, and Nicholas wondered if he really was an angel. Sometimes he brought gifts, and sometimes he sang with the men.

In October, Nicholas began to feel ill. Captain Toler and Nicholas Jr. worried that he had the same sickness that had taken Seagull Sal. Gabriel brought tea for Nicholas and he began to improve.

In November, word arrived that a new batch of prisoners would be taking the cell. The prisoners who had been there longer would be moved to the dungeon.

The men had heard of the dungeon. Previous victims whispered of the dreadful darkness and the muddy floors. Other prisoners were transferred to the windowless hole—and never returned. Despair filled the room. Nicholas told Gabriel the news that evening.

The next morning a guard arrived, and Nicholas and Nicholas Jr. were told to follow him. Nicholas looked at the others, confused. He embraced Captain Toler and the other men in their Scripture group. Nicholas and his son followed the guard to a private room. The door clanged as the guard locked them in. Nicholas admired the sleeping mats on the floor. Barred windows overlooked a garden of white ginger flowers.

"The Savior has been so good to us," Nicholas said to his son. "But it feels unfair that I got a nicer room when the other men are thrown into the dungeon."

"When will we get out of here?" Nicholas Jr. asked.

Nicholas sighed. "I wish I knew."

Nicholas and his son enjoyed the room for only a few days. They had been accused of plotting to escape with the governor's son. The governor and his son were at odds, so Nicholas and Nicholas Jr. were thrown into the dungeon with the others.

It was a shallow earthen cellar and none of the men could stand upright. Pools of water stood in the lowest spots. The dry season had begun, but still the cellar was damp. Only one bucket was provided as the toilet for seventy prisoners, and it overflowed every day. Two lanterns hung from the ceiling.

Nicholas was glad to see Captain Toler and the other men, including his sailors from the *Golden Swan*. However, in the dungeon, his dysentery returned and he became dehydrated. Other men became sick as well, and the sounds of coughing and hacking filled the damp cellar.

The morning and evening worship services continued, but the singing was weak and punctuated with coughing. Whenever Gabriel visited, he brought another lantern so the men could enjoy better light. When Nicholas finally could not get up, Gabriel tried desperately to get him moved to a hospital. But it was to no avail.

"I'm going to move you to Santiago," Gabriel finally said. "I have a friend who thinks he can help me get an order to have you moved."

"No," Nicholas said.

"Why not?" asked Gabriel. "It's a port city and ships will be coming and going. You will have hope of being exchanged and freed."

"I cannot be moved alone. The others must come too. This is a hell on earth, Gabriel, not fit for a beast."

Gabriel looked around the miserable dungeon. "Ah. Let me see."

A few days later, the order arrived: all seventy prisoners in the dungeon would be moved by ship to the castle in Santiago—the same castle where Nicholas had been imprisoned as a boy. And once again, it was almost Christmas.

The Admiral

Christmas 1740

A surgeon aboard the ship visited frequently. Nicholas had arrived on a bed, so weakened he could not walk. Gabriel had seen to the details of his transportation, and then had recommended him to the captain.

"I need a trustworthy man who can speak Spanish to be in charge of the prisoners," the captain had said. "Will he do?"

"Yes, if he has the strength he will do very well," Gabriel answered.

From his sick bed, Nicholas functioned as the overseer of the prisoners on the short sail to Santiago. He communicated requests for medical care to the surgeon. He spoke with the ship's purser[1] about the number of mouths to feed. With the help of Captain Toler he led the men in prayer and singing. When announcements came from the captain, he passed them on in English to the prisoners.

The castle warden escorted Nicholas, Captain Toler, and Nicholas Jr. to a small room. He barred the door after showing them in, so they knew they were still captive. After the dungeon, however, the castle room felt like luxury.

Each of them had a simple bed with a straw mattress and a blanket. A window looked out over the water. They could see the morning sun and listen to the call of birds. Their toileting bucket was emptied twice a day, and the rice and beans palatable.

Nicholas grew stronger. Every day, he walked more laps in the room. The guards let them out to walk in the afternoon sunshine. Nicholas had never known before

---

[1] A purser is an official responsible for papers and accounts and the wellbeing of passengers on a ship.

how wonderful sunshine is to those who have been deprived of its presence. They walked up stone steps to the parapet where armed guards guns watched the harbor and large cannons on wooden trucks stood at the ready.

With strands of cotton thread from a shirt, the three prisoners laid a checker board at the side of the room where it would not be disturbed. They played countless games of pebbles against straw. Nicholas Jr. soon began to beat his father and Captain Toler on a consistent basis.

"Could I write a letter?" Nicholas asked a prison guard one day. A week later paper, quill, and ink were delivered.

"May I have some paper?" Nicholas Jr. asked, touching the sheets.

"You may, but there is only one pen," Nicholas said. "We will have to share."

> Dear Christina,
> Nicholas Jr. and I send you our greetings. We are well, and have been wonderfully preserved by the Savior, who even sent us a man named Gabriel who treated us as an angel might have.

He knew it was important to say that first. She would scan the entire letter for words that said they were alive and well.

> I continue to recover from my illnesses. We miss you all very much, and at last are recovering hope of seeing you again. I cannot spare the paper to tell of all our adventures now. We are currently Spanish prisoners, but have every reason to think that we shall be exchanged.
> If you are able to write, address your letters to San Pedro de la Roca Castle, Cuba. Hopefully, we will be home before your letters arrive.

When he finished, Nicholas gave the pen and ink to his son. At the exercise break that day, Nicholas Jr. sat against the stone parapet and sketched. He looked up at the outline of stone against the blue sky and then down at the paper. That afternoon, he worked on fleshing out the sketch. Nicholas looked over his shoulder occasionally, but he knew the boy would be self-conscious if he watched too long.

"Can I send this to Mother and Susanna?" he asked that evening.

Nicholas took the paper. Nicholas Jr. had sketched the stone fortress, with the Spanish flag flying at the top and the wooden bridge set in a corner between two walls. In the corner, a lookout stood posted with a gun. He had drawn the window of their room with its border of thin bricks.

"This is a very good drawing, son," Nicholas said. "Do you think it will frighten them?"

Nicholas Jr. looked at the drawing as he considered. "Did you not write that we are in prison? I think they would like to know what it looks like. I would, if you were here alone and I were at home."

Nicholas considered this. His son knew far more than he did about the loneliness and desperation of waiting to hear from a loved one at sea.

"I never thought about it like that, but I think you're right," Nicholas said. "We will send it with the letter."

The dry season passed, and the rainy season began. It was summer again, a whole year since they had left Staten Island. No word had come from Christina. Any number of things could have happened to their letter, and Christina may never have gotten it. Or perhaps she had gotten it and her reply had been lost.

"It's your birthday today, my son!" Nicholas said on June 26. He had been able to get a small book to write in, and here he kept the date and a journal of their prison stay. "Fifteen years old! Even with prison fare, you are almost as tall as I."

On Nicholas Jr.'s tray that night, several pieces of paper and a writing quill came with his food. Nicholas smiled at his son's delight. It had taken effort to beg for a birthday present without his son overhearing.

"Captain Garrison." They had only taken a few bites when the voice came at the door. "Captain Garrison, the presence of yourself and your companions is requested by an English party. Gather your belongings."

The three looked at each other, then sprang for their few possessions. Nicholas Jr. gathered his birthday gift and a few papers from the past months. Nicholas got his journal and New Testament.

Two soldiers escorted them down the long hallway and under the arched doorway to the exercise area on the parapet. They went down a set of stone steps, across a courtyard, and up a few steps. They crossed a wooden bridge set over a moat filled with black, sluggish, stinking water and refuse. Then, they walked through the iron gate and down the long stone corridor to the harbor. Nicholas remembered the night Joaquin had led them out the back way of this very same castle, more than twenty years before.

The two soldiers in front of them, and the two behind, kept an impressive marching rhythm to the water's edge. An English sloop was anchored offshore under a flag of truce. Nicholas could see the several Spanish officers on board, wearing red and black uniforms.

The three men were put into a small boat and rowed out to the sloop.

"Captain Garrison, Captain Toler," the English captain in the sloop addressed them. "I am here under orders of Admiral Vernon to exchange you for two Spanish captains." The imprisoned captains stood behind him. The English captain looked at the Spanish officer, and they all nodded in agreement. Then the Spanish prisoners and officers descended into the boat and rowed off, and the sloop weighed anchor.

That's it? Nicholas wondered. In all his adventures of capture and escape, he had never been exchanged before. Less than an hour earlier, they had been sitting in their locked room in the castle. Now, they were aboard an English sloop, and the San Pedro de La Roca castle was already growing smaller, a strip of aqua water widening in front of it.

"Are we free?" Nicholas Jr. asked at his elbow.

"I believe so," Nicholas said. "That's the best birthday present of all, is it not?"

Nicholas Jr. stood with his hands on the railing which circled the forecastle. He lifted his face into the sea breeze, the thin white shirt collar fluttering. He was blinking back tears.

"I didn't know if we ever would be free again," Nicholas Jr. said quietly.

Nicholas considered that in the mind of a young man just turned fifteen, a year must feel like a lifetime.

"Captain—" Nicholas turned to call for his friend who had endured the year with them, but he was standing right behind them. Their gazes locked, and tears filled both men's eyes.

"Thank God," they said simultaneously. They prayed for the rest of the seventy men who had come to the castle with them. Were they still imprisoned within its walls?

As the last rays of sun flooded their world with gold, they sang the song by Isaac Watts they had sung so many times in the castle. "Oh God, our help in ages past/Our hope for years to come/Be Thou our guide while life shall last/And our eternal home!"

"How far to Jamaica, Father?" His son's shining eyes mirrored his own joy. They were traveling again!

"About one hundred miles. Maybe a day or two depending on the breeze. It will be a much better journey than we had when Joaquin helped us escape in a fishing boat."

Nicholas Jr. begged to help the crew, and the captain permitted him to join one of the watches.

"Old Grog hasn't had a good time down here," the captain informed his comrades.

"No?" Nicholas asked. "I'm sorry. Do you mean the admiral?"

"Ah, yes! He wears that grogram cloth, so he's been called 'Old Grog' as long as I can remember. Have you heard of his battles or his work in Parliament?"

"I have heard of him but never met him," Nicholas said.

"He had a great victory over the Spanish in Panama end of last year," the man continued. "There's a new song going around called *Rule Brittannia,* in honor of him taking Porto Bello with only six ships. While there we had such a problem with drunkenness that Old Grog made a new rum recipe: three-fourths water and one-fourth rum. Can you guess what the men are calling it?"

"Grog?" suggested Captain Toler.

"That's right!" the captain said with a laugh. "After that victory, we attacked Colombia. We had a lot more ships and men, but people began to die of disease. Old Grog was angry with the commander of the infantry on land. He thought they should be more aggressive. But it was the rainy season, and the men on land were dropping like flies from dysentery and yellow fever, and we were losing men from scurvy. We finally retreated. We've been back in Port Royal only a few weeks, which is why we are only now exchanging prisoners."

"We were with seventy other prisoners," Nicholas said. "What of them?"

"Some have been exchanged, I believe, and more to follow."

Nicholas sensed that the captain did not know but was trying not to reveal his ignorance, so Nicholas let the matter pass.

In the early morning two days after their release, the captains received an invitation to board the *Princess Caroline* of Admiral Vernon, the man who had freed them. Nicholas and Captain Toler made an attempt to straighten the rumpled clothes they had worn for the last year. Their captain's coats had been returned, but they were in a sorry condition. Nicholas Jr. at least had received new clothes, having outgrown the ones he came in.

As the three came through the entry port and straightened up on deck of the massive warship, the ship's musicians struck up "Rule Britannia."

> Rule Britannia, Britannia rule the waves.
> Britons never will be slaves.

"If the last year wasn't slavery, I don't know what it was," Captain Toler whispered to Nicholas with a smile.

"How did you know what I was thinking?" Nicholas asked. It wasn't the first time that Captain Toler had spoken his thoughts.

"By sharing the same cell for a year."

They snapped to attention as an officer motioned them to follow him to the quarterdeck. Leaning over the railing of the upper deck, the tropical sun slanting across his face, a tall figure stared down at them. Nicholas was surprised at the simplicity of his brown overcoat. Most naval captains, and especially admirals, decked themselves in blue and gold. However, noting the way the other men gave him space, Nicholas was certain this was their liberator.

"Gentlemen," the admiral said, "what a pleasure to have you aboard. Will you come down to my cabin?"

They followed the admiral down the companionway to his expansive cabin. The admiral and several officers took seats on the side of the table by the great stern windows. Possibly he sat in front of the window by design, knowing that his guests across the table would be more visible with the light on their faces. With the light on his back, the admiral's own face was obscure, veiling his unruly eyebrows and the decided sag of his jowls. The admiral folded his wrists on the table, the massive cuffs of his overcoat flopping about. White ruffles peeked out of the cuffs and a white scarf adorned his throat.

Nicholas knew they were expected to report the basic account of their imprisonment and any interesting facts about the Spanish they may have learned. He used the opportunity to share how the presence of the Lord had encouraged, maintained, and even saved them in the course of the year.

"Interesting," the admiral said, as Nicholas described the walk through the jungle and the hunters' decision to kill them. "Do you think they were cannibals, Mr. Garrison?"

"I don't know, sir," said Nicholas. "There was nothing in their manner too delicate for such a deed."

The admiral asked Nicholas and Captain Toler a few more questions. Then he looked at young Nicholas. "Young Garrison," he said, "how many times have you been to sea?"

"Only this once, sir," Nicholas Jr. replied. Nicholas leaned back in his chair and rubbed his son's shoulder as everyone in the room laughed.

"No man can promise you a trouble-free life at sea," the admiral said, "but I hardly think your experiences so far can be called typical."

"He has done very well, sir," Captain Toler said. "And his father has been teaching both of us navigational skills through the long months. Captain Garrison is much more accomplished at the octant than I, sir."

"I thought as much," one of the officers said. "I know you, Mr. Garrison, I feel sure. I remember you as a boy on the *Ella* out of New York. Even then you could not be kept away from the charts. You might remember me as Clark, the lookout."

"Sir!" Nicholas cried with pleasure. "I do! Perhaps if I had seen red hair I would have remembered you more quickly."

The admiral's face lowered, and Nicholas hoped he had said nothing wrong.

"Aye," the man sighed. "It will be a lovely day when Harrison finishes his sea clock. There is much to be said for any man with an interest in navigation, as we learned the hard way at Scilly in 1707. That is what I thought of, Mr. Garrison, when they spoke of your interest as a boy."

"You were there at Scilly, sir?" Nicholas asked.

Years earlier Old Pete had told him the story of four warships and two thousand men sinking off the coast of the Isles of Scilly. He thought of Old Pete now and wondered if he had escaped from the Spanish warship and made it back to Liverpool.

"Aye, in one of the ships that did not sink," the admiral said, shaking his head. "It is a memory hard to shake. But come now, boys, you must be thinking of how you will get home. I will be sending a ship to New York in a few weeks, possibly a couple of months. If the time comes and you have no other plans of departure, I will facilitate your journey on that ship."

43

The Warship

"I'm afraid we have no room for the boy, Mr. Garrison."

Nicholas stared at the captain of the warship which would soon be heading for New York. Would they really refuse to let his son accompany him home after so many months?

"He can be put to work, sir." Nicholas said, although of course the captain was aware that a boy could be put to work.

"I understand, but we are overcrowded as it is. I have plenty of boys. I have received orders from the admiral to conduct you to New York, and that I shall do if you wish it."

Nicholas conferred with Captain Toler, who was ready to head home to England on a merchant ship.

"I could speak to the admiral," Nicholas said. "But to put myself in the displeasure of the captain seems unwise."

"Does the boy wish to learn more of the sea?" Captain Toler asked. "I could take him with me for the time."

"There's no man here I would rather see him accompany," Nicholas said slowly. Except himself, of course. Nicholas felt a physical pang at the thought of parting with his son after all the dangers they had endured together. He remembered his father looking at him in the old kitchen at home, saying, *I was wondering when you would ask.* Now he understood the pain his father had experienced.

With Captain Toler, Nicholas Jr. would have not only a trustworthy sea mentor, but a spiritual mentor as well.

"I will let him decide," Nicholas said. "If he does not wish to go with you for further experience, we will wait here together and find a different passage home."

He found Nicholas Jr. on the huge deck, beating someone in checkers. The warships were preparing to go into battle against Cuba, and Nicholas was glad to think of heading the other direction.

Nicholas Jr. glanced up.

"Finish the game," Nicholas said.

"It's already finished," his opponent grumbled.

Under the moon and stars, Nicholas and his son talked.

"I would like to go home," Nicholas Jr. said when his father presented the options, "but I would also like to have more experience. Perhaps a voyage without getting captured." A smile played on his lips.

So the warship left Jamaica with only one Garrison on board.

Nicholas felt a deep loneliness as the ship sailed north. He had spent over a year with this son. He had spent months with the other English prisoners. All the prisoners from the *Golden Swan* had been released by the admiral except for Seagull Sal.

Seagull Sal had been freed by God himself. Nicholas missed him. In prison, Nicholas had experienced envy for Seagull Sal, more than grief. Now, back in the free world, he missed Seagull Sal's golden hair and his songs and even the food dripping around him.

Nicholas was given a narrow bunk in the wardroom. He knew the men below were allotted about fifteen inches each for their hammocks, so he thanked God for the generosity of the captain in giving him an actual bed.

On the second day out of Jamaica, Nicholas ate porridge with the officers in the wardroom, taking time to thank God for his food. He was glad to be in the mess room beneath the captain's cabin because this deck also had light from the stern windows.

"Maybe I should pray over my food," an officer said. "Does that make it better?"

The others all laughed, and Nicholas remembered the prison room full of vile men. However, he laughed with them. "Yes," he said simply. "It does make it better, as I learned in prison."

The men looked at each other and fell silent. Spoons scraped bowls and coffee slurped into throats.

Nicholas retired to his bunk to drink his coffee and spend time in prayer. "Heavenly Father," he prayed, "your Son suffered so much on earth. Speak to my heart and give me courage and joy!"

Nicholas' mind flashed back to Brother Friedrich on St. Thomas. Brother Friedrich had visited him as he recovered. Despite bouts of illness himself, Friedrich had determined to speak to every slave on the four or five dozen plantations on the island. Day by day, he doggedly pursued this goal. Night by night, he sang and prayed and renewed his spirit, still taking time to care for Nicholas.

If Brother Friedrich could visit all those slaves, Nicholas could surely meet each of the several hundred men on this warship. It was not acceptable for the captain or officers to make small talk with the men, but he was not a captain here. As a visitor who had been in prison, the officers would surely give him grace.

As he meditated, he thought too of Brother Josef and how he had befriended the other passengers on the *Golden Swan*. Although merchant ships carried much smaller crews than warships, Nicholas was not physically ill as Brother Josef had been.

Nicholas smiled and breathed thanks, his fingers cradling the coffee mug. God was so faithful at bringing these things to his mind through the still small voice of the Spirit.

Nicholas got up and stretched as well as he could in a small area where he could not stand to his full height. Then he stepped out into the gun decks, where the men not on watch were passing the time. A boy about the age of Nicholas Jr. was sitting off to himself, working on a piece of rope.

"Are you practicing your knots, lad?"

The boy jumped and looked up. Nicholas smiled kindly, and the boy's shoulders relaxed.

"No, sir."

He looked at the rope in his hand with frustration and then glanced up questioningly. Nicholas squatted beside him to study his handiwork.

"I'm trying to make a bracelet for my mother, sir," he confessed. "But I think the rope is too thick."

Nicholas took the project and held it up to the light falling through the portholes. "Can you not separate the rope into strands?" he asked.

"Maybe I could!" the boy said. As he unwound his braiding, Nicholas asked about his family.

"My father was killed at sea, sir," he said. "My mother lives in Denmark."

"How do you come to be on an English warship, my boy?"

"I was impressed in London after a merchant voyage, sir," he answered simply.

"Ah." Nicholas knew that the royal navy was forceful when necessary. He felt a deep sympathy for the boy, who really was a young man, probably sixteen or seventeen.

"What is your name?"

"Christian Jacobsen, sir. You are the merchant captain who was a prisoner, are you not?"

"I am," Nicholas smiled. "I will check later to see how your ropework is coming."

Nicholas walked on to where several men off duty were engaged in a game of backgammon.

"Wish to play, Cap'n?" one asked him gruffly.

"Just watching," Nicholas said. "I am a checkers player."

"Oh, I will play you in checkers!" called a voice from behind him.

The men sometimes drilled during the day. They practiced cleaning and loading the guns with shot and powder. They ran the guns out on their wooden tracks, touched the priming powder with a lit match on the end of a staff, and blasted their shot into the sea.

This was a skill he was not adept at, and he was grateful he was not. He admired the discipline of the gun crews, however. Each man had his role with the cleaning and loading. Together, they heaved on the tackle that pulled the heavy guns forward and through the porthole. With a blast, the gun would shoot back until it caught on its breech rope and the process was repeated.

Up on deck, when Nicholas visited, he could not stop being amazed at the numbers. Where merchant vessels used five men, the navy could spare twenty or thirty. The boatswain's whistle or the piping of the musicians provided the music for the heaving and pulling, rather than raucous songs from the men.

Nicholas received permission to make observations with borrowed instruments when the captain and first mate had finished their measurements. He found that he was their equal, or better, and soon won respect on the quarterdeck.

"I hear you are in conversation with the men a lot," the captain said one evening, brow furrowed in a frown.

"I do enjoy passing the time in company and learning to know new people," Nicholas said. "Although I understand that as a captain this leisure is not possible." The captain relaxed and shrugged, and Nicholas breathed a prayer of thanksgiving.

"Sandy Hook!" came the call one morning. Nicholas' heart rate picked up as familiar land came into view. He walked toward the quarterdeck, keeping clear of it until invited.

"Come on up, Mr. Garrison," said the captain. "These are your home waters, I believe."

"They are," Nicholas said.

He had not allowed himself too much anticipation on the voyage. He was on a warship, after all, which at any time could have been put into action and sunk.

As they sailed farther and farther north, the chance of being intercepted by the Spanish became less.

A wave of joy flooded Nicholas as Staten Island came into view. He had written Christina from Jamaica, telling her he was hoping to find passage home. Did she know the warship was arriving?

With the pilot beside the helmsman, they made the turn north and carefully picked a course to the channel past the Watering Place and the wooden skeletons in the shipyard. Then it would be a short sail to Manhattan and all things familiar: the ships from other nations, the shrieking block and tackle, the coffee houses, the taverns, and the many languages in the streets.

"Sir," Nicholas said suddenly without stopping to consider whether it was prudent. "Could your men row me to shore here?"

"Is Staten Island your home?"

"It is, sir."

"Ah."

Nicholas could imagine the wheels turning in the captain's head. Even the smallest delay to put a man out in a boat would be much against his wishes.

"It would be hard for me to deny a released prisoner the chance to see his family as soon as possible," he finally answered. He nodded at the boatswain, who rushed off with his pipe to prepare a boat.

Nicholas hurried to his bunk and collected his few possessions in a bag. As he climbed the steps, Christian Jacobsen followed him. "All the men are sad to see you go," he said. "Myself especially."

Nicholas clasped the young man's hand. "Come to Staten Island if you get the chance," he said. "There's a ferry that will bring you. My wife and family will be more than happy to have you."

"Take this to Mrs. Garrison," Christian said.

It was a rope bracelet similar to the one the boy had made for his mother.

"Thank you! She will be honored. Do come see us."

As Nicholas prepared to climb off the ship, he saw that men were up in the yards and the captain and officers were lined along the quarterdeck, watching him.

The captain called, "Three cheers for a merchant captain released from Spanish prison!"

"Huzzay! Huzzay! Huzzay!"

Nicholas paused at the porthole, stunned. He turned and looked back at the hundreds of men and removed his hat. He then stepped through the porthole. Along the Staten Island shore, he saw the ferry pushing off toward them.

"Ahoy! Is that Captain Garrison?" someone from the ferry shouted. "We'll take him from here."

Nicholas could not stop the tears forming as he bid farewell to the men in the small boat. He did not remember their names, but he was sure he had spoken to each of them. "God bless you!" he said.

One of them gave him a boost from the small boat and he dropped into the ferry. The boat was quickly returned, and the warship moved on to Manhattan.

On shore at last in a daze of joy, Nicholas hired a horse and then realized he had no money. The tavern owner waved him off. He rode over Iron Hill until he came to the Church of St. Andrew. He did not consider himself a member of the Church of England anymore, but it seemed like a fitting place to pour out his gratitude to God. He leaped off the horse, tied it to a tree, and slipped through the church door. Falling to his knees at the front of the church, he wept with gratitude. God had not only spared his life, but had also sent many tokens of His presence along the way.

He noted the day—Saturday, September 16, 1741.

"This day I will keep as a day of thankfulness to you, heavenly Father," he prayed, "until the day you call me to yourself. I never want to forget your love and faithfulness in rescuing me. Again."

He wiped his eyes on his handkerchief that was no longer white, and leaped onto his horse, already sore from the ride over the hill. It had been almost a year and a half since he had ridden a horse. For the first time in his life, he was returning with no present for his wife, only a rope bracelet from the boy he had befriended.

"Let's go home," he whispered to the horse.

In the clearing before the Garrison house, a boy was hauling water. Nicholas could scarcely believe that twelve-year-old Jan could be so tall. Beside him toddled a little girl who was just getting her land legs, the daughter he had never met. His son saw the horse coming, dropped the water, and ran to the house, screaming.

"Mother! Come quick, Mother! Father's here! Father is home!"

The Day of Peace

September 1741

Utter chaos descended on the Garrison house when Nicholas arrived. Christina ran outside, her face first pale, then ecstatic. The children tumbled along beside her, wide-eyed. Footsteps pounded in the upstairs loft. Nicholas barely had time to dismount before the wave of bodies hit him.

Everyone was crying and talking at once. Blandina, just over a year old, wailed in the puddle beside the bucket that Jan had dropped.

With a cooking spoon clasped in her hand, Mary arrived on the scene, puffing from the exertion of running. She burst into tears and loud thanksgiving, muffled by the apron thrown over her face.

"Christina, my dear!" Nicholas said through his tears. "Did you know I was coming?"

"No! I mean yes, but I—no!"

Nicholas kissed her and everyone laughed and shouted and shoved. Christina ran to get Blandina and the other children piled into Nicholas' arms.

"Susanna, you are a young woman!" Nicholas exclaimed.

"I'm thirteen," she said. She smiled up at him with her mother's smile.

"I turned twelve two days ago," Jan said. "Mother asked what I wanted for my birthday, and I said I wish Father would come home. And you did, Father! You did!"

Lambert was nine now. Benjamin was six. Katie was five. Little Seger was three.

"Blandina," Christina said to the baby. "This is your father!"

Nicholas reached into his cloth bag and pulled out the rope bracelet that Christian

Jacobsen had handed to him.

"Look at this, baby girl," he said, taking her from Christina. "It's for your mother, but she won't mind if you get the first look." The baby grasped the thin rope in her tiny fist, then flung it to the grass and reached for Christina with a wail.

"That's all right, Blandina," Nicholas said, handing her back. "I don't blame you at all."

He squatted on the ground.

"Seger, my little man, do you remember your father?"

"No, he doesn't," Lambert said.

"Yes, he does!" Benjamin said, as if he was afraid Lambert would next say that he, Benjamin, did not remember.

Seger stared up at Nicholas with big eyes. "God get Father out of castle," he said.

Surprised, Nicholas looked up at Christina. She smiled at Seger, but said nothing.

"God did get us out of the castle, Seger. And he got us out of a muddy dungeon too. When we get settled I'll tell you stories," Nicholas promised, picking up the three-year-old.

"Mary," Nicholas said over the heads of his family, "are you going to stand out there ignoring me?"

"And here I am giving you a minute to say hello to your family!" Mary exclaimed, stepping in. "If you was a day younger I would swat you with my spoon."

Besides a few gray hairs, Mary had not aged much. Nicholas realized she was in her seventies.

"If you only knew how many prayers we prayed and the tears we shed, now didn't we, Miss Christina."

"We certainly did."

"And little Jan says to his mother, he says, I just want Father to come home, and I thought, what if maybe he'll be a-coming this week! And there I am a-stirring the—*Oh!* The beans! I'm burning the beans, Miss Christina, and that man hasn't had a decent bite since he left here!"

Mary whirled and disappeared into the stone house. Christina leaned against Nicholas and sighed as if a weight had rolled off her shoulders.

"Boys, take care of the horse," she said softly. "If only our oldest son would be here, my happiness would be complete."

After a noisy meal of Mary's fresh bread and perfectly-cooked beans, the children crowded around Nicholas showing him things.

"Look at what I drew!" said little Benjamin.

"I made this leather pouch," said Lambert.

Nicholas looked up on the wall and saw the drawing Nicholas Jr. had sent.

When the children were all in bed, Christina poured her husband a cup of tea. "I have something to tell you," she said.

"Just one thing?" he teased.

"One of great importance," she said. "Thomas Noble's wife Mary has been talking with me about the Moravians and the death of the Savior—many things she learned from Brother Josef. She told me how there is nothing we can do to save ourselves, not even by living right and being good."

"Hmmm," Nicholas said. "She is right."

"One day last winter when we had no word of you, I was in despair, and I cried out to the Lord for help. I asked Him if He could just send one small thing to show that He is really a merciful, personal Savior like Mary said.

"That afternoon there was a knock on the door. I opened it and found Thomas and Mary Noble and Brother Josef and a few other Moravians standing outside, their arms full. They brought presents from the Noble's store: candy for the children, fresh fruit from the South, cheese and spices. The children were so happy! I was so overwhelmed that God had answered my prayer that I could hardly speak."

Christina's eyes filled with tears. Nicholas covered her hand with his and squeezed.

"He really does care!" Christina rejoiced. "I knew it was going to be all right, even if you never came home. I knew God was real and that He sent Jesus to die for me. I don't know how to describe it. I talked with them late into the night. And they have been encouraging me ever since."

Nicholas sighed as if a burden were falling from his shoulders. "I am filled with happiness!" he said. "I prayed for you every day, my dear. What a strange thing that God should use my imprisonment to speak to you. He is so good!"

The fall of 1741 was full of joy. Nicholas and Christina laughed and cried and studied Scripture, together.

In early December, Nicholas received word that Count Zinzendorf had arrived in New York and would be passing through to the settlement of Moravians in Pennsylvania. Could he stop at the Garrison home?

Nicholas and Christina accepted eagerly, inviting friends and family for the occasion. Thomas and Mary Noble and Nicholas' sister Elizabeth, with others who were interested in the Moravian community, met at the stone house. They packed tightly into the parlor while Count Zinzendorf spoke to them about the blood of the Lamb. The count's sixteen-year-old daughter Benigna had come with him. In Europe, she had injured her foot and the doctors did not think it could be healed. They had talked of the need to amputate it. On the voyage to America, however, the foot had healed, and Benigna was walking without a limp. Together, the company praised God for this physical healing.

When the time came for the count and his party to head to Pennsylvania, Nicholas accompanied them to Brunswick. There, he bid them goodbye and returned home.

In the short time he had been gone, little Seger had fallen ill. Nicholas found Christina's face tight with worry. He had suffered some bouts of coughing before the visitors left. Now, a fever had settled over him like a heavy fog. He lay on his parents' bed, his breathing rapid. His eyes were closed.

"Seger," Nicholas whispered.

The little boy did not respond.

"Seger! It's Father. Can you open your eyes?"

The eyes opened slowly, but the fog still covered them. Seger did not seem to notice or care that his father had returned.

Nicholas and Christina knelt by the bedside and prayed. Nicholas forced himself to take deep, slow breaths to fend off the choking sensation of helplessness.

He watched Seger breathe. His throat hurt as he remembered his brother Seger, drowning in the waters of the Fresh Kills. It hurt as he thought of the orange and white cat, drowning in the wide ocean. It hurt as he recalled Pine, suffering from the disease that took his life. It hurt as he remembered his own suffering on the *Golden Swan* after God had miraculously spared his life.

I couldn't save my brother, Nicholas thought. *I couldn't save the white and orange cat. I couldn't save Pine. Now, my son is dying and there is nothing I can do. If only I could take his suffering away!*

Nicholas paced the bedroom floor, crying out to God for healing. He asked for peace and strength to bear the sorrow if Seger did not get better.

Give up, the enemy taunted. *God doesn't care. And there is nothing you can do!*

There is nothing I can do, Nicholas agreed. *But God is not limited! Oh God, help me to accept your will! Help me to hear your voice of truth.*

Mary kept a pot of water boiling to make the room warm and humid. Christina changed cloths on Seger's forehead every hour, day and night. Nicholas sent for a doctor in Manhattan. The doctor drew blood from the little boy's arm in an attempt to draw the infection out of his body. He made a plaster of herbs and placed it on his chest.

Little Seger continued to suffer. Finally, a week before Christmas, the little boy passed away in Nicholas' arms. As life moved out of Seger's body, Nicholas relaxed for the first time in days. In that moment, God answered his prayer for peace.

"He is in the arms of the Lamb," Nicholas whispered to his wife.

"I know," Christina sobbed. "I can just see how happy he must be, free from the struggle to breathe! But I will miss him so much."

Christina wiped her face, and took a knife from Nicholas' writing desk close by. Gently, she cut a wisp of Seger's hair.

"What is that for?" Nicholas asked.

"I will show you sometime," Christina said.

45

The Moravian Community

Spring 1742

In the spring, Nicholas visited the Moravian colony at Bethlehem.

He had taken another trip to the West Indies for Thomas Noble. He stayed on St. Thomas, meeting Brother Friedrich again. Brother Friedrich was not well, and the brothers on the island urged him to go with Nicholas to America to rest. Nicholas accompanied him all the way to the Moravian community in Pennsylvania, where the Lehigh River met the Monocacy Creek.

A tour guide met them when they arrived. There was always a tour guide in Moravian communities to show people around and answer questions.

Nicholas and Friedrich looked at the newly-constructed buildings. A larger building with four chimneys stood on the rise of ground above the Lehigh River.

"Why was the name Bethlehem chosen?" Nicholas asked the guide.

"Last Christmas, Count Zinzendorf arrived from Europe," the man said.

"That was right after he visited in our house," Nicholas said.

"You see the *Gemeinhaus*[1] with the four chimneys," the guide said. "The count and all the Moravians ate a Christmas Eve meal there, although the building was not completely finished. Then, everyone walked down the hill to the First House for a communion service. You can see it there below the hill."

Nicholas, with a surveyor's eye, noted the way the land fell, both to the Lehigh River and to the Monocacy Creek. The creek and river created a rough western and southern

---

[1] *Gemeinhaus* is the German word for church house. The Moravians used the building for church services, meetings, a school, and a minister's residence.

A View of
BETHLEHEM
one of the Brethren's
Principal Settlements in
PENNSYLVANIA
1757

1. *Gemeinhaus* (Congregation House) 2. Married Brethren and Sisters' House
3. Single Brethren's House 4. Single Sisters' House 5. Girls' School (Bell House)
6. Burying Ground 7. Stables and Barns 8. First House
9. Monocacy Creek 10. Lehigh River 11. Crown Inn

Artist Nicholas Garrison Jr.

boundary for the community. The dormitory and community buildings stood high above the water. Industries requiring running water clustered below the hill along the creek. He turned his attention back to the guide.

"It was late evening by the time the communion was finished, and the count led the group into the stable, which was bitterly cold. They started singing a hymn: *Nicht Jerusalem, sondern Bethlehem, aus dir kommet was mir frommet.*[2] That's how the town was christened Bethlehem."

The words of humility embodied the beliefs of the Moravian church. The confidence and joy found only in Christ was evident in Bethlehem, where the small group of pioneers was carving out a community.

"On St. Thomas, they have a twenty-four-hour prayer chain," Nicholas said. "Does the prayer chain go on here?"

"Oh yes! And the calling out of the night hours by the watch," the guide said.

"The count dreams of this land as being a place where people of all nations may serve the Lord together," the tour guide went on. "You will see that people of all races are welcomed here. And be sure to address the count as Brother Ludwig," the man added. "That is his request both to us and to the sea congregation that has just arrived from Europe."

"Sea congregation?" Nicholas asked.

"Yes, they arrived just six days ago. Our lodging places are filled to bursting."

Nicholas listened with interest to the description of the floating church. The sea congregation had traveled from Europe to America in a ship filled with Moravian believers. As they did on land, the sea congregation maintained an orderly schedule and daily inspirational services. The brothers and sisters were each assigned tasks such as cooking, caring for the sick, or cleaning the berths. Some of the brothers were on standby should the sailors need assistance with anything a land man could easily do.

"A general economy is practiced here at Bethlehem," the tour guide said. "When anyone joins the community, they give their possessions to the brotherhood. If they decide to leave, they take with them as much as they had when they came."

"The record-keeping sounds challenging," Nicholas said.

"It can be," the man agreed. "Although we take meticulous notes of every detail. But that is one reason why we are slow to allow new members to join us. We want them to understand fully before committing. They need to know that everything is decided by a committee: which buildings we should build, who will work where, when we will cut trees."

The guide took them farther up the hill. He showed them the flat gravestones that marked a new graveyard surrounded by trees. From this higher ground, the guide

---

[2] Not Jerusalem—lowly Bethlehem / 'Twas that gave us Christ to save us. (This translation is not literal, but it is the accepted English translation.)

pointed to cultivated fields surrounding the community, both on their side of the Lehigh River and on the bluffs across the river. Many trees had already been felled to clear the ground for crops.

Next, the guide took them inside the *Gemeinhaus* and up the stairs to the *Saal*. Rows of backless benches filled the *Saal*, with one side for the women and one for the men. An open Bible rested on a table at the front of the room. Non-Moravians could observe the communion service through a window from a side room. Count Zinzendorf had an office in another side room, and other rooms housed visitors and members of the community.

Nicholas stayed in Bethlehem for several days. One evening, four couples were married in the *Saal*. Brother Peter Bohler delivered the sermon, speaking on Ephesians 5:32: "This is a great mystery, but I speak concerning Christ and the church." Brother Bohler explained how marriage symbolizes Christ and His bride, the church.

The next day, Brother Ludwig shared his observations about the other Christian groups who had settled in William Penn's land. Some groups criticized the Moravians for the use of the lot to decide matters of the church. Brother Ludwig explained their concerns, but he encouraged the community to continue to use the lot to the glory of God.

Nicholas couldn't wait to return home to Staten Island and share with his wife what he was learning. "Christina," Nicholas said when he had told her everything he could remember, "I can't stop thinking of the sea congregation. Imagine serving as captain of a ship filled with followers of the Lamb!"

"You would find that so pleasant after all your other experiences," Christina said with a smile. "I believe you enjoy commanding a ship as much as I enjoy making something out of cloth or yarn."

They were in the main room of the old stone house. Their daughters were at the kitchen table working. Susanna, now fourteen, sliced apples in half. Katie, who was six, carefully pulled out the stems of each apple and tried to pick out the seeds with a spoon. Blandina, the only little one now that Seger was gone, ran around her father's feet. She had just turned two.

Christina sat nearby in her rocking chair, knitting a blanket. She propped her work on her expanding waist. She often told Nicholas how knitting helped her relax from the cares of the day. Standing behind the table where his daughters were at work, he watched as she finished her row and slid the last stitch off the needle. After a moment, she looked up at Nicholas.

"You would do well at commanding a Moravian ship, I think," Christina said.

Nicholas rested his hands on the back of Katie's chair. He lowered his head, thinking of the wickedness he had been a part of and how he still struggled at times to put his faith in God.

"I don't know if God will call me to be a captain again," he said. "Right now it seems God wants me to live faithfully where I am—here at home with you and the children. And this time, I intend to be home when you need me."

Christina sighed and smiled. Another child was expected in late summer or early fall.

Nicholas reached an arm around Katie and sneaked an apple slice from her bowl. Katie shrieked as her father popped the slice into his mouth. Nicholas wrapped her in his arms so she could not move and she shrieked some more.

"Katie, do not scream so loudly," her mother admonished.

Nicholas saw his wife looking at him in a gentle suggestion to be a little less provoking. He laughed, kissed Katie on the forehead and let her go. He crossed the room to his wife's chair, still swallowing.

"Have you been feeling well?" Nicholas asked quietly.

"Yes, I think so," she said, wistfully. "Just tired like I always am at this stage. And somehow I miss my other sons a bit more when I think of a new baby . . . Nicholas . . . and Seger . . . and the two little babies. But we have seven living children. I cannot complain."

"Father! Father!" urgent boyish voices shouted from outside the house. Nicholas sprang to the door. Jan, Lambert, and Benjamin had been harvesting summer apples. Perhaps someone had fallen.

"Father! A letter!"

On the road, Nicholas saw a hired man from the ferry waving to him and he waved back. A piece of mail delivered by hand? Christina got to her feet as quickly as possible when she heard the word "letter." The entire family gathered around as Nicholas broke the orange seal and opened the packet addressed to Captain Garrison.

" 'Dear Father and Mother,' " Nicholas read, "I am doing well. I have been taken up by Admiral Vernon's ship again. It is so hot the deck planks are sticky with tar in the afternoons. Perhaps if we set sail for England before long, I will obtain passage back to New York from there. Give my love to Susanna, Jan, Lambert, Benjamin, Katie, and Seger.' "

"Look, here is a sketch of the ship!" Nicholas said.

He lowered the letter, and all the children pressed around. Christina touched the paper and kissed it with happiness.

"I wish it would say more, but at least we know he is well," she said. "Why is he back on the warship?"

"I wish I knew," Nicholas said. "Hopefully nothing happened to Captain Toler."

Nicholas spoke little the rest of the day. He kept thinking of the environment on warships— the frequent floggings, the hard tack, and the maggot-infested water.

I should never have taken him to sea, Nicholas thought. Then he turned his eyes to the Lamb, as he was learning to do when he felt helpless.

That evening, Nicholas sat down at his writing desk to reply to the letter. Jan came to his side. "Father."

Nicholas turned to look at his son.

"I want to ask you something."

Nicholas froze. The pen in his hand shook. His breath caught. In his mind he was twelve years old again, standing by the front door shortly after his mother had died. He saw his younger self trying to tell his father how badly he wanted to go to sea. He remembered how he had grabbed a wooden spoon to steady himself while he stumbled out the words.

Father, I want to ask you something. It was the same scene in a different corner of the same house.

I cannot let another son go to sea! Nicholas' heart cried. Nicholas put the quill pen into the inkwell, so his son would not see his hand shaking. "What is it, Jan?"

"Father, did you not say the Moravians at Bethlehem have workshops where boys can learn trades? Could I go there to learn a trade?"

Nicholas' breath rushed out in relief. He saw Christina behind Jan, settling Blandina in her bed. She was listening to Jan as well. He felt the world settle back on its foundation.

"Well, Jan, perhaps you could. I didn't know you wanted to do such a thing. We should pray about it first and I will talk about it with Mother."

"Good!" Jan said, his face bright with relief as well.

On Jan's thirteenth birthday in September, Nicholas sent the children to the barn and called for Mary. Jan would share his birthday with a new baby brother, whom they named Seger in memory of his uncle and brother.

"Thank you, God, for a healthy son," Nicholas whispered as he leaned over his wife and the red-faced baby in her arms. He turned the wet cloth on his wife's forehead and smoothed back her hair.

46

The Wind at Scilly

December 1742

In December Nicholas took Jan to Bethlehem to live and learn a trade. Brother Friedrich met Nicholas with joy and kissed his cheek.

"What a blessing to have a Garrison boy move here with us!" he said. "Come, Nicholas, let us show you the new buildings. We are still cramped, but there is ongoing construction."

When it was time for Nicholas to leave, he embraced his second son. "Pray to the Savior whenever you are in distress," Nicholas told him. "And write to Mother and me as often as you can."

Jan was excited about his new adventure. Nicholas was the one in the most distress, even though he knew his son would be in the hands of people he trusted.

Brother Friedrich rode with him through the woods as far as the Delaware River.

"No matter how many children are left at home, it is always hard to part when they leave," Nicholas lamented as he waited for the ferry.

"You can count on me to be a friend to your son as long as I am here," Brother Friedrich assured him.

"I know I can," Nicholas said.

"My heart is in St. Thomas, though, Brother Nicholas. As soon as I have opportunity, I will return to my people."

"I admire your devotion," Nicholas said. "But please wait until you are well."

The ferry bumped against the near shore. Brother Friedrich waved to him from the shore as the ferry moved away, rolling in the current.

On the day after New Year's Day, 1743, the Garrison family heard the sound of horses outside the house. Nicholas went to the window.

"It's Count Zinzendorf—Brother Ludwig!" Nicholas called to Christina.

Nicholas, Lambert, and Benjamin wrapped themselves in coats and scarves to attend to the horses. Susanna and Benigna, Brother Ludwig's daughter, ran into each other's arms.

"What a pleasure to be with you again, Brother Garrison," the count said when he and the other guests had settled before the kitchen fire.

"I would entertain you in the parlor, Count Zinzendorf," Nicholas apologized, "but it is warmer in this room."

"Oh, this is ideal," the count said. "And please, I wish to be addressed as Brother Ludwig."

"Do have some tea," Christina said, as Susanna and Katie scurried to bring cups. Mary was dumping flour and sugar and cinnamon into a large bowl.

"Thank you, Sister Garrison, I believe I will," said Brother Ludwig. "It's a bit chilly outside today.

"Brother Garrison," he continued, "we are about to embark for Europe on the ship *Jacob* with Captain Ketteltas. We hope to bring a second sea congregation to America."

"I am glad to hear that God is blessing Bethlehem," Nicholas said. "Does Captain Ketteltas bring you back then as well? I believe I have heard of him."

"Well," Brother Ludwig said, "perhaps he could."

Nicholas realized that everyone in the room had fallen silent. The girls stood waiting with more hot water, but not one guest lifted the tea to their lips. Mary stood as still as the poker in her hands. Red coals glowed inside the big Dutch oven, heating the bricks to bake Mary's raisin biscuits.

Brother Ludwig took a sip of his tea and cleared his throat. "I will delay no longer in sharing the objective of my visit," he said. "We hope to obtain a ship in England by which to return. We are wondering, Brother Garrison, if you would be willing to come with us. Could you convey the brothers and sisters back to America in that ship as captain and chief elder?"

Nicholas found himself unable to speak. A pool of joy rose in his inner being like a sudden tide. He felt his wife's hand on his shoulder, squeezing lightly. The room seemed to swell, as if the ceiling beams were not strong enough to hold it together. He bowed his head and thanked God silently before looking at the count.

"I—I believe—it would be an honor," he said simply.

He felt for his wife's hand and looked up at her, then back to Brother Ludwig. "However, I have left my family far too often in my life as a captain. Perhaps the question should be put to my wife, who has borne the burden of my absences."

"Sister Garrison," Brother Ludwig said, "do you support your husband in this? Perhaps we should give you some time to think and discuss."

"I do support him," Christina said simply. "It pains me to have him leave us, but I released him to the Savior when he was imprisoned in Cuba. And he is an excellent captain, sir. The other captains speak well of his abilities."

"I believe you," Brother Ludwig said. "Thank you for your support. If you are willing, Sister Garrison, a family from Bethlehem could stay near you and your family. Then while your husband is gone to sea, you will not be alone."

"That would be wonderful!" Nicholas said.

"Yes," Christina said. "That would be wonderful."

After Brother Ludwig and the others moved on to Thomas Noble's home in Manhattan, Nicholas and Christina made plans.

"Do you think I could take Susanna?" Nicholas asked. "Would she want to go? Benigna will be sailing too."

Christina's face fell and Nicholas saw the struggle in her eyes. Another child gone from home?

"Let's ask her," Christina said.

When they brought the question to their daughter, Susanna's eyes opened wide. "Could I?" she asked.

Ten-year-old Lambert would be the oldest child in the house.

A few weeks later, the *Jacob* sailed past Sandy Hook and into the Atlantic Ocean. Nicholas stood on deck with Brother Ludwig, Benigna, and Susanna. Captain Kettletas leaned against the binnacle on the quarterdeck. Nicholas found it strange to be on a ship and not be its captain, but he soon realized how much more relaxed he felt as a passenger. He had seldom been on a ship when he had no responsibilities, and it had been years since he had been something other than commander-in-chief.

"Father," Susanna whispered. "I don't feel well."

Nicholas looked down at his daughter. Her face, surrounded by a thick wool scarf, showed a green tint. Nicholas knew the symptoms. "Let's take you downstairs to rest," he said.

"I will be doing the same," Brother Ludwig said. "Much as I wish it were not so, the sea usually affects me for the first few days. Although when I went to St. Thomas on the occasion of our first meeting, I begged the Lord to spare me due to the numerous things I needed to accomplish. I was only sick one day before we weighed anchor. Do you ever experience seasickness, Brother Garrison?"

"I have never truly been seasick," Nicholas said.

Nicholas helped Susanna lie down. "Do you need a bucket?"

She nodded, her lips pinched together. She swallowed, and Nicholas could see that she was miserable. He grabbed a wooden bucket and got it to her just in time.

"Father, I wish I would have stayed at home. If only I could lie on my own mattress by the chimney! Are the waves bad today?"

"I'm sorry, my dear. No, this is just a mild sea breeze."

"Did Nicholas get sick when he went with you?"

Nicholas thought of his son and tried to remember. "I don't think he felt too bad," he said. "It's all right, Susanna, most people get sick, even captains and admirals. But almost always they feel better after a few days."

"A few days?" she said, a tear dripping. "What if there's a real storm? Then I'll probably get really sick."

Nicholas had to compose his face to keep from smiling at his daughter's dramatic words. He went to his sea chest and withdrew the wool blanket Christina had sent. He laid it over the coarse linen cloth which Susanna had wrapped around herself. "I'll be here whenever you need anything."

Of the twenty Moravians aboard, thirteen were ill the first three days of travel. The other passengers cared for them, emptying buckets, brewing tea and coffee, reading Scripture, and singing hymns. Susanna's sickness lingered, but on the sixth day, Nicholas found her walking toward him on the deck.

"I'm finally feeling better, Father!"

"I see that!"

Nicholas reached out and steadied his daughter as the ship lifted and dropped in a swell. She gripped his hand to keep from falling.

"How did you learn to walk on a ship?" she asked.

"I need to relearn on every voyage," he said. "Although I scarcely think of it anymore."

On the fourteenth of February, the ship's crew was interrupted in their singing. The Isles of Scilly had been sighted the night before. They were now passing south of the islands, and the wind, which had been following and aiding them, had suddenly swung around and was pushing at them from the south. The sails snapped, the masts creaked, and the ship plunged toward the deadly rocks of Scilly.

"All hands!" called the first mate.

Nicholas was on deck when the alarm was called. They would have to stop the ship, or it would sail north and wreck on the rocks. But they could not stop the ship unless they found a ledge of solid ground on which to cast anchor.

Nicholas remembered the stories of the British navy fleet that had plunged toward these same rocks in 1707. The flagship of the admiral in command had gone down in three or four minutes, with the admiral on board. Nicholas could scarcely imagine a huge warship dropping into the water in mere minutes—hundreds of sailors, so alive one moment and meeting a watery grave the next.

On the *Jacob*, the men aloft fought with the sails. Another sailor worked the sounding lead, searching for ocean floor where the ship could cast anchor. Whitewater broke over the shoals as the ship continued to be pushed toward danger. Nicholas looked down into the water. The four navy ships were down there, somewhere.

We may join them soon.

He was not the captain. That thought consoled him, but only a little.

The crew, having taken in the sails, were standing on the bulwarks, frozen with terror. The singing had stopped. Only the squeaking of cables and the whistle of the wind could be heard.

"Any ideas, Captain Garrison?" came the voice of Captain Ketteltas behind him. "It's a bloody poor time for a south wind." Despite the calm facade, Nicholas saw terror in the man's eyes.

"I think you're doing all you can, sir," Nicholas said.

He hurried down the hatch. The Moravians had been alerted to the danger by the call of "all hands" and they were praying. Nicholas silently joined them. Brother Ludwig motioned for him. "You look very grave, Brother. Is the danger really so great?"

"It is. We are headed straight into the rocks where four navy ships went down when we were boys."

The count rested his hand on the curved side of the ship. "Ah, Brother. We will all come to land safely and happily."

Nicholas said nothing. This was a matter where he was the expert, not Brother Ludwig. He turned and paced in the narrow space.

"Brother Garrison, it will be over in two hours. Let us trust to the Savior." Nicholas stared at Brother Ludwig. He did not want to doubt his sincere faith, but no man could know the future.

One of the Moravians began a song, and the others joined in. Nicholas went to Susanna's bunk and sat beside her, wrapping an arm around her shoulders. If the ship went down, he wanted to be beside his daughter. He prayed, begging God to spare their lives. "God, we are sinners saved by grace," he said within himself. "Please have mercy on our souls through the blood of the Lamb, and on the souls of those who are with us!"

He joined in the singing as best he could, feeling every roll of the ship and expecting at any moment to hear the ripping noise of rock through wood.

"Brother Garrison." It was Brother Ludwig.

"The two hours are up. Will you go up on deck and see what is happening?"

"Yes."

On deck, Nicholas found that the ship was still heading to disaster. It was much closer now to the white water, and despite the struggles of the helmsman, another two hours of the south wind would bring their ruin. Nicholas walked around the perimeter of the vessel.

He had not made a full circuit when a cry came from the helmsman and captain.

Nicholas felt the wind drop off. The storm was breaking! Clear sky showed in the west. The wind began again, but this time it was from the southwest.

The captain nodded. The first mate began yelling, and the crew sprang to action to catch the west wind. In minutes, the sails were filling and the ship was headed away from the death trap. The men before the mast began to cheer.

"Huzzay! Huzzay! Huzzay!"

Stunned, Nicholas remembered Brother Ludwig's prophecy. He ran back down the hatch. "We are out of danger!" he exclaimed. "A west wind has come up to push us past the rocks."

"Will you all join me in returning thanks to God?" Brother Ludwig asked, his face aglow.

That evening, Nicholas and Brother Ludwig walked on deck together, watching a delightful sunset. "You must know my question," Nicholas said. "How could you know the precise time the storm would be over?"

"I will tell you," Brother Ludwig said, "since I don't think you will make bad use of my words. For more than twenty years, I have enjoyed intimate communication with my dear Savior. When I am placed in a critical situation I first examine myself to see if I am at blame. If I find anything with which He is not satisfied, I immediately ask His forgiveness. My gracious Savior then allows me to feel His forgiveness, and usually tells me how the matter will end. But if He does not answer, I think it is better that I should not know it. But this time, He let me know that the storm would be over in two hours."

Nicholas stared at his companion. Could God truly be so confidential with man? In the Church of England, he had heard more of the judging and jealous nature of God, rather than His unfathomable love and care for man.

"Thank you, Brother Ludwig," was all he could say.

Three days later they arrived at Dover and set out over land to London. Here they found rooms with members of the Moravian church. While eating breakfast the morning after their arrival, Nicholas heard that Admiral Vernon had just returned to London from Jamaica.

He leaped up from the table, leaving his English sausages to grow cold. He ran to Susanna's room and pounded on the door. "Susanna!" he called. "Hurry, we must get down to the wharf!"

47

The Moravian Sea Captain

Spring 1743

Fifty Manhattans would not have equaled the population of London, and that was not the only difference. In Manhattan, there were new boards, new shingles, new windows, new fences. Here in London the buildings were hundreds of years old. The people were packed into houses stacked in long, tight rows along narrow streets. Back alleys between ancient homes were piled with trash and peppered with chickens and stray cats. Carts rumbled, horses whinnied, delivery men shouted, and children screamed.

Nicholas and Susanna reached the Thames River and found the *Princess Caroline.* Admiral Vernon was not on board, but they could speak to the first lieutenant if they wished, a midshipman informed Nicholas.

"Well," Nicholas began, but he was interrupted by a glad shout.

"Hey, that's my father and my sis!"

It was Nicholas Jr., almost six feet tall. He had been scrubbing the deck of the *Princess Caroline,* likely as payment for his passage. He threw down his mop and ran toward them. Nicholas was glad that his son wasn't too grown up to hug his father and sister.

"I haven't seen you for so long!" Susanna exclaimed. "Look how tall you are. I would hardly have recognized you. Oh, I wish Mother could see you. And Mary. She would burst her seams!"

Nicholas Jr. explained that Captain Toler had perished of a tropical disease after one run to England and back to the West Indies. Nicholas shook his head. "After all we lived through in prison!"

Nicholas dashed off a letter to Christina, knowing it would make good time from London to New York. Christina would want to know that her family was together.

After Nicholas Jr. had been cleared from the warship, the three Garrisons left with the Moravian passengers for the Netherlands. A few weeks later they arrived at Marienborn, near Frankfurt, Germany.

Marienborn was a main base of the Moravians. In front of a green hill, a stately castle towered over community buildings and rows of cultivated trees and shrubs. Smaller buildings marched in neat grids, interspersed with trees. The Garrisons were given an official tour.

"Everything was broken down and filthy when our brothers and sisters first moved into the castle at Ronneburg," the guide explained. "Homeless people lived on the grounds. Animals wandered in and out of the castle. But our brothers and sisters stood the test. They cleaned the castle, planted crops, cared for the homeless, and started a school.

"Then a neighboring landlord offered them the Marienborn castle. This place has now become the headquarters for our people."

The guide took them into the *Saal,* which was very different from the meeting room in Bethlehem. Tall windows were cut into the thick outer wall. Nicholas counted the panes of glass, nine high and six across. Fifty-four panes in just one window! A cord could be pulled to close the curtains, with the drapery hook at the top of the window acting as a pulley.

However, some things were similar to Bethlehem. A simple table holding an open Bible graced the front of the room. Women sat on the backless wooden benches on the left side and men on the right, the guide said. He explained the service schedule to them.

The guide showed the visitors where they could stay. "If the young people are interested in staying permanently," he said, "the choir[1] houses for the single sisters and single brothers are both in Herrnhaag. It isn't far from here."

In the next few weeks, Nicholas listened much and spoke little. He had written a letter to the church, requesting membership. He took Susanna to Herrnhaag to join the single sisters' choir. She began wearing the traditional dark dress and a tight fitting bonnet with a pink ribbon. The color of the ribbon showed she was part of the single sisters' choir.

At Herrnhaag, Nicholas met an Englishman by the name of John Valentin Haidt. Brother Haidt was a painter, the son of a goldsmith. Brother Haidt had learned

---

[1] A choir in this sense refers to a group of Moravian believers of the same gender, near the same age.

to know the Moravians in London. Much like Nicholas, he had been touched by meeting Brother Josef Spangenberg.

Brother Haidt had moved to Herrnhaag in 1740. There, he used his skills to paint portraits and Bible scenes, which now decorated the *Gemeinhaus* buildings in both Herrnhaag and Marienborn.

"I could not forget Brother Josef," Brother Haidt told Nicholas. "He was dressed like a farmer, but he spoke like a scholar. Then, I attended a Moravian love feast in London. I invited myself, I'm ashamed to say, not knowing what it was!"

Nicholas and the painter laughed heartily.

"I also could not forget Brother Josef," Nicholas said. "The man radiates peace and simplicity. And I also remember the first love feast I observed, only mine was on St. Thomas."

"I could not believe," Brother Haidt said, "the love which these brothers had for each other. They even kissed each other on the cheek! I was astonished."

Nicholas laughed and nodded, interlacing his fingers behind his head. "My shock was the same on St. Thomas. A kiss is not a typical part of London culture then either, is it?"

"Not between men," Brother Haidt said. "But they did it with joy, because it is commanded in Scripture. They explained that it was a way of expressing what Jesus was most adamant about, that we love one another."

Nicholas nodded. "On St. Thomas, the group was even more diverse—white men and black men, white women and black women—all mingling together. The white plantation owners hated the love that the brothers and sisters showed for each other."

The two men talked late into the evening, struck by the many things they had in common. Both had been following the longitude problem with interest. As an artisan in the watchcase field, Brother Haidt had met John Harrison, who had made a new sea clock. Though bulky, it did not lose time at sea. Both hoped that Harrison could make his idea practical for all seafaring vessels.

Brother Haidt was living his dream as a painter for the Moravian church. Nicholas was about to embark on his dream to be a ship captain for the Moravians. Ever since Nicholas had heard of the first sea congregation, a longing had filled him. Would it be possible to do the work he had always loved and serve the Lamb at the same time?

On a warm April morning, Nicholas walked to the *Saal* at 4 a.m. for worship. He found his place with the other married men and joined in the songs of praise to the Lamb. Flickering chandeliers threw light around the high room, and the sun soon filtered through the tall windows. That afternoon Nicholas was taken into the church. Brother Ludwig himself officiated, and a number of brothers welcomed Nicholas into the fellowship. Nicholas wept as they kissed him and called him brother.

He was home.

Taking part in a communion service is one of life's most sublime acts, Brother Josef had said. For that reason, the Moravian church was very cautious about letting people take part in this service. If there was questionable, ongoing conduct in anyone's life, they were kept from the service.

"We would rather make the door into our fellowship very narrow, and the door out very broad," Brother Josef had explained. "If people want to leave our community, they can leave with no trouble. But we subject them to strict scrutiny before we allow them to enter our group."

Would he be allowed to join the communion service? As thoughts of his sins flooded his mind, Nicholas shook his head. He must think, not of his past sin, but of the Lamb of God, who shed His blood to take away the sins of the world.

A few months later, Nicholas did take part in the monthly communion service. The leader called for all members to look to the Lamb and His sufferings and death as the solution for their sin. By eating bread and drinking the fruit of the vine, they would remember Christ's broken body and shed blood.

As he ate the bread and drank from the cup, Nicholas shed more tears. What a relief, to know the Lamb of God! What a joy to be with others who loved Him! In the eyes of those around him, Nicholas saw a reflection of the same love that he experienced from Christ.

Next, the brothers and sisters demonstrated that love. Nicholas knelt on the stone floor of the castle hall beside a bowl of water. A brother whom he did not know well was seated on the wooden bench, with his feet in the warm water. Awkwardly, Nicholas washed the man's feet. This ordinance would be easier for the women, he thought. At least they were used to bathing children.

After washing and drying the man's feet, Nicholas traded places with him. This, he found, was equally strange. But as the man dried his feet Nicholas realized this was true humility, unity, and love, to do as Christ had taught by word and example. Yet to allow another to serve oneself required just as much humility, and bound both brothers in the love of Christ. Nicholas swelled with happiness. He wished his whole family could be with him.

"Brother Garrison," Brother Ludwig said a few days later, "you are part of our brotherhood now. You can fill a role that none of the rest of us can. Are you ready to go to London to find the ship to sail to America?"

The *Little Strength*

September 1743

Nicholas paced the deck of the *Little Strength* in the September sunshine. The blue sky and scattered clouds made him think of his mother, and he sighed. His father had come to the Netherlands as a young man to pursue an education. Had he ever visited Rotterdam or stood on this place in the river? Perhaps he had fished here as the small boats nearby were doing. Perhaps he had eaten a smoked fish from a street vendor.

He thought of Christina. Was she regretting letting Susanna go? Their daughter had settled into the girls' choir house in Herrnhaag and wanted to stay. She treasured the hymns, the love feasts, and the skills she was learning in the school. She didn't mind the clothing standards or the early rising. And she did not want to board a ship again.

Nicholas' dream of going to sea as a Moravian captain was now a reality. He had purchased a ship and assembled a crew, which included his oldest son. Captain Gladman, who had taken the first sea congregation across the Atlantic, was with them as well. Nicholas still missed having Seagull Sal at the helm. But he knew Sal would not wish to return to earth.

"Captain Garrison!" shouted one of the men in the yards. "Barge ho! I think it carries some of our passengers."

He was right. Pilgrims from Marienborn and Herrnhut arrived within an hour. A stream of young people climbed the sloping gangplank. Nicholas, Captain Gladman, Nicholas Jr., and mate John showed the newcomers around the ship.

Brother Josef Spangenberg's wife scurried up and down the stairs to the women's quarters, arranging things for the best comfort. Bunks were provided for the women in rooms on each side of the middle deck. In the hallway, benches and seats nailed to the floor planks gave the feeling of a home.

The men hung their hammocks above the luggage and provisions on the lower deck. Nicholas had the cabin at the stern, and Captain Gladman and mate John each had a smaller room nearby. Nicholas Jr. hung his hammock with the men.

The *Little Strength* would take on more Moravian passengers in England. A small group left by packet boat to alert them to prepare.

Those on the ship in Rotterdam celebrated a love feast. Under canvas awnings that formed a kind of chapel on the deck, the brothers sat on one side of the table and the sisters on the other. Most were newly married couples in the prime of life. At Marienborn, thirty couples had recently been married in one day. The leadership felt that young people had the energy needed to settle in Bethlehem and Nazareth.

Nicholas felt fear surge inside him. What if the ship were lost at sea, with all these young people who hoped to serve the Lord in a new land? What if they hit the rocks of Scilly? What if they were delayed and began to die of scurvy? These things were risks on every voyage, but Nicholas' fear of being responsible for this sea congregation increased in proportion to his joy at the privilege.

On the sixteenth of September, the *Little Strength* began her journey down the Rhine River toward the North Sea and around to a Dutch port city. There they would pick up Brother Josef Spangenberg, who planned to accompany them for a few days.

The journey to the North Sea took longer than expected, but this allowed the passengers to adjust before hitting the open sea. One evening the weather was especially fine, with little wind. As the sea congregation sang hymns, the inhabitants of the Dutch village they were passing ran to the river bank to listen.

This interest encouraged the travelers. Not everyone had been so friendly. On their journey to the ship, a group of Moravians had been eating at a hotel. As they sang a hymn, the gathering crowd had thrown stones through the hotel windows. The sounds of shattering glass and mocking cries echoed in their minds.

After six days they sailed into the Dutch port and met Brother Josef. Nicholas ordered the small boat to be lowered and climbed into it with the men. Sitting in the stern, he took the tiller himself and brought the boat to the shore.

"Brother Josef," Nicholas said with pleasure.

"Captain Garrison!"

"Can you not call me Brother Garrison?"

"I believe I shall call you captain, sir, for the sake of order," Brother Josef said with a twinkle in his eye. "Only while we are on the ship." He took Nicholas' hand and stepped into the boat.

As the *Little Strength* sailed into the North Sea and the waves rocked it up and down, many people grew seasick, especially among the women. But the women had an excellent caretaker in Sister Mary Wahnert, who remained well. She brought tea and blankets, emptied buckets, and sang hymns to the miserable women.

By morning the coast of England could be seen. Nicholas and Captain Gladman kept the ship sailing through the English Channel to Cowes on the Isle of Wight, near Portsmouth. Here, English passengers waited with London friends who had come to see them off. After an evening service the London friends went into the countryside to obtain fresh milk and vegetables for the voyage.

The next day more fresh foods were added and fresh water and ballast were placed in the hold. At the custom house Nicholas cleared the ship for sailing. As he interacted with the tide surveyor, he thought of Old Pete, who had done the same job in Liverpool. Had Pete made it back after serving as surgeon on the Spanish ship?

Nicholas called to weigh anchor the next day. During the next five days, Brother Josef made his rounds among the 130 passengers and sailors. All but three of them were Moravians. When they neared the place where the Spangenbergs would part from the group, Brother Josef called everyone together.

"I encourage each of you who may work in a secular job in America that this work is no less 'spiritual' than the work of a missionary. One of the worst problems our missionaries to the Lenape people have is that many white men call themselves Christians, yet their conduct is worse than that of the natives. Converts need to see what it means to match words to deeds. In Christ, a blacksmith is a better blacksmith. A miller is a better miller. A tailor is a better tailor. No job is more or less important in Christ's economy!

"And now, has anyone changed their mind about going to America?" he asked. "Perhaps due to sickness or any other problem?"

No one responded. Everyone wanted to continue, even the sister who was still sick in bed. "She wants to go on," Sister Wahnert reported. "She feels strongly that this is the work the Lord has for her right now, even if she should die on this ship."

On the second day of October they neared the ocean. After Brother Josef led in morning prayers, they said their farewells and the Spangenbergs stepped into the fishing boat that would take them back to land. The passengers stood at the rail and waved. Nicholas ordered up all the sails, and with a favorable wind behind them, the *Little Strength* moved quickly. Before nightfall no land was in sight.

Nicholas was now considered the chief elder, assisted by a committee of seven.

The eight men met morning and evening in Nicholas' cabin. Evening church services were held in German on the middle and lower decks. The man reading the liturgy stood on the stairs between the two decks. Nicholas led English services in his cabin, which could admit thirty to forty people.

The Moravians formed two night watches, from 10 p.m. to 2 a.m., and from 2 a.m. to 6 a.m. The two brothers on watch kept the lanterns burning and spent much time in prayer. They were also on call to assist the sailors. At 6 a.m. the retiring night watchman rang the rising bell.

Bells were rung on schedule throughout the day. Morning prayers were at 7 a.m. and breakfast at 8 a.m. German and English language classes were offered in the forenoon, and those not in class were assigned to useful tasks. Brother Reuz, stable and level-headed, was chosen as the main cook, and others assisted him. The main meal of the day was served at noon and supper at 6 p.m. Love feasts for birthdays or special services were occasionally held on the weather deck. Evening prayers at 7 p.m. ended each day on an inspiring note.

Nicholas remembered his experiment on the warship en route to New York, and he wanted to learn to know each person on board. Groups of five or six ate meals together, and Nicholas joined a different group each day.

On fine days more passengers came on deck, and Nicholas marveled at the fourteen nationalities. People from England, Wales, Scotland, Ireland, Holland, Germany, Denmark, Sweden, Norway, Wendish Lusatia, Bohemia, Poland, France, Switzerland and Italy were among the passengers. Yet everyone worked together. One evening, Nicholas mentioned this. How could everyone live together in unity?

"I think, sir," one of the brothers said slowly, "that we are all setting forth on a spiritual journey. We see the danger all around us out here in the middle of the ocean. Yet our calling to work for the Lord makes petty things unimportant."

Nicholas nodded. Most ships were full of bickering, whining, malice, and lust for the next port. He could not thank God enough for the privilege of captaining the ship of peaceful believers. He was also glad for calm weather, enabling him to spend time with Nicholas Jr. and the others on board.

Two weeks into the journey, the steward of the food and water provisions ran up to Nicholas, breathless. "Sir! Our water casks are leaking! I was just down to fetch one when I noticed a pool of water beneath them."

Nicholas hurried to the lowest deck. With several brothers helping, they inspected every cask and found that twenty-three were leaking. All hands helped bring up the leaking casks and pour the remaining water into stronger casks. "We will have to ration the water," Nicholas said.

"Aye, aye, sir."

49

The Test of Trust

On the first of November a severe thunderstorm sprang up. Nicholas and Captain Gladman cast an uneasy eye on the dropping barometer. Nicholas felt fear tighten in his stomach again at the thought of all the young lives in his care. "This looks like hurricane weather," he said.

"All hands!" shouted mate John, banging on the forecastle hatch. Captain Gladman went to the galley to make sure the cooking fires were put out. Nicholas stood on the quarterdeck, hand on the rail.

"Should we help, sir?" one of the Moravian brothers asked.

"This is a storm for experienced men, I'm afraid," Nicholas said. "Even the sailors are at risk for going overboard. Aye, look at that!"

The ship gave a dreadful pitch and Nicholas tightened his grip on the rail. The masts bent so low that the men on the yards were splashed by a high wave. The Moravian brother fell against him. Though in danger himself, Nicholas maintained an eye aloft to his men.

"Keep the passengers below deck!" Nicholas hollered. "And hang on to something as you go!"

The hurricane winds blew in behind the thunderstorm. They had done everything they could to stabilize the ship, but still the *Little Strength* threatened to capsize.

It was his first voyage as captain of a ship of the Brethren and it might be his last, along with 130 others. Sick with fear, Nicholas descended the ladder to check on his passengers. The Moravians below deck were singing. They were less fearful than he was!

He shook his head in amazement and went to his cabin. Soon, he heard a knock on the door.

"How goes it, Captain?" Brother Wahnert asked.

"We are in danger of swamping at any moment," Nicholas said. "How can those people be so calm?"

Brother Wahnert clutched the table as the ship rolled again. "I think, sir, that they have a firm conviction that wind and waves cannot keep them from the Savior's presence and love. Shall we pray to Him now, Captain Garrison?"

A few hours later, the wind died down. Back on deck, Nicholas was ashamed that he had not trusted God more readily. A splendid sunset dropped below the horizon. He looked up at the masts and rigging of the ship. They had come through a fierce storm, but nothing was broken.

A few weeks later, a rainstorm hit the *Little Strength*. Using canvas sheets held by four people, the floating church gratefully collected fresh drinking water. "We are getting close to land," Nicholas encouraged. The ocean floor was sloping up and forty-five fathoms had been sounded.

However, a wind sprang up, pushing them back out to the ocean. The fresh water was nearly gone. Nicholas pinched his lips together with frustration and wished for Seagull Sal at the helm. Tacking, changing direction by turning the bow into the wind, was difficult in these conditions, but Seagull Sal had been a master.

On the evening of the twenty-fifth, the man with the sounding lead announced a depth of only eleven fathoms. "If it wouldn't be for this haze, I think we could see shore," Nicholas said to Captain Gladman and mate John as they squinted into the fog.

Then, another strong wind sprang up. "This wind will push us aground," Nicholas snapped, leaping to call the men. "We need to get off this shallow bank." All evening long and into the night, the sailors sounded as the ship tried to fight its way back out to deeper seas. They could not sail directly into the wind, so they tacked, first to starboard, then to port, adjusting the jib sails with each turn.

Nicholas paced the quarterdeck, again feeling his trust in God growing thin. Captain Gladman had taken the wheel, and John shouted the orders that Nicholas gave. Around midnight, the strong wind died down. They were safe. Nicholas retired to his cabin, angry at himself for doubting.

The morning fog was still so thick that they could see nothing, even at eight fathoms. Nicholas had never before experienced such a difficult entrance into the New York Harbor. Finally the mist rose, and Sandy Hook appeared.

America! Solid ground! Fresh water! Everyone cheered and sang and cried. Carefully, they made their way into the harbor. The Moravians sang as the ship turned north along Staten Island.

"Captain Gladman," Nicholas said, "my son and I would like to visit my wife and family. If we anchor here, will you take charge of the ship?"

"Happy to do that, sir."

They cast anchor close to the Watering Place. "What will Mother say?" Nicholas Jr. wondered as they climbed into the small boat.

Nicholas smiled. "She will hardly recognize her oldest son."

He was right. Christina and the younger children could hardly believe that Nicholas Jr. was the young man as tall as his father. They were warmly greeted, but Nicholas could see a new sadness in his wife's eyes.

"Is everyone well?" Nicholas asked. He looked at each of the children in turn. "Where is Blandina?"

"She . . . has gone home," Christina said brokenly. "The other children had small pox, and Blandina did not recover. Mary and our friends from Bethlehem tried to help, but it was no use."

Nicholas sighed deeply, wishing he had been at home. He had not been home at her birth, and now he had missed her death as well. He remembered the little girl tossing the rope bracelet to the ground and toddling around the kitchen. He recalled her sweet kiss before he left for Europe.

"But I am too happy to have *you* back for much sadness right now," Christina said, "and I am glad Susanna is happy in Germany. Can you stay the night, or must you go back to the ship?"

"I will go back in the morning, my dear. I will spend every moment with you I can. And, if I'm not mistaken, I smell Mary's cooking."

Nicholas met the *Little Strength* in Manhattan the next day. Several other Moravian brothers had come to greet those who were disembarking. One of them collected letters from the passengers and hurried off to Bethlehem with the news of their arrival.

"Brother Noble!" Nicholas cried when the merchant came on board. "I wasn't sure if I should expect you here or not!" His friend Thomas had been indecisive about the Moravians and had been discouraged during a discussion with them several years before.

"Ah, Captain," Mr. Noble said, "the Presbyterians sent a minister to try to convince me to have nothing to do with the Moravians. While he was in my house, I received a set of letters intended for the Moravians in Bethlehem. Those letters convinced me that the Moravians are children of God.

"But now! You are all tired and hungry, I'm sure. I would happily host everyone, but I do not have the room. But if you and some of the other leaders of your floating church will join me this afternoon, I will do all I can to help your passengers and their luggage reach Bethlehem."

"Excellent," Nicholas said. "We will come. The men loaded fresh water last night, and my wife sent apples. We will have a love feast tonight, and I hope you will join us!"

"I will," Brother Noble agreed. "Nicholas, I am so sorry about your little daughter. We brought the best doctor from Manhattan, but it was to no avail."

Nicholas swallowed and nodded. "Thank you, Brother, for helping. I just wish I could have been home."

The elders made plans at Brother Noble's house. Everyone who was able to travel the eighty-some miles on foot would set out in two bands. The others would travel to New Brunswick on a small boat along with the luggage, and then on wagons to Bethlehem.

"Would you like fresh bread for tonight?" Brother Noble asked. "I know just the bakery to get some, even for 130 people." The love feast that evening was a joyful time as the passengers laughed and talked and sang and thanked Captain Garrison.

The *Little Strength* returned to its mooring off Staten Island. Most of the passengers spent the weekend visiting the Garrison house and meeting other Moravians in the area. On Monday, December 2, Nicholas approved the able-bodied travelers to head out on foot.

Across Staten Island they went, over the Arthur Kill by ferry, and then on foot through the hills to Bethlehem. Captain Garrison and Captain Gladman took charge of the largest group, while Brother and Sister Wahnert took the smaller group and went out ahead.

The days were exhausting. They plodded on mile after mile, one foot in front of the next. Although they had eaten well over the weekend, their diet aboard ship had been lacking in fresh foods and abundant water. By Friday night, Nicholas' group could go no farther. They found an inn where they could stay out of the cold.

"Captain Gladman," Nicholas said, "I think I should go ahead and let our family at Bethlehem know we are all right, but that our group is much in need of a rest. Will you stay with them?"

"Aye, aye, sir! That is, if you're sure you can make it the rest of the way tonight."

"I have been through much worse," Nicholas said, pulling on his coat. He left the inn, carrying a lantern. They were only six miles from their destination, but to the exhausted travelers it might have been six hundred. Nicholas hurried down the frozen stagecoach track and reached Bethlehem in two hours.

"Brother Garrison!" Peter Bohler greeted him. He was one of the leaders of the Moravians and preached inspiring sermons. Nicholas remembered sitting under his teaching.

"Father!" a younger voice cried.

"Jan!" His son ran into his arms. "Oh, it's good to see you, my son! You are growing so tall."

"I like it here," Jan said. "But I missed you."

The Wahnert party had just arrived. Now, with all the newcomers, the group celebrated with a love feast. The home people heated water in huge kettles and poured it into basins. After the meal, they washed the feet of the weary travelers.

Early the next morning Peter Bohler led a prayer time and read Ephesians 6, reminding the group to "take on the whole armour of God" and to pray for each other. Captain Gladman and the rest of Nicholas' group began to arrive. The blisters on their feet caused them to limp, and their clothes were stained and damp, but they were cheerful.

A fire was crackling in the *Saal* when Nicholas walked through later that day and found Peter Bohler alone with his Bible open. Maybe this brother could help him.

"Can I speak to you for a moment?" Nicholas asked.

Brother Bohler pulled a second chair to the table and motioned for him to sit down. "What can I do for you, brother?"

"Well, I . . ." Nicholas sighed and shook his head, then plunged in.

"Brother Bohler, I was so full of joy when I was asked to be the captain of the floating congregation. But there were several storms that filled my heart with fear. In fact, before we ever weighed anchor I worried that my ship would sink and I would be the cause of death for all of these devoted young people." Nicholas paused.

"Whose ship?" Brother Bohler asked.

Nicholas looked up, startled.

"Go on," Brother Bohler invited. "I interrupted your thought."

Nicholas paused to gather his thoughts. "It seemed as though the prince of darkness were spending his last resources to prevent our passage to America.[1] My trust in God grew weak and I began to give orders like the old Captain Garrison. I have been used to living in the power of my own mind and wit, I fear. I was so worried that I would somehow fail this congregation. But I believe I failed the Savior even more by worrying so much." Nicholas fought the tears that were threatening again. He had shed many of them overnight.

Brother Bohler leaned back in his chair, his fingers fanning the edge of the pages of his Bible. He was silent for a moment, then he raised his head and looked Nicholas right in the eye.

"Did it make you happy, Brother, to live in the power of your own mind and wit? Was that a good system?"

Nicholas sprang to his feet. He paced to the fireplace, leaned against the mantle,

---

[1] "It . . . America" is a quote from the journal of Nicholas Garrison.

and laughed. Brother Bohler joined in his laughter, the sparkle in his eyes glowing with the special light that came when a soul found relief in Christ.

Nicholas picked up an iron poker and poked at the fire methodically for a minute, then returned to the table, tossing the tool between his hands.

"No, Brother, you knew the answer, did you not? Living for myself did not make me happy. There were times over the years when I thought I was happy, there under the sails. But my mother's Scripture verses kept reminding me that there is something better to life. Christ was pursuing me, and I could never sin with abandon—those verses kept coming to my mind."

Nicholas paused, still holding the cool end of the poker, his elbows resting on his knees.

"Why did I want to trust myself again, Brother Bohler? I have proved it an unhappy way to live. Yet I still have not learned to trust God fully."

He got up again, set the poker down, and walked to the fireplace. He picked a roasting hazelnut off the hearth and fingered it. Brother Bohler watched him.

"Ah, friend. You have a deeply sensitive and anxious nature. Perhaps this is from your mother's teaching, and though it can be a weakness, it can also be a gift. But we must remember that we do not perfectly attain the character of Christ in this life. We are changed into the image of Christ from glory to glory. Did your mother forget to teach you that verse?"

The two men exchanged warm smiles.

"Have you asked the Savior to forgive you?" Brother Bohler prompted. "Don't ask me if you think He will. You know the answer, my friend."

Nicholas came back and sat down, sighing with relief. Brother Bohler had reminded him of what he already knew.

"I do know the answer. I first learned the forgiveness of Christ on the island of St. Thomas as Brother Friedrich nursed me through my sickness. I will never forget my relief."

"Then don't give up," Brother Bohler said. "If I'm not mistaken, God has much more for you to do, perhaps even harder things that will test your faith even more. But as long as you know Him, you can 'take the wings of the morning and dwell in the uttermost part of the sea,' and even there His hand will lead you."

"How did you know those were the words my mother taught me?" Nicholas asked, astonished.

"I did not," Brother Bohler said. "But the Spirit did. It is just one more reason we can be assured of the Savior's love for us. Go in peace, my brother. And be sure to stay for the service tomorrow. Has your son told you what will take place?"

"No," Nicholas said.

50

The Spanish Privateer

At Bethlehem the next afternoon, three young men were taken in as members. Nicholas' eyes filled with happy tears as he watched his son Jan, now fourteen. Standing before the church, Jan and the others were welcomed with warmth and love. It was not easy to gain admittance to the congregation.

The Bethlehem group had discussed this with Brother Ludwig. "All denominations and sects strive to grow larger and stronger," the count had said. "But our rule must remain that of keeping the door open for anyone to leave us, yet being cautious to admit them. There is more danger that in time our church may weaken due to its largeness rather than its smallness." To this end the Moravians interviewed people persistently, and then put the matter to a lot to see what the Savior wished.

On the day Jan was taken in, Brother Bohler preached on the final judgment. That afternoon the last travelers from the *Little Strength* arrived and were received with joy. Brother Bohler had prepared a new hymn for their arrival.

Before Nicholas left for Staten Island, he toured Bethlehem. The wooden structures and beautiful masonry completed since his last visit encouraged him. Glad in heart, he headed home.

Nicholas spent the winter with his family and planned another Moravian voyage in March. Passengers would include Bishop Nitchshmann, Brother and Sister Wahnert, and a converted Lenape couple whom Peter Bohler had recently married at Bethlehem.

"Christina," Nicholas said, "one of these times you should go with me!"

"I will," she said. "I want to . . . but the baby . . ."

Christina would give birth to their twelfth child in the fall. Nicholas hoped to return before that event. Of their eleven children, four had died.

"Do be careful, Nicholas. I know you are serving the Lord and doing a very good job of it, but I still . . ."

"I know, my dear. We will be careful."

The ocean crossing with the *Little Strength* went well. They were only days away from their destination, sailing through the English Channel, when the lookout in the topmast called down with an announcement.

"Sail ho!"

Nicholas was standing on the quarterdeck. In the choppy waters of the channel he liked to be on deck as much as possible. He pulled his telescope from his pocket and searched the horizon, but he could see nothing from the deck. He pocketed his telescope and swung himself onto the ratlines, climbing to join the lookout.

Was the sail friend or foe? They could not tell from this distance.

"Keep a sharp eye on that vessel," Nicholas told the lookout. "We need to know if they are following us."

It's just another ship passing, Nicholas told himself. *Nothing to worry about.*

Bishop Nitschmann and Mate John stood below, surveying the situation. "What do you think?" the bishop asked when Nicholas leaped back onto the deck.

"It's hard to tell yet," Nicholas said. "But we need to keep a sharp eye on them."

"Crowd on all the sail you can," the bishop suggested. "Just in case it is an enemy, we can get a head start."

"Yes, call the others up and bring the spare sails," Nicholas said to Mate John. "We can hang more canvas."

By the time the new sail had been hung, the ship could easily be seen.

She was obviously pursuing them.

Nicholas ate his noon meal on the quarterdeck, not allowing himself to sit. Back and forth he paced, forcing himself to take deep breaths—and praying continuously. By early afternoon, the chase looked as if it would soon be over. The *Little Strength* was not close enough to any English harbor to make it to safety. If only darkness would come soon, perhaps they could escape.

At 3 p.m. everyone on board heard the booming challenge of the other ship's cannon. Nicholas watched as the other ship, only about a mile away, hoisted an English flag. He doubted the ship was really English. Either way, he had already decided what they would do.

"Run up the white flag, John," Nicholas said to the mate.

The other ship, a Spanish privateer, pulled down the English flag and hoisted a Spanish flag instead. The ship pulled close and a voice boomed through a speaking trumpet. "Bring your captain over with a boat's crew."

"Bring down the boat," Nicholas sighed. He was the first one down the rope. A small group of sailors went with him.

The Spanish privateer sent nineteen men onto the *Little Strength* to take over. Nicholas, standing on the deck of the Spanish ship, watched the ragged soldiers swagger on board his ship, their pistols and cutlasses clanking.

"God have mercy," he breathed. He tried to pick out the Spanish comments around him, but he had not spoken the language much since Cuba. He could see the sailors stripping clothing from the people of the *Little Strength* in exchange for the rags from their own backs. Next, he saw the Spanish rifling through the sea chests, taking anything of value and leaving the rest strewn on the deck.

Both ships turned south, rounding France on their way to Spain. Within six days, they passed between the green and white cliffs at the edges of the St. Sebastian harbor and sailed around a rocky island. They anchored in beautiful blue-green water.

Soldiers escorted the Moravians to shore and took them to a stinking prison. The stench and the darkness reminded Nicholas of that long ago day when he had met Captain Toler in Bayamo, Cuba.

"Por favor,"[1] Nicholas said. He used his best Spanish to ask for a better place for the sisters, and they were granted to live in a house.

"How were you treated?" Nicholas asked the men who had stayed on the *Little Strength*.

"Very well, at first," said Mate John. "They took our clothes and gave us these rags. They let us stay in the cabin and hold our prayers and worship services. But as we arrived in harbor we were forced to hand over the keys to our private luggage. They made us give them our money and watches and sent us ashore with only these tattered clothes."

"Tell Captain Garrison what you wrote on the beam in his cabin," another man coaxed. So Mate John recited the lines.

> Poor *Little Strength,* which once hath been
> The ark of our Eternal King,
> In which the servants of our God
> Passed o'er to bear the news of blood.

---

[1] Please.

But since tho' took yet will be bold
To tell to Spain and all the World,
That Jesus Christ Lord and God
Has bought them by His death and blood!"[2]

The poem brought courage to everyone in the stinking pit and they began to sing. "Do any of you know the song 'O God, Our Help in Ages Past'?" Nicholas asked. "That is the song we sang the last time I was imprisoned by the Spanish."

The next day, naval officers questioned the prisoners then exchanged them for Spanish prisoners and set them free. The *Little Strength,* stolen by the Spanish, was a total loss to the Moravians, but Nicholas praised God for sparing the lives of every person on board.

Nicholas visited Susanna at Herrnhaag. His sixteen-year-old daughter ran into his arms.

"Father, I love it here!" Susanna said. "Is Mother well?"

"She misses you," Nicholas said. "I brought a letter for you."

"Oh, good! I miss her too," Susanna said. "But I have so many good friends, and they are teaching me what it means to have faith in Jesus Christ. And I am one of the evening cooks. It's not hard because Mary taught me so much about cooking, although they do things differently here. And I love singing with the girls. Sometimes I feel that we will sing ourselves right up to heaven to the presence of the Savior. Singing together is such a wonderful thing!"

"It is, my dear," Nicholas said when she stopped to catch a breath. "I am overjoyed that you are finding it so."

After a short stay at Marienborn, Nicholas and Brother Josef Spangenberg were commissioned to return to New York and order a new ship to be built for the use of the Brethren. Sailing on the *Jacob,* they reached New York without incident.

* *

As they stepped onto the dock, Thomas Noble met them. Without a word, he handed Brother Josef a document.

"An act for securing His Majesty's Government of New York," the men read.

"It's directed against the Moravians who are missionaries to the Lenape people in northern New York," Thomas Noble said.

Brother Josef and Nicholas read the act. On September 21, the governor of New

[2] John W. Jordan, "Moravian Immigration to Pennsylvania, 1734-1767," *Transactions of the Moravian Historical Society,* Vol. 5, No. 2, 1896, p. 62. <https://www.jstor.org/stable/41179779>, accessed on June 25, 2019.

York had written a law forbidding anyone to live with the Indians and evangelize them. The next day, a second law had been added: anyone who wished to live with the Indians needed to swear an oath of allegiance to the British Crown. This the Moravians would never do. Last, the Moravians were ordered to stop teaching and depart the province. The ink was hardly dry on the document.

Thomas Noble shook his head. "There are a lot of aggravating factors. Our missionaries have exposed the corruption of the settlers who are illegally selling liquor to the Lenape. We have also helped the Lenape understand the legal system so they do not get cheated. But I'm ashamed to tell you that the Presbyterian ministers with whom I used to worship have pushed for this as well. They feel that missionary work among the Lenape is somehow a threat to civilization. Would the two of you be willing to visit the village of Shekomeko and find out how things are?"

Nicholas stared at Brother Noble, astonished. *I'm a sea captain, not a missionary in the wilderness of New York,* he thought. *Am I really being asked to carry out a mission in defiance of the Crown?*

"We would be happy to do that," he heard Brother Josef saying.

Nicholas turned and looked at his friend. He opened his mouth, then closed it again.

"The believers here in New York feel that the two of you would be well suited to this venture," Brother Noble said. "And perhaps Sister Spangenberg as well."

The trails to upstate New York bristled with robberies and murders. Many rivers and creeks lacked bridges or ferries. Sometimes the native people lay in wait for white men. Even worse, what if a copy of the document in their hands reached Shekomeko before they did? They could be arrested by the justices who were posted all along the route north.

"Brother Garrison?" It was Brother Josef's soft voice.

The word *brother* brought peace. While at sea Brother Josef had called him *Captain Garrison* to maintain order. Now that they were on land his use of *brother* reminded Nicholas that he was part of a family. The Lenape of northern New York were part of the same family. Many of them had visited Bethlehem, and some had chosen to live there. If the government edict against the missionaries prospered, fewer Lenape would come to know salvation through the blood of Christ.

"I must visit my wife first, Brother," Nicholas said. "I cannot delay as she is to give birth any day. Then I will go with you to Shekomeko."

Nicholas was too late. Baby Abraham had already been born, and was keeping the home lively with his squeaks and wails. Everyone loved him, and Nicholas held him as much as he could before he and Brother Josef set off.

51

The Wilderness Missionaries

November 1744

"Venison stew, gentlemen."

The burly innkeeper ladled the stew into pewter bowls and set them on the heavy boards of the table. A large platter of roasted potatoes, carrots, squash, and onions was plunked in front of them. Three taper candles burned in holders on the table.

"Perhaps a little pepper on the vegetables? I just got a fresh box from Manhattan."

"Please," Nicholas said.

Nicholas and Brother Josef sat in the low-ceilinged inn before a flashing fire, protected from the cold November night. Sister Spangenberg was traveling with them, but she had retired to another room to refresh herself. The three travelers had spent the entire day riding on horseback through the woods.

The two men bowed their heads, and Brother Josef prayed aloud, thanking God for the gift of Jesus and for protection during the day's travels.

The innkeeper turned from rolling a log into the fire. "Could you be some of the Moravian missionaries?" he asked.

"We are on our way to visit them," said Brother Josef, then turned to his wife. "Ah, Maria, do have a seat and try this delightful stew."

The men made room for her at the table. Nicholas looked at the innkeeper, whose thick arms showed he was a man of the wilderness. What were his feelings about the missionaries? Did he agree with the government act against the Moravian work?

"We just had two missionaries stop a few nights ago," the man said, balancing the poker on his palm. "They had three Indians with them."

"Ah, how interesting!" Brother Josef said. "Were they doing well?"

The innkeeper shook his head in bewilderment. He seemed to be looking at something that was not physically present in the room.

"Yes, I think so," he said. "I was—uh—shocked at the conduct of those savages. They prayed and sang hymns and thanked God as if they could understand religion like a white man! They treated each other and myself with kindness and respect." He shook his head again and hung his poker on a fireplace hook with a clang.

"And so they can," Brother Josef said. "You have blessed us with this report, my friend."

Nicholas lay down to sleep. In all his ideas of where his life might go, he had never imagined himself on the road north to visit a Lenape village. His father had told him about the days of the Lenape people on Staten Island and how they had all been required to sign the land deed. He had seen a few Lenape on Staten Island himself, but most of them had left.

He remembered the watchword the day before they left on their mission: *From morning to night in the joy of God.* Despite the hardships and imprisonment, he had found joy in salvation. He was taking the wings of the morning to places he never thought possible, but God was with him. Comforted and strengthened, he fell asleep.

In the early morning their breath hung in the air as they saddled the horses by the light of the lantern held by Brother Josef's wife Maria. Despite heavy coats and mufflers, the cold penetrated their clothes like liquid, but they quickly mounted and rode off. As the sun came up over the trees, they rejoiced at the beauty and splendor of the handiwork of God. They felt warmer by the time they stopped for breakfast at the place the innkeeper had told them about.

"Come in, travelers," the justice said as his servants rushed to crack eggs and slice cheese. "I am Justice Merlin. Do you have any good news for me?"

Brother Josef looked at Nicholas with a twinkle in his eye. Nicholas knew that the justice was about to get more of an answer than he was looking for. "Good news?" Brother Josef repeated. "The best news is that poor sinners have a Savior."

"Oh!" said Justice Merlin. "You surely are one of the Moravians."

The next day was the most difficult journey over the mountains. The horses reached for good footing, but sometimes their feet slipped. The travelers clung to their horses' manes to keep from sliding off backwards. The road followed the creeks, and pools of water sometimes lay in their path. The horses kicked up globs of mud that landed on the travelers' clothes and boots as the ground thawed. Then, as they descended the other side, they had to steady themselves to keep from sliding onto the horses' necks. Exhausted, they finally reached a place where they could spend the night.

"And where are you bound?" asked the man of the house. He had served as judge at the trial in which some Moravians had been accused for not swearing oaths. Nicholas could see that the man was undecided about the Moravians.

"We are going to visit Shekomeko, sir," Nicholas said.

"I do believe your missionaries are doing a good work among the Indians," the judge said. "But I could wish they would not take their religion so seriously."

As exhausted as they were, the three travelers could not miss the opportunity. This was why they had come, to defend and support the mission to the Lenape.

"Sir," Brother Josef said, "we worship a Savior who took our need for salvation very seriously. Are you acquainted with the suffering and shame that attended the death of Jesus Christ?"

"I have heard the Scriptures of course," the judge said slowly, smoothing the curls of his wig.

Nicholas couldn't help wondering why he wore the wig here in the wilderness. It was the accepted custom of the day, but it did not seem at all practical here in the north.

"Many people have suffered and died," Brother Josef continued. "But the motivation of Christ's suffering makes Him unique."

" 'He was wounded for our transgressions,' " Nicholas quoted, remembering the verses his mother had taught him. " 'He was bruised for our iniquities . . . with his stripes we are healed.' Sir, I have been flogged aboard ship. Yet I suffered for my own wrongdoing. But this Jesus suffered because I could never be good enough or righteous enough in my own power."

The candles burned lower and lower as the judge talked with his guests.

So it continued as they journeyed north. Everyone knew something of the Moravians. Most of them supported their work with the Lenape, having seen the positive effects.

They lunched with Justice Wilsy, who lived just a few miles from Shekomeko. After feeding the travelers bread and ham, he saddled his own horse to accompany them the last miles into the Lenape village.

"Have you heard about the act decreed against the Moravian missionaries?" Nicholas asked Justice Wilsy. Brother and Sister Spangenberg rode in front, and he and the judge rode side by side when the road allowed it.

"I have," Justice Wilsy said. "I would rather lose my hand than put Moravians in jail for their work among the Indians. I have seen with my own eyes the miracle that has come over them when they turn to the Savior as the Moravians preach. It is always a good change, resulting in benefits for our whole community far and wide." They rode in silence for a time.

"Just around that grove of trees ahead and we shall be entering the village!" Justice Wilsy called.

As the horses trotted into the village, a man stood by the road, waiting. Perhaps he had heard the approaching hoof beats.

"Brother Johannes!" shouted Brother Josef.

"Good morning!" the man cried, coming toward them eagerly.

Nicholas and Brother Josef leaped off their mounts and a Lenape brother greeted them warmly. Soon they were warming their hands before a fire in a house made of bark where the Moravian missionaries lived. A group of Lenape converts met them there.

"Brothers and sisters!" Nicholas cried. "I can see the effect of the grace of our Savior on your faces."

Johannes translated his words to the others, who smiled and nodded, their brown faces glowing with love for their visitors and for the Savior of them all.

Nicholas looked around the simple house. It was stacked full of provisions for the winter. Squash, potatoes, onions. Dried vegetables, herbs, and strips of dried meat. In the dim corners, smoked meat hung from the rafters. The missionaries had been diligent not only in spreading the Gospel, but in providing for their own physical needs.

The three travelers visited the homes of the Lenape people, where only bare necessities were present such as fire, food, and water. Privately, Nicholas and Brother Josef noted how vibrant the community was despite the poverty. "If poverty makes it easier to trust the Lord, is it not a greater blessing than wealth?" Brother Josef remarked.

The next day they met with the Lenape brothers and sisters in the *Saal* built in the Moravian style. Brother Josef and Nicholas discussed community issues with them, encouraging them and teaching them from Scripture.

"Will you conduct a service for us this evening?" Brother Josef asked Nicholas. "I'm sure Johannes will translate."

Nicholas felt alarm. Preaching in a bark house to these dark-skinned believers with their silent ways and mysterious gestures was so different than leading a worship service in his familiar cabin at sea. But he steadied himself. "I can preach the salvation of Jesus Christ through His death and resurrection," he said quietly.

"That is all that needs to be preached," Brother Josef said.

The next day Brother Josef and Nicholas went on, leaving Sister Maria with the missionaries at Shekomeko. They crossed the Hudson River near Albany and then moved deeper into Indian country. They safely forded the Mohawk River. On their return, they came to the river at a different place.

"Do you think we can cross here?" Brother Josef asked. Nicholas studied the swirling water, foaming white around the rocks. Together they picked a crossing.

Halfway across the river, Brother Josef's horse stepped into a hole and went down. As its nose dipped under the water, Brother Josef was thrown over its head. Nicholas leaped from his horse, and extended a hand to his friend, who had caught hold of a large rock. Brother Josef's horse sprang forward, then turned and fled to the shore from which they had come.

Nicholas' mind spun. Getting Brother Josef across the river was paramount. If he turned to pursue the retreating horse, he stood to lose both horses and his friend.

"Are you all right?" he yelled over the noise of the rushing water as Brother Josef found footing on the slippery rocks.

"Blessed by the mercy of the Lord!" Brother Josef shouted. "I do believe I am unharmed, just a bit bruised."

"Here, take my horse," Nicholas said. "I need to go after the other horse."

When both horses and men had at last arrived safely on the other side, the men gave thanks to God. The horses shook themselves, showering the men with drops of water.

Brother Josef and Nicholas returned to Shekomeko. "There was a funeral while you were gone," Sister Maria told them. "It was a child. At the grave, a Lenape elder prayed earnestly for the Lord to receive the child. He then prayed that all those listening might come to understand the Lord's mercy in sending Jesus as our Savior. It was beautiful!" Her eyes shone with tears of gladness.

Dozens of baptized believers gathered for a love feast before the travelers departed. The women had baked bread for this occasion, and the travelers shared chocolate from Manhattan. As they sang and preached and fellowshiped, tears streamed down both brown and white faces. What a shame it would be if the authorities forced the Moravians from the land! Yet Nicholas knew that the Spirit of God could preserve the Lenape no matter what happened.

"Brother Garrison, will you lead us in a closing prayer?"

"Dear Savior," Nicholas prayed as Johannes translated, "we have felt your presence with us today. Thank you for coming to this earth to die for sinners. Thank you for shedding your blood, for bearing shame and spitting because of us. We pray a blessing on these brothers and sisters in their labors of love together for the glory of your church. May we all meet safely around the Lamb in heaven someday, rejoicing that we have been given the blessing of salvation."

"Now, brothers and sisters!" Brother Josef said. "Let us love each other above all. Let us express our love to each other not only as we part with a kiss, but also through our words and daily actions." White men and brown men, white women and brown women, kissed each other on the cheek. Many wept, moved by the extraordinary experience of worshiping with people so different from themselves and yet so much the same.

The three travelers arrived back in Manhattan filled with comfort. They did not know whether the Moravian missionaries would be expelled from Shekomeko. But they had heard from nonbelievers of the good effect of the mission effort, and they had experienced it themselves. Nicholas gratefully returned home to his family. Brother Josef and his wife accompanied him.

"Children, shall I tell you how your father helped to save my life in the river?" Brother Josef asked the young Garrisons. The children loved Brother Josef and eagerly crowded around him for the story. Christina and Maria talked at the table, where the childless Maria was fondly holding baby Abraham. After the children went to bed, the four adults talked late into the night.

"Christina and I would like to move to Marienborn," Nicholas said. "Our daughter Susanna is there, and I was so blessed while living there with the believers. Our children can be educated there, although some of them want to stay in Bethlehem. My deepest desire is to see my wife and all our children brought into the Moravian fellowship. We could spend more time together between voyages and learn to know the Moravian communities even after the new ship is built."

"Ah, yes," Brother Josef said. "Perhaps you could. Will you hire someone to build the ship here on Staten Island before you leave?"

"I will," Nicholas promised.

The Seasickness

1745

Mary slapped a lump of bread dough with all the force of her hand, shaping it into submission. "I didn't think I would live to see the day," she huffed, "but if it must be, it must be."

"Elizabeth will be so happy to have your help, Mary," Nicholas said.

"Oh, don't you go trying to make me feel better about losing my boy Nicholas and his family," Mary said. "I shall do my best to your sister and her children, but it won't stop me from shedding tears for Nicholas and Christina. Oh no, it will not!"

Mary swatted another loaf of dough. She checked the coals inside the big Dutch oven and scraped them into a tin bucket. Using her long-handled peel, she slid half a dozen loaves of bread dough deep into the oven onto the piping hot bricks. Then, she sealed the opening with its metal lid.

Christina listened from her rocking chair, where she caressed the silky head of baby Abraham. "I'm so glad to finally get a chance to go to sea with Nicholas," she said to Mary. "But I always thought I would go when we had no babies. And here little Abraham is not more than six months old!"

"And little Abraham will grow up and not even know who his old Mary is," Mary lamented.

"The older boys will be here in Bethlehem. They won't forget who their Mary is," Nicholas pointed out, but he realized he was pleading again, trying to make Mary feel better.

"Oh, that shall be a comfort, having them a three-days' journey away!" Mary said sarcastically.

"I'm sorry, Mary," Nicholas said. "You've been in my life since I was a small boy, and you've been a faithful servant all these years. Are you sure you won't go with us to Europe?"

"Me, tossing across that old ocean on these aching knees?" Mary sniffed. "Going to a country where I never been before?" She whisked a cloth across the table with irritation, chasing beads of stray bread dough and flour. "But I do hope you come back before this old body gets laid in the ground," Mary said, and burst into tears.

Jan, Lambert, Benjamin and little Seger would all live at Bethlehem for the time. It was a difficult decision to put all of the boys there, but there was opportunity both for education and apprenticeship to a trade. Nicholas and Christina discussed it several times and finally concluded that Bethlehem would be a safer place than journeying to Europe. They both expected to visit Bethlehem frequently.

Susanna was still in Germany, and Nicholas Jr. wished to go back to Germany. Baby Abraham and Katie, who was almost nine, would go with their parents to settle at Marienborn.

Not long after Brother Josef and Nicholas had returned from visiting the Lenape believers, a delegation from the government had arrived in Shekomeko demanding that the Moravian missionaries leave. Several had been seized and put into prison in Manhattan. Amid giving directions for building a new ship, planning for the move to Germany, and taking communication between the imprisoned brothers and Bethlehem, Nicholas found the days flying by.

In April Nicholas and Christina boarded a merchant ship, the *Queen of Hungary*, under command of Captain Hilton. Other Moravians were aboard as well, including Nicholas' friend and mentor, Peter Bohler.

In the buzz of ship-loading excitement, Nicholas carried their sea chests into their small cabin.

"What a tiny space to live in for six weeks!" Christina said. She was sitting on their lower bunk, arranging blankets in a sea chest to make a bed for little Abraham. Katie would have the top bunk.

"Ah, my dear, our son Nicholas has much less space forward with the men. And on a warship the men have barely over a foot of space to hang their hammocks."

"But did you not have more space as captain?" Christina asked.

Nicholas regretted that he would not be captain on his wife's first voyage. On the one hand, he was glad he would have more time with her and the children, especially if Christina should grow seasick. Still, the more comfortable cabin would have been ideal.

"Yes, the officers' cabins are a bit bigger," Nicholas admitted.

Christina showed Nicholas what she had brought in her chest. Besides blankets and clothes, she brought her drawing pencils and the silver locket that Nicholas had given to her years before when he asked her to marry him.

She opened the locket and Nicholas saw that she had saved four wisps of hair. The wisps were not alike.

"Who . . ." he began. Then, he remembered Christina collecting a wisp of Seger's hair after his death.

"Little Benjamin and Garret," she said, "Seger and Blandina."

She knew which belonged to each child. She closed the lid and it locked with a soft click. "I hope I never need to add more hair to this locket," she said. "It does break my heart though to leave Seger and the big boys here in America."

"We will come back if God wills," Nicholas said.

"You seem to have a tendency to get captured at sea," Christina noted with a smile.

"I have had some bad experiences, yes," Nicholas agreed. "But we will pray for God's protection."

After their belongings were stowed they returned to the deck "Look, Christina," Nicholas said as the *Queen of Hungary* moved toward the Narrows with the pilot on board. "The new Moravian ship is being built there in the ship yard! Look at the hull!" Amid the forest of scaffolding, the curving ribs of a ship could be seen.

"How wonderful that the New World is capable of manufacturing such things!" Christina said.

"Yes," Nicholas agreed. "We will still import the rigging and tackle from Europe."

"Are they cheaper there?"

"Yes. But the masts and the wood for the hull are from here. Besides being cheaper, the trees are bigger and better than what is available in England."

The next day, Christina was heaving into the bucket beside her bed. Katie felt fine, so Nicholas took her and baby Abraham up to the deck. Nicholas held the baby himself. It felt wonderful to be at sea with his own little children. "Look, Baby Abraham," Nicholas said. "Do you see the land far away? That's America, getting smaller and smaller!"

Abraham soon became a favorite of the entire ship. Despite his noisy beginning, he was a calm baby, and happily allowed the Moravian passengers and even the crew to pass him from one set of arms to the next. Katie kept a watchful eye on her baby brother and sometimes reclaimed him if she thought he was being treated too roughly. Captain Hilton himself spoke to Abraham often and allowed him to touch his telescope.

After a few days, most of the seasick passengers felt better. Nicholas bent over Christina's bunk. "Are you feeling any better, my dear?"

Christina's eyes opened slowly. "No."

Nicholas knelt beside her. He had known people who were seasick for an entire voyage. Surely Christina would not be one of those! "I'm sorry, my dear. Is there anything I can bring you?"

"No, I can't keep anything down," she said. "I don't know how Abraham will get enough milk. But I am looking to the Savior's sufferings on the cross. It is the only thing that comforts me right now." A tear slid from her eye.

"There are a few goats on board," Nicholas said. "I will check about getting milk for Abraham. Try not to worry about him, my dear. Katie is taking such good care of him. Besides, he is the favorite of the ship."

Christina did not improve; it seemed that riding the waves would always make her feel sick. Nicholas and Christina had hoped to travel together in the future, and this was a deep disappointment.

One day, when she was feeling less miserable than usual, Christina came on deck for a few minutes. "It is beautiful," she said, looking over the water. "I think if I would feel well, I would understand why you love the sea so much."

"I so wish you could enjoy it more!" Nicholas said.

"It's so-so vast," she said. "The water, I mean . . . and even the ship itself. I did not know ships had music."

"Music?" asked Nicholas.

"Yes, the cracking and snapping of the canvas . . . the pulleys shrieking . . ." She looked up, and then looked down immediately, grabbing the deck rail.

"Ah, my dear," Nicholas sighed. "You are dizzy still. Best to stay lying down."

They reached the Isles of Scilly in a favorable breeze, passing under them in safety. *Thank you, God,* Nicholas breathed.

Nicholas and Katie were eating their monotonous meal of salt pork and sea biscuit with their Moravian friends. It was a fine day, so they had spread their oilcloth on the deck. Baby Abraham slept on Nicholas' knee, comfortable after a meal of goat's milk. Now that they were past Scilly, Nicholas considered telling Katie the story of the wind that had threatened to destroy the *Jacob* with him and Susanna aboard. He opened his mouth to speak when he heard a call from aloft.

"Deck there!" bellowed the lookout.

Captain Hilton took his speaking trumpet, calling back and forth to the lookout. He snapped his telescope open as the ship came into view.

"Is there danger, Father?" Katie asked.

Nicholas felt his spine tingle as he weighed his answer. The shortest and best answer was the simplest. "Yes."

"Deck there!" the voice called again. "Two vessels dead ahead!"

53

The Long Way to Marienborn

Spring 1745

By evening, the ships—French warships—had come within range of the *Queen of Hungary*. As soon as they fired a warning shot, Captain Hilton ran up a white flag.

Were they really going to be captured on his first journey with his wife and two small children? Nicholas' only relief was that he was not the captain. As captain, he would likely have been separated from his family.

The prize crew boarded, ordering Captain Hilton to the French ship. They clattered into Captain Hilton's rooms and took over the administration of the ship.

The Moravians met for their normal evening service, gathered around Christina's cot so she could hear the singing and prayers. Everyone looked to Nicholas, knowing he had the most experience with such situations.

"I have never been captured by the French before," Nicholas admitted, "but I have no reason to think they will handle us with cruelty. They want the ship and its cargo to make a profit, not the people on board. We might prepare ourselves for some clumsy sailing, if the English are right in their stories."

The Moravians committed their situation to the Lamb. Little Abraham lay beside his mother, waving his arms and babbling. Christina pulled him close while Katie huddled against her father.

A few days' journey brought them in sight of a walled city with towers and stone architecture that reminded Nicholas of the Cuban castle. In the harbor, a boat met them and a pilot leaped aboard. Nicholas could understand why. The ocean floor sloped so gradually here that huge fields of sand lay bare. The pilot directed the ship around the sand field.

"I believe this is St. Malo," Nicholas said. "Look, Katie, it is low tide and the water leaves sea creatures on the sand. See all those people? They are getting food for their next meal."

The French crew hustled the passengers off the *Queen of Hungary*. They stood in a group, awaiting orders. Nicholas took baby Abraham until they would need to pick up the sea chests and move. Abraham, with no understanding of the situation, babbled and waved his arms as usual.

"Oh, I'm so tired," Christina whispered to Nicholas, from where she sat on a sea chest. "But it is so good to be on land!"

Nicholas shook his head ruefully and put his arm around her. "I have a bad record when taking my family members to sea," he said. "Remember what happened when I first took Nicholas Jr.?"

"Oh, I am glad we are not in a Cuban prison," she said. "And the Savior has released you every time!"

"We may end up in a French prison, I fear," Nicholas replied.

"Wherever we go," Christina said, "He will go with us. Was that not what you found in Cuba?"

"It was," Nicholas said.

After being questioned by a French official who spoke poor English, the Moravians were waved away. "Go," the official said.

Go. It was easy for the official to say but much harder to do. However, the Moravians were grateful to be released. Nicholas rejoiced that their personal possessions had not been taken. He remembered the sea chest he had lost to the Spanish warship.

The hot, bumpy wagon ride across France exhausted Christina even more. Little Abraham struggled to get the nutrition he needed and began to cry more and babble and laugh less. Finally, they reached a port city where they arranged passage to the Netherlands. On board ship, Christina fell ill again.

They transferred to a small boat to go inland by river. Christina improved slightly, but the baby had become drowsy and weak. Nicholas and Nicholas Jr. went into a village along the river and bought cow's milk. With a small spoon, Christina dropped the milk into Abraham's mouth.

Christina's face was still drawn and pale, but her heart continued to rejoice in the Savior. She seemed so confident in the presence of the Lamb that Nicholas envied her. "My dear, you have done so well in keeping up your courage! This has been a difficult journey."

"Ah, yes, Nicholas," she said, shaking her head as if to say that she had no idea how difficult it could be. "Yet, we felt assurance of the Savior's direction to come to this place. So even if we meet great suffering or even death, I will try to endure it gladly."

One afternoon in June the party of travelers in two wagons finally arrived at Marienborn. The Moravians poured from the buildings and surrounded the wagons. They helped the tired men and women to the ground, lifting all the luggage themselves.

Christina's eyes were full of tears. She would not relinquish baby Abraham to anyone. Nicholas reached an arm out to steady her. "Are you all right, my dear?"

"Yes. Only so happy to be here. I think Abraham will recover now that we can live in a settled way."

"Ah. Christina, I see Brother John Haidt! He has come to welcome us—perhaps Susanna has come with him!"

Brother Haidt wove his way through the crowd. "Brother Garrison. So glad to see that you made it safely. We received news of your unhappy adventures with the French."

"They are most unhandy seamen," Nicholas said with a grin. "But the Lord preserved us. Might you have brought our Susanna with you?"

Brother Haidt's shoulders sagged, and Christina's tired eyes caught the motion. "Is she all right?" Anxiety tinged her voice.

"She is beyond the reach of sickness," Brother Haidt said quietly. "So in that way, she is all right."

"Oh!" Christina collapsed against Nicholas. He caught her, even as his own heart broke at the startling news.

"It was the smallpox," Brother Haidt said sadly. "March 12 to be exact."

"Just a few months ago," Nicholas said huskily. "Perhaps if we would not have been delayed by the French . . . But no, we were still on the other side of the ocean."

Christina looked unbearably tired. She looked skyward and spoke bravely. "Even if it is true that the French delayed us from seeing her, we can know for sure that the Savior allowed us this grief. And what joy she must be experiencing!"

As he had many times before, Nicholas marveled at his wife's strength. He saw her pain and the tears in her eyes, yet she was not only calm, but confident.

"What a lovely younger daughter you have!" Brother Haidt said when Katie was introduced. "But come, we must get you to a place of rest. Is the baby ill?"

"He will do better now that we are here," Christina said.

But that night, Abraham also passed from his short sojourn on earth to the arms of the Savior. Six of their twelve children had gone home.

Christina rested for weeks after arriving at Marienborn. She visited the graves of both Susanna and baby Abraham. She had not summoned the strength to attend the baby's funeral. Yet, despite her grief and physical weakness, she maintained her trust in her Savior.

"I am so happy here in this community, Nicholas," Christina said one night. "But wouldn't it be nice to hear from Bethlehem about our dear boys?"

Christina stood at the door of their house, looking toward the choir houses where Katie and Nicholas Jr. lived. Both enjoyed the dormitories. They enjoyed learning skills, studying lessons, and singing hymns. Nicholas Jr. was experimenting with drawing, occasionally going to Brother John Haidt for tips.

Nicholas went to stand beside her. After Abraham's death, he had worried that he would lose her too. He had been afraid to go to the baby's funeral for fear he would come back and find that his wife's spirit had fled after her children.

He had not lost her though. Christina recovered. She watched the communal life of Marienborn with interest. She attended the love feasts and listened to the beautiful singing and tasted the special foods. She watched the brothers and sisters share in communion. She made friends with the married women, and when she was able, she helped care for the children of the community. She made sure that Nicholas Jr. and Katie came home as often as possible. She had just written her letter to the *Gemeine,* asking to be admitted as a member.

It was almost time to walk to the *Saal* for the evening service. The sun threw its last rays over the Marienborn castle and the buildings around it. "We will pray to hear something from the boys, Christina," Nicholas said. "There are passengers coming from America soon, are there not? I think we may receive a letter."

Just then a group of young boys burst between two houses. Christina and Nicholas glanced their way—then stopped and stared. One of the boys looked so familiar. He stopped running when he spotted them. Then he ran into their arms.

"Benjamin!" Christina gasped.

"Benjamin!" Nicholas repeated. "What a surprise!"

"Did you not get the letter?" Benjamin asked, looking up at his father.

"No."

"Oh." The boy stood silent, Nicholas clasping his hands into fists, then unclasping them. Apparently, the letter had said Benjamin would be arriving. But perhaps there was bad news as well which Benjamin had hoped his parents already knew.

54

The Painter's Thoughts

Nicholas and Christina stared at Benjamin, too surprised for words. What a blessing to see one of their sons!

"How are your brothers?" Christina asked.

"Lambert is making shoes!" the eleven-year-old said eagerly. "He made these for me." He held out one foot to show them. "And Jan is working as a coppersmith and learning to make kettles and spoons and plates."

Christina's face glowed. She clasped her hands and looked up at Nicholas whose face was also full of joy.

"How is little Seger?" she asked.

Benjamin's face fell, and Nicholas knew then what had been in the letter. No! It could not be.

"A fever came to the little children's house in Bethlehem," Benjamin said quietly. "He is buried with some other little boys on the hill above the *Gemeinehaus.*"

Nicholas put his arm around his wife mechanically, but his thoughts whirled in an eddy of disbelief. He had lost two Segers before. Surely not a third!

"Oh—we should have—brought him with us," Christina said brokenly.

"My dear," Nicholas said. "You know what happened with Abraham. There is no . . . but come, let us sit down. Benjamin, you must stay with us tonight."

Benjamin sat with his parents by the fireplace. Nicholas threw on an extra log as the setting sun withdrew the warmth of the day and the landscape faded from green to black.

"Seger was with four other little boys in school, and they got along really well," Benjamin told them. "The others were David, Peter, Gottlieb, and Thomas."

Christina, her eyes shining with tears, drank in his words. She could picture the little boys playing and singing with her son, even though she had never met them.

"Gottlieb and Thomas died of the fever too," Benjamin added. "Gottlieb's father was the missionary to Shekomeko who died while serving there."

"Yes, I remember his father!" Nicholas said.

After sharing the sad news, Benjamin talked of other things late into the night, cheering his parents. When they finally headed to bed, Nicholas found Christina kneeling before the chest she had brought from Staten Island, weeping.

"My dear!"

"Oh, Nicholas, I am so glad that the Lamb has suffered for us and understands what it means to suffer! And because He rose from the dead, there is new life for our son! I only wish—I know it is a silly human thing, Nicholas—I only wish I had a little wisp of Seger's hair."

Then he saw that her fingers were wrapped around the silver locket.

"Did you get some from Abraham?"

"Yes. But not from Susanna. And now I am missing our second Seger, too."

She sprang the clasp open. It was hard to distinguish by lantern light, but Nicholas thought he could count five wisps. The first Benjamin. The baby Garret who never breathed. The first Seger. Blandina. Abraham.

Now, there should have been seven. Seven of the twelve! He too was glad that the Savior understood sorrow.

The next day, as soon as word could be sent to Nicholas Jr. and Katie, the family met together. The fresh pain of Seger's death made the fellowship with the other children even sweeter. In the afternoon Nicholas suggested a visit to Brother John Haidt, the painter who lived at Herrnhaag, a few miles away.

A few days later they visited Herrnhaag. The community had been built according to plan. The castle stood on a wooded hill, and down on the plain the town was laid out in neat squares with large houses for the choirs. They found Brother Haidt hard at work, surrounded by colors and brushes and the tangy aroma of paint.

"Ah, Brother Garrison!" he said. "I have just received word that I am to do your portrait!"

Nicholas gulped. "That is certainly not why I am here!"

"Of course not. But Brother Ludwig thinks a portrait of our sea captain would be a fitting addition to our collection. Now that I am working at painting full time, I can get more done."

"We do not wish to bother you," Nicholas said. "Could we observe?"

"That you can," the painter replied. "But even a painter needs breaks and I will stop my work in a few minutes and speak with you."

Nicholas and Benjamin and Christina, all lovers of art, watched with awe as Brother Haidt's hand moved across his canvas without fear. The painter began to talk about portraits.

"When a group of people is painted, the important people must be in the middle. So when I make a painting with Christ, I will place His figure in the center of the canvas. Also, it's important to have a light source with the light coming from the side. Mid-morning or mid-afternoon sun makes wonderful lighting."

That night the children visited the choirs of the young people, while Nicholas visited with Brother Haidt and Christina chatted with Catherine, Brother Haidt's wife.

"My wife has just recently joined the *Gemeine*," Nicholas said, after sharing the sad news from Bethlehem. "It is such a joy to see my family a part of the brotherhood! My wife was not at all sure about the Moravians at first."

"Ah," said Brother Haidt. "Then our experience has been quite similar. When I first proposed to move here from London, my wife flatly refused. But our servant woman, Hannah, was a Moravian. She told my wife that it is a great blessing to have a husband who cares about serving God. So my wife agreed to move here if Hannah would move with us. Still, after we moved here, my wife and Hannah made plans to run away. My wife could speak no German and living here was such a trial to her. But I began to hold English services just with them. One day, my dear Catherine was profoundly affected by the story of the Savior's sufferings, and her mind was changed."

Nicholas nudged a log that was threatening to hop out of the fireplace. "Yes, that is quite similar to our experience," he said. "Brother Haidt, what do you think of the change toward more feasting and extravagance among the Brethren in recent years?"

"Ah. I think perhaps we feel alike on that issue too," the painter said. "For some time I had served as a minister. Recently, I asked to be released from those duties to focus on painting. I did not tell Brother Ludwig the real reason, but I will share it with you."

Brother Haidt had noticed that the joy of the brothers and sisters had become frivolous at times. The huge feasts with hundreds of candles lighting the *Saal* had become a greater focus than the sufferings of Christ.

"Yes, I have noticed this as well," Nicholas said. "Yet I know that the children of God should be full of joy."

"Indeed! But should they not be filled with joy primarily because they are washed in Christ's blood and raised to new life? I spoke to some of the Brethren about this, and I preached on Christ's sufferings. Yet this seemed to make them wary of me, as if they thought I were judging them. You see, the count's son is the leader of much of this mirth. There is also an obsession, which I'm sure you have noticed, with the physical wounds of Christ, especially the spear-hole in his side."

"Yes." Nicholas nodded. "Yet, I do have great respect for Brother Ludwig! I have seen his devotion to God, and I have seen the Savior working through him."

Nicholas told Brother Haidt about the storm near the rocks of Scilly several years earlier, when they were saved at the exact time that the Savior had told the count they would be.

"Oh, yes," Brother Haidt said. "And I cannot deny the depth of mercy and grace I have personally experienced. The Moravians have brought together believers of tribes and nations and skin colors from all sides of the Atlantic. I will cast my lot with them even if some things are less than perfect."

In the next few days, Nicholas and his family viewed many of the paintings Brother Haidt had completed. His portraits of the Moravians had a unity of expression. They were peaceful, yet the subjects looked as if they could jump off the canvas and begin serving, however the Savior desired. Brother Haidt often painted an object in the subject's hands or a significant scene in the background.

They visited the *Saal*, which could hold up to a thousand people. Count Zinzendorf had asked Brother Haidt to create paintings for this room.

"As a young man, the count traveled across Europe to see the world, as was common for noblemen," Brother Haidt explained. "He saw the painting of Christ by Domenico Fetti, entitled *Behold the Man*. Under the painting were the words, *I have done this for you. What have you done for me?* This gave him a lasting impression of the power of a painting."

In the center of the ceiling twenty-eight feet above them, they saw Brother Haidt's painting of the ascension of Jesus. In the four corners of the ceiling were scenes from after the resurrection: Mary Magdalene in the garden, the Savior with the disciples on the road to Emmaus, Thomas thrusting his hand in the wound in the Savior's side, and Peter leaping out of the boat to swim to Jesus who was making breakfast on the shore. The walls of the *Saal* displayed paintings from before the Resurrection, two from the Old Testament, and two from the New Testament, including the Passover and the Last Supper.

"Think about what you wish to pose with for your portrait," Brother Haidt said to Nicholas in parting. "Perhaps some tools from your trade."

"I'll think about it," Nicholas said. "I do enjoy my navigation tools."

55

The Greenland Voyage

Despite the grief of losing three children in a short time, Nicholas and Christina experienced a blessed year in Marienborn. Nicholas stayed at home as much as possible to comfort his wife and encourage her. They embraced the practices of the church and attended the services. They also talked together as a family about the things that concerned them in the Moravian church. Perhaps one day they would move back to America and live at Bethlehem.

At the beginning of 1747, Nicholas was asked to take a load of lumber to the mission in Greenland.

"What do you think, my dear? Is this something you would like to do?" Christina asked, her knitting needles flashing.

"I would!" Nicholas said. "I haven't been to sea for awhile, and never to Greenland. I will have to request a warmer coat from the tailor though."

"Take plenty of lanterns," Christina said. "They say it is mostly dark there in the winter."

"Soon the ship being built for the church will be finished, and we can sail in our own vessel," Nicholas said. "You will want to go with me to Staten Island to take it on its first voyage, will you not?"

Christina let her knitting fall into her lap. "Hmmm. Yes, it would be wonderful to visit Staten Island again. I do dread the voyage though. You may love it, Nicholas, but I do not."

"By the mercy of God, we will make it without being imprisoned this time!"

Nicholas said. "I know you do not want to go to Greenland, my dear. But will you prefer to stay at home here rather than travel with me back and forth across the Atlantic on later trips?"

"I will do what I am asked to do," Christina sighed. "And I hate to think of being separated from you for all those months. But I just do not look forward to being aboard ship. Perhaps Jan and Lambert could come here!"

Nicholas was excited to make the journey with Christian David, one of the founders of the Moravian movement in Herrnhutt and one of the first to take the Gospel to Greenland. They headed out on horseback toward the seaports. The horses' hoofs bit into the frozen snow. Both men wore furs under their regular overcoats, knowing it would get colder as they neared their destination. As they rode, Christian David told Nicholas the story of the Greenland church.

"We were close to death so many times in those first five years," Christian David said. "Brother, when we first saw those unsmiling Inuit men paddling canoes around the ice floes and those depressed Danish traders blinking at us from their boats among the rocks, we didn't know what we had gotten into. One year, no ship arrived and we nearly starved.

"But do you know what finally brought the people to salvation? We quit preaching about the holiness of God and the need for right living, and we started to preach nothing but Jesus Christ and Him crucified. Slowly, person by person, they came, until now there are three hundred who meet. And now that they know Christ, they are learning righteousness and the ways of God."

On the Greenland voyage, Nicholas learned to navigate around icebergs and to use seal oil in a lamp. He marveled at the gathering of the believers in their sealskin coats, and their excitement and gratitude at the arrival of wood for their *Gemeinhaus*. Five Inuit planned to travel back to Europe with them.

When the ship weighed anchor and pulled away from the shores of Greenland, Nicholas stood on the quarterdeck. Behind them, the snowy hills of Greenland stood like a memorial to the most fascinating place Nicholas had ever visited. Up in the masts, the breath of the sailors fogged in the chill air as the men moved to the tasks they knew so well. To the south, the sun rose into a cloudless sky. The days would lengthen quickly with the coming of spring, but ice and snow still encased the huge island.

Nicholas reached into the binnacle and pulled out his octant. A surge of excitement welled. He smiled at his own childish delight in taking measurements from the heavens.

"It never gets old," Nicholas said to the helmsman. "God has been so good to give me a role in His church that I so much enjoy. I never imagined such a privilege would be mine!"

"I'm glad for you, sir," the helmsman said. "But God has shown His goodness to me by sparing me the grief of having to take measurements!"

The men shared a laugh.

Behind him Nicholas heard a rustle. One of the Inuit men had ventured from below and was stepping carefully across the deck.

Nicholas stepped down from the quarterdeck. He enjoyed learning to know the people he transported, but this time the language barrier perplexed him. Although some of the Inuit men spoke German, this man did not. He just smiled, as if being on deck in the fresh air was a great relief.

The ship rolled, and the man grasped at the standing rigging. With his free hand, he pointed in wonder at the octant Nicholas held. Nicholas held the metal object out to him, allowing him to run his fingertips along the shining brass. Then, he pointed to the sun and the horizon, using both arms to show the angle between the two.

"Measure," he said. "I measure our location with the sun. You can come up on the quarterdeck to watch if you wish."

• •

Nicholas arrived in the Netherlands, eager to see his family and to introduce his five new friends from Greenland. They made the last leg of the journey by horseback, with their guests riding along in a wagon. As they approached Marienborn, a cluster of men came to welcome them.

Brother John Haidt, the painter, was in the group. Nicholas remembered how Brother Haidt had met them to tell of Susanna's death, and he shivered at the memory. Then he shook himself. How unkind of him to associate his friend with bad news! Of course, Brother Haidt would want to be part of the welcoming committee. He would want to meet the five Inuit passengers from Greenland and maybe make a painting of them someday.

"Brother Haidt!" Nicholas cried, leaping off his horse. "What a blessing to have you here waiting for us!" The two men kissed each other on the cheek.

"We praise God that you have returned safely," the painter replied. He smiled, but Nicholas had heard his wooden effort to speak polite words.

Nicholas felt his heart rate rise and a knot form in his throat. He looked from one face to another. The men were all looking at him.

He did not want to ask.

How could there be more bad news? He turned his eyes heavenward. *Savior, help me! Spare me!*

"Is—is everything all right at home?" he asked.

"There was an influenza at Marienborn while you were gone," Brother Haidt said. "I am sorry to tell you, Brother, but your wife and daughter Katie have both gone home to the Lamb."

· ·

In a daze, Nicholas performed the necessary duties of introducing the Inuit guests to the welcoming committee. He pointed out his sea chest so it would be delivered to the correct house. He gave a brief report to the men on the success of their journey, so the welcoming committee could share a little news with the rest of the community.

Then, he walked toward the settlement with Brother Haidt beside him. As they walked, memories flooded Nicholas' mind.

The trees above them, just beginning to bud, reminded him of the trees around the old stone house on Staten Island. He thought of the other times he had returned from voyages. Christina had always been there, running to the door to welcome him. He remembered her joy when he returned from captivity in Cuba, her joy when he returned from *anywhere*. Never before had he returned to an empty house.

When they climbed a rise, he thought of Iron Hill, where he had taken Christina to ask her to marry him. She had looked out over the water, asking if he would go back to sea. He pictured Christina with the silver locket, making plans for their wedding. He recalled her beauty on their wedding day, and how Pine and Mary had raced around in the background, making everything perfect.

A group of children ran across the path ahead of them. Nicholas thought of their own twelve children. He remembered Mary attending the young Christina at Nicholas' birth. He recalled the two babies who had died without taking a breath, of little Seger dying in his arms, and of little Blandina dying while he was gone on a voyage. Then, in quick succession they had lost Susanna, Abraham, and little Seger. Now, Katie.

How will Christina handle this? Nicholas asked himself before he could catch his mistake.

She would not have to handle it. He was the one who would have to handle it, alone.

Alone. For too many sad years he had been unfaithful and Christina had been alone in their relationship. Still, she had been faithful to him. Always, at the end of every voyage, he knew she would be there. The tears fell silently onto the wagon road.

"Is there anything I can do for you, Brother?" the painter asked him as they approached Marienborn.

"No," Nicholas said. "Well—perhaps you should explain to our Inuit guests that I will need some time alone. And perhaps you should show me the graves."

The snow was gone now. Fresh earth was still settling on the mounds in the graveyard. There were many fresh graves, as the influenza had spread through several of the choir buildings. Brother Haidt took Nicholas first to Katie's burial spot in the row of graves of young girls. Then he took him to the women's section.

"Thank you," Nicholas whispered. "I think I will spend some time here alone. Could you take care of the horses?"

"Exactly what I would want to do," Brother Haidt said. "I will take care of the horses. I love you, brother. Do let me know if I can do more."

Nicholas squatted at the grave and picked up a handful of the loose earth. It was too soon for the flat grave marker to be placed. It would not stay flat in the unsettled soil. But someone had written neatly with charcoal pencil on a piece of board:

Christina Van Woogelum Garrison 1707-1747.

Only forty years old!

He wept as his fingers sifted the dark earth. She was with her Savior, the merciful Lamb. She had found Him to be her best comfort in sorrow and misery. Nicholas thought of Christina's joy at his conversion and his own joy when she became convinced to throw in her lot with the Moravians. What patience she had showed through her long seasickness! What courage she had displayed when they were captured near St. Malo! How strong had been her hope that Abraham would recover when they reached Marienborn!

How great her faith must have been as she walked through the valley of death into the arms of her Savior!

I wasn't with her, Nicholas mourned. *I should have been with her.* Nicholas let his head fall into his hands, and he sobbed.

"Father!"

He wiped his eyes, composed himself, and stood up. Nicholas Jr. and Benjamin had come to join him. Nicholas opened his arms and they both ran into them in a group hug, all three crying.

When they released each other, Benjamin opened his hand. "Mother gave this to me," he said. "It's for you."

It was the silver locket.

Nicholas opened it. Christina had grieved that she had no lock of hair from Seger or Susanna. There were now six tiny wisps and one larger lock of hair, each tied with a tiny ribbon.

Nicholas frowned, then looked at Benjamin. "You finished it, did you not?"

"Yes, Father."

"This—" Nicholas touched the larger lock with the tip of his finger—"is your mother's?"

"Yes."

"Well done, my son. Do you two know the story of where this locket came from?"

They both looked up at him, shaking their heads.

"Come to the house, and I will tell you."

56

The *Irene*

May 1748

"Huzzay! Huzzay! Huzzay!"

"There must be a thousand people here," Nicholas said to Brother Josef. "I believe there may be," Brother Josef replied.

Nicholas smiled as the newly christened ship, the *Irene,* eased into the water. The brand-new anchor was heaved over the side and fell with a splash.

Brother Josef's demeanor had not changed a bit since that day when they had first met aboard the *Golden Swan* in the green waters of the West Indies. He was still unruffled by peer pressure, undisturbed by clamor, and undaunted by danger.

Now, they were together again on Staten Island watching the new ship of the *Gemeine* make its first descent into the sea. There was no man Nicholas would rather have had at his side.

The ship was not quite finished. The finer carpentry work inside the cabin and lower decks would be finished by joiners in Manhattan, where the ship would be towed the next day. The tackling and sails, which had come from Europe with Nicholas, would be added there as well.

Nicholas admired the fresh white paint of the *Irene*'s bulwarks, contrasting with the black which striped the hull. The keel had been painted dark red but would rarely be seen now that the boat was afloat. Two masts fresh from New England forests towered at the fore and waist of the ship. A third shorter mast behind the mainmast identified the ship as a snow.

The Moravians provided a meal for the workers who had spent the last three years preparing the ship. They served it in the upper story of a warehouse newly built on Staten Island to accommodate shipbuilding supplies and space for the sail makers.

So much had changed since Nicholas had last been on Staten Island. Most important was the absence of Christina and the presence of Marianne.

When the question of Nicholas marrying again had come up in Marienborn, Nicholas had confided in his friend, the painter. "The house is really lonely, Brother Haidt," he had said. "Part of me just wants Christina back, but I know I cannot wish for that. Christina is in a glorious land of no sorrow, and she is with our other children. I think she would only wish for me to be happy. But what about my children, Brother Haidt? I remember how I felt about my father marrying again. It was hard for me to think about going home."

"Pray about it, Brother. And remind your children how much you love them."

Nicholas talked to Nicholas Jr. and Benjamin and told them that the church was recommending that he marry again. They were sitting together in Nicholas' house.

"It's all right, Father," Nicholas Jr. said.

Benjamin nodded his agreement. "Could I have the silver locket?" he asked slowly. "I know it's a woman's thing, and if Susanna or Katie were still here, I would want one of them to have it. But perhaps someday I will have a wife who will value it."

Benjamin wiped a tear with the back of his hand. So many people had left them

The Moravian ship, Irene.
Drawing by Benjamin Garrison, son of Captain Garrison.
From the collection of the Moravian Historical Society, Nazareth, PA. Used by permission.

in such a short time! Susanna, Seger, Abraham, Katie, and Mother.

Nicholas looked at his oldest son. "He may have it," Nicholas Jr. said. "Although I would like to have her drawing pencils if there are some here."

Nicholas opened his sea chest. There were pencils for Nicholas Jr. as well as a leather-bound book in which their mother had copied verses and quotes in her beautiful calligraphy. Nicholas Jr. took this as well.

After the wedding, a simple exchange of vows at a love feast, Marianne had invited the boys for a meal. She was more outgoing than Christina had been. She had been single for many years, and could tell wonderful stories. The boys liked her.

"How does it feel to you?" Marianne asked Nicholas once. "I cannot imagine being married to someone for more than twenty years and then marrying someone else. You have so many memories with Christina!"

"Yes," said Nicholas. "But she is gone and much happier than either of us can be on this earth. I don't expect you to take her place. Our marriage will be the beginning of a new adventure."

God had answered their prayers for direction about whether Christina should go along on future voyages. She had suffered so much at sea, and now she did not have to deal with another voyage. Nicholas pictured her in heaven, talking with the Savior she loved, surrounded by eight of their children.

Marianne, on the other hand, had been to sea a few times and loved the experience. She had the uncommon blessing of never getting sick, not even in the worst storms. And so, she had eagerly accompanied Nicholas to New York.

After the christening of the *Irene*, Nicholas went alone to his sister Elizabeth's house, where he knew he would find his old friend Mary. Elizabeth met him at the door and gave him a hug. "Where is Marianne?" she asked quietly.

"She is with friends in Manhattan," he said. "I had to come here first and see you and Mary."

"Ah. I'm glad. Mary has been filling my ears with her grief for her boy Nicholas and how she 'just don't see that any woman could ever take the place of Miss Christina.' "

Elizabeth's imitation of Mary was so accurate, Nicholas chuckled.

A boy peeked up at Nicholas from beside his mother. Nicholas squatted down to his height. "What is your name?"

"Nicholas," he said.

Elizabeth laughed. "We agreed to use your name after the first two boys," she said. "But then we had three girls! So now we finally have our Nicholas. We must send to Bethlehem and bring Jan and Lambert here. They will be so excited to see you! Oh, I hear Mary coming!"

Mary's steps shuffled more than they had when Nicholas saw her last. But her face still looked the same. For once, she was speechless. She stared at Nicholas as he walked toward her.

"Mary! It's so good to see you again!"

In answer, Mary burst into tears and threw her apron over her face. "And I don't mean to be crying up a rainstorm when I should be glad to see you again," she finally gasped. "But, oh, it just reminds me of my dear Miss Christina and my sweet Katie and Susanna!"

"I know, Mary," Nicholas said. "Being here on Staten Island makes me think of them too. I lost all my daughters and my dear wife."

"But you've done gone and married a new woman, and I can't say it's a bad thing," Mary said, clearly trying to convince herself. "I don't say it's a bad thing, and a man ought to have someone to keep him company, oh yes, he ought, if the good Lord makes it possible, just like your father done. But Nicholas, I never shall forget my Christina, even as I never shall forget your mother."

"I won't forget them either," Nicholas said, tears coming to his eyes. "And I'll bring Marianne to meet you later. I think you'll like her."

After the visit with his sister and old friend Mary, Nicholas returned to Manhattan. Christina was not the only person missing from New York. Thomas Noble's wife Mary had died and Thomas had sent their children to attend school in Bethlehem. Then, Thomas Noble himself had died during a visit to Bethlehem. Nicholas missed his friend's presence and coffee shop invitations.

On the day after the christening, the *Irene* was scheduled to be towed to Manhattan. The plans were to dock her in a slice of water called Old Slip, where she would receive her final work at the hands of craftsmen.

Nicholas and Marianne walked down to the dock to wait for the ship. Brother Josef came with them. As they left the shelter of an alleyway between warehouses, close to the site of the break-in of Nicholas' childhood, a sharp wind hit them.

"Aye," Nicholas said, stiffening. "And they are on the way already!"

"What do you mean, Captain?" Brother Josef asked.

"This wind. It may cause some trouble to a ship being towed by oarsmen."

Sure enough, as the ship grew closer, they heard shouts and saw the ship rocking in the waves. The pilot on board would know if they were in danger, but Nicholas felt his breath quickening all the same. Finally, they cast anchor, rather than make the rest of the voyage into Old Slip.

"Good choice," Nicholas said, feeling his breath escape in a rush. "That would be most unfortunate to slice a hull on the rocks before the ship is even fully finished!"

"Why do ships not always cast anchor rather than hit the rocks?" Marianne asked, puzzled. "I'm sorry, Nicholas, I know nothing about the finer points of sailing."

"Sometimes they don't know the rocks are coming," Nicholas said. "This bay is a busy place and has been very well charted. The pilots know exactly where every obstruction lies. Other times, the crew can see the white water that marks the presence of shoals or reefs. They know the danger is present, but the ocean floor is too deep for the anchor."

"Ah," Marianne said. "So the anchor must be able to grab the ocean floor to be effective."

"That's right," said Nicholas, secretly amazed that this was not instinctive knowledge to all humans.

The next day, under quieter winds, the *Irene* was brought safely into Old Slip. The carpenters were given their instructions and Nicholas was officially named captain. A few days later, Nicholas finished his morning coffee and walked toward the ship. A voice called to him. "Captain Garrison!"

Nicholas turned and stared at the young man. He knew the face, but he could not place it.

"Do you remember me? Christian Jacobsen, sir, from the British warship that brought you here to New York after your captivity in Cuba."

"Christian!" exclaimed Nicholas. "How are you?"

"I have just returned from a merchant voyage where I served as first mate," Christian said. "We went to London, and I made contact with the Moravians there. I have never forgotten what you taught me about the Savior, and I have tried to find out more about Moravians at every port. I went to find you on Staten Island a few years ago, but you were gone, although I spoke with your sister Elizabeth."

"What a blessing!" Nicholas exclaimed, grabbing the boy's hands. "Are you committed for another voyage? I could use a first mate on our new ship, the *Irene*, which will be bringing Moravian Brethren over from Europe and carrying other cargo and passengers as needed."

"I would be honored," Christian Jacobsen said simply.

Brother Ludwig had instructed Nicholas to take on outgoing merchandise as space in the hold allowed. With the help of agents who connected ships and cargo, Nicholas posted an advertisement in the *New York Gazette*.

> FOR AMSTERDAM DIRECT
> The Snow "Irene," Nicholas Garrison, Master,
> will sail by the 1st of August next at furthest.
> For freight or passengers agree with said Master,
> at the house of Jarvis Brinckerhoff.

Jan and Lambert came to New York to see their father and new stepmother. The four spent many happy hours together on Staten Island. Nicholas showed his boys the hill where he had proposed to Christina and the place in the Arthur Kill where his brother Seger had drowned. They visited the Church of St. Andrew. The boys' grandfather Lambert, whom they had never met, had helped to build it. They visited the family burying ground and together cut back the brush and righted the sinking stones. Nicholas thought of his brother, his parents, and his children who lay there. This made Nicholas think of something else. "Let me make a trip with you boys to Bethlehem," he said.

Bethlehem was growing fast. Several hundred people lived there now and both agriculture and industry were expanding. The girls' school which Brother Ludwig's daughter Benigna had started had just moved from the *Gemeinhaus* to its own building, called the Bell House.

Lambert and Jan took Nicholas up the hill behind the *Gemeinhaus* to the wooded plot marked with simple white gravestones. There, in the sixth row, he found the grave of his little son Seger. Close by, were the graves of other little boys who had died of the same sickness. Nicholas rested his hand on the stone. He ached for his son, but as he squatted by the grave, he thought of the perfect happiness and health that Seger enjoyed now and how he was with his mother. He thanked the Savior for His goodness and love.

It was September 8 before the passengers and cargo were loaded and the *Irene* was ready to sail. The *Irene* was smaller than most of the ships Nicholas had commanded. In addition to himself and Christian Jacobsen, there were only seven other men making up the crew. They sailed under the flag of the Moravian church, a white lamb on a red background.

Nicholas no longer wore the flashy gold and blue he had once worn as a captain. He dressed in a pin-striped blue shirt and the double breasted brown coat he had worn since joining the Moravians. Around his neck, he wore a red scarf. Many Moravians kept a small red ribbon or handkerchief in honor of the blood of Christ. At first, Nicholas was not sure he could wear red because it reminded him so much of Captain Parker. But he was now controlled by Christ, not Captain Parker. He wore a smooth brown sea cap over his brown hair instead of the wig and pretentious hat of his contemporaries.

In Amsterdam, Nicholas took 104 Moravians on board, including his old friend Christian David whom he had met on the Greenland voyage. Three natives of Greenland, who had been visiting Europe, came with them as well. The *Irene* arrived in New York trouble free on May 12, 1749. Nicholas and Marianne accompanied their passengers to Bethlehem.

Nicholas' children were still divided between Bethlehem and Germany. In Bethlehem, he spent time with Jan and Lambert as well as Benjamin, who had joined his brothers in Bethlehem. Only Nicholas Jr. remained in Germany.

On June 9, a love feast like no other was held at Bethlehem. The Greenlanders were there, dressed in sealskins. From Suriname, Arawak Indians were present, looking remarkably similar to the people from Greenland. From America, Indian believers from five tribes had gathered. Behind them sat the missionaries who had taken the Gospel to them and learned their languages. Hymns were sung in each language.

* *

In the fall of 1749, Nicholas set off for Europe once more, again making a pleasant and rapid passage of only thirty days. Brother Josef Spangenberg was on board, and the two spent many pleasant hours talking and praying together. The voyage back, once more full of Moravian passengers, was again made in record time.

In late summer 1750, Nicholas and Marianne and a company of brothers set sail from New York to Europe, shortly after the death of Brother Friedrich Martin in the West Indies. Nicholas was glad to think of his friend in company with the Lamb he worshiped and loved, even though it pained him to think of never seeing him again on this earth.

"Got a bit of a Noah's ark this time!" mate Christian Jacobsen said, breaking into Nicholas' thoughts.

"But let's not land on Mount Ararat," Nicholas replied.

They carried a number of animals: seventy chickens, a few geese, a young bear, several pigs, and four fine horses, two destined for Count Zinzendorf.

As the pilot guided them out of the bay, a strong wind came up. The chickens squawked, the pigs screamed, and the horses whinnied as the *Irene* rocked. Both the longboat and the yawl, the small vessels used to launch landing parties from the ship, broke loose and were damaged on the rocks.

"Let's take the yawl with us," Nicholas said. "We can repair it at sea. We'll have to leave the longboat to be repaired here."

When they finally cleared Sandy Hook, Nicholas and Christian Jacobsen looked at each other. The voyage had barely started and they already had damage and lost a small boat. "I hope that's the end of the excitement for this voyage," Nicholas said. But it was not to be.

57

The Newfoundland Seas

1750

Two weeks into the voyage, Nicholas was exhausted. The wind was contrary, and he felt the need to remain on the deck for long hours. He rarely returned to his cabin to sleep.

On September 9, Nicholas paced the quarterdeck, carrying his coffee mug and watching the menacing clouds. The *Irene* had been riding medium-high seas all night, with single-reefed sails. The mercury in the glass barometer was dropping lower and lower. Nicholas almost told the cook to put out the fire and serve a cold breakfast.

He was glad for his coffee as well as the cooked oatmeal which he had eaten hastily. The coffee's warmth buoyed his spirits. He took a final swallow and got a mouthful of grounds. He must have gotten a dipperful from the bottom of the copper kettle. He walked to the bulwarks and spit them into the sea.

"Captain, I think—"

Christian Jacobsen was standing at the helm, but his words were cut off in a blast of wind. If Christian had been about to predict a gale of hurricane force, he was right. Nicholas, for the first time in years, almost fell. He caught himself on the binnacle and looked aloft. One man was in the lookout and several more on deck. He ran to the forecastle and pounded on the hatch with his empty coffee mug.

"All hands!" he yelled but he heard nothing come out of his mouth. He wrestled open the hatch. The face of John Vanderbilt was framed in the opening; the men were coming up. He leaned over the hatch and yelled into John's ear, gripping the edge of the opening.

"Take in all sail!" he yelled. He flung the coffee mug to the side. They would have worse things than a coffee cup going overboard before this wind blew itself out.

The men would know that this was the next step, but they always listened for orders. Nicholas fought his way back to the tiller. "I'm going up with the men!" Nicholas called to Christian.

"No, sir, let me go!" the mate shouted. "We need you on deck!"

They could barely hear each other. Christian shot up the ratlines of the mainmast almost before Nicholas could answer.

A huge wave crashed onto the quarterdeck. The stormy sea, with waves already giant-sized, had taken them by surprise. The ship heeled, swinging the men on the yards low to the water. Nicholas caught his breath as the men clung to the yards while the masts lay parallel to the deep.

Would the ship right itself, or would it simply fill with water and sink like a stone?

With a rush, the ship came up, flinging the men the other way as they fought to pull in the sails. Chicken feathers caught in the wind as a cage of the birds swept overboard. The horses would be next.

Then the rain hit. Nicholas felt the drops drive against his skin like pins. As the men fought with the sails, he manned the tiller, doing his best to keep the bow pointed into the wind. The effort was almost futile. One by one, the men wrapped in the sails. All the while, the ship tossed and the waves grew into mountains, black moving masses that threatened to capsize the *Irene* and swallow her whole.

The men dropped back onto deck, each clinging to the rigging to keep himself aboard.

"Everyone here?" Nicholas shouted.

"Yes, sir! One more big knockdown and she won't come up, sir!" Christian yelled.

"I know! I want to go up and cut off the main topgallant mast to take away some of the drag," Nicholas said.

"You will die!" Christian yelled.

"The odds are pretty high anyway!" Nicholas yelled back.

Amazing how things could change so suddenly. Another wave swamped the deck. Water rushed around the feet of the men standing with him on the quarterdeck. The chickens washed away by the dozen.

"Who will go up with me to cut off the main topgallant mast?" Nicholas asked, pulling an ax from the binnacle. "This is for volunteers only."

The men knew that *volunteers only* meant the odds of returning alive were poor. If anyone spoke, his words were whipped away in the wind, but John Vanderbilt raised his hand.

"Let's go," Nicholas said.

He was forty-nine years old, but he had never allowed himself to slacken on the rigging of a ship. He made frequent trips up and down the rigging to keep himself in shape. This training helped him now as he grabbed the black ratlines and swung himself out over the foaming water.

As he left the deck, he saw one of the Moravian brothers peering from the hatch. He hoped the passengers would have enough sense to stay below deck.

Up, up, up, he climbed, with John Vanderbilt climbing the opposite side. At the top, Nicholas steadied the ax and began to chop.

After a few blows, John reached for the ax. Nicholas released it, realizing his mistake in taking on something that the younger man could do more quickly.

"I'm going out on the yard to cut the rigging," Nicholas yelled to John, then made his way out on the foot ropes. No ship was engineered well enough to withstand hurricane force winds indefinitely. Something would break.

At the end of the yard, he cut the rigging with his knife, then moved to the opposite side. He focused on the solid matter before him, the yard to which he must cling, the mast they must cut off.

When the mast was weakened and the lines were cut, Nicholas stood across from John and watched the waves and the roiling water. With a dreadful heel, the *Irene* flung over on her port side.

"Now!" shouted Nicholas.

John had been waiting for the signal and gave the mast a mighty blow. With a cracking noise it broke loose, fell as the ship began to right, and disappeared instantly.

Just that long, Nicholas realized, was all it would take to swallow a man. Today, perhaps, would be his day to meet the Savior. Many men had gone to a watery grave before him, and many would after him. Perhaps everyone on the *Irene* would go together.

He and John had survived the cutting of the mast. They scrambled back down to the deck.

"You made it back!" Christian said with relief.

The ship heeled again, and one of the horses fell, then washed into the ocean.

"Go to your bunks," he told the men. "Protect yourselves from the storm. There's nothing more to do."

Nicholas knew it was day from his pocket watch, but the atmosphere was so dark it felt like night. He ran to the hatch to check on the people below. "Is everyone all right?"

"Yes, sir! Are you all right on deck?"

"So far!" Nicholas yelled. "All fires are out?"

"Yes, sir!"

Nicholas returned to the quarterdeck. He could not bring himself to leave, but he could think of no further interventions. The remaining chickens and horses had washed over. One horse returned to the ship and put two forelegs over the gunwale, begging to be saved. But the next instant the ship was tossed by a wave, and the horse disappeared.

Finally Nicholas opened the hatch and ran down the steps. The Moravians would be gathered in his cabin. He burst through the door and shut it behind him, then sank in utter weariness upon his bed.

"Are you all right?" Marianne asked.

He only sighed. He was physically well, but watching a ship flounder was almost more than he could bear. In all his years at sea, he had never been in a situation as desperate as this one. To be in command of the vessel and the lives of the people in it, watching life slip away to almost certain loss was the hardest thing he had ever known.

He understood now how people died in shipwrecks. He had wondered sometimes if captains were simply not watching, to allow themselves to drive straight into horrible storms. But this storm had come almost without warning. He had known that something bad was coming, but he had not known what.

"Now let the Lamb be the Captain," he whispered.

The Moravian Seal

58

The Lamb, the Captain

The Moravians sat in the cabin, hand in hand.

"I wish we could let our brothers and sisters in Bethlehem know," someone said. "I think we will go to the Savior."

"I am ready to go to the Savior," one of the women said as she comforted some younger boys who were crying. "But I don't believe we shall go yet."

About an hour later, a terrible convulsion shook the ship. "Are we on the rocks?" someone asked.

Nicholas shook his head. "The masts."

He walked to the hatch and looked out. The foremast had snapped off seven or eight feet above the deck. The main topmast had snapped, breaking the yards as it fell. Nicholas watched the bulk of masts and spars fall over the side of the ship, where it dangled and caught in the rigging, dragging the boat down with its weight. Water was already covering half the deck.

"We've got to cut those masts free," Nicholas said, leaping onto the deck and grabbing the ax from the binnacle.

"Let me try," Christian said.

"Rope," Nicholas said.

They wrapped two sections of rope around Christian so a sailor could hang on to him from either side. With this moderate security, he swam across the deck, striking blow after blow with the ax, and finally breaking the chunks of wood free.

With the success of this operation, the ship rode just a bit higher in the water.

The men returned to their quarters, and the cabin crew thanked God for this small success.

All night long the storm raged. The next day they could tell it was abating somewhat. At 10 o'clock, Nicholas stepped onto the weather deck.

The *Irene* was devastated. Nicholas had never before seen such wreckage on a ship that was still floating. The wind was still blowing, but it was less fierce. Despite the rolling and rocking of the ship, all the sailors and several passengers came on deck. They stood in shock, saying little.

The mainmast, the foremast, and the bowsprit were all gone, with only stumps of wood where they had been. All the animals that had been on the weather deck had perished. The men had moved the small bear to the second deck, along with some pigs, and they were alive.

Nicholas and Christian walked amid the wreckage, formulating a plan.

"Let's wait for the wind to die down more," Nicholas said. "And then we can try to make some repairs. We have a spare topmast we can use as a foremast so we can raise a sail."

Over the next few days, they made as many repairs as they could. On the second day, they spotted a sail on the horizon.

John Vanderbilt waved a spare piece of canvas to get the ship's attention. To everyone's joy, the ship headed their way.

"Ahoy!" the captain shouted when the ship was close.

"Nicholas Garrison with the *Irene* of the Moravian church," Nicholas called through his speaking trumpet. "Newly from New York."

"Captain Cremick of the *Hull Marie* of St. Christopher! I see you have been in trouble. Can I offer you any assistance?"

"Thank you. Do you have any spare yards?"

Captain Cremick and several of his men came aboard the *Irene* with the supplies they could spare. With additional yards, the men of the *Irene* were able to rig sail and make their way forward.

A few days later, Christian shouted, "Sail ho!"

Perhaps they could borrow more yards. They were still running short.

"I do believe she's just driving in the wind," Nicholas said as the *Irene* approached.

The sea was up, so Nicholas made sure they did not get too close. This ship had kept her rigging better than the *Irene,* although a few of the sails were blowing loose. But she made Nicholas think of a graveyard. The men of the *Irene* shouted and shouted, but there was no response. They circled the ship, which was a snow like the *Irene.*

"The rudder's broken," John said.

"Right you are," Nicholas agreed.

"We can't board her in this sea," Christian said, looking at Nicholas.

Nicholas nodded and narrowed his eyes. Could there still be someone on board, alive in the lower decks?

"We'll stay by her and see if the wind dies down and lets us board," Nicholas said.

"Aye, aye, sir."

They spent the night a safe distance from the lonely ship. In the morning another gale sprang up. They moved to the safety of open sea and rode out the storm.

"I think she went down, sir," Christian said. "I was watching her and can't see her anymore."

"Hmmmm." Nicholas couldn't get the ship out of his mind. "That could have been us," he murmured.

"Sir?"

"That could have been us, all dead. God must have a merciful eye for our little *Irene*."

In his cabin, he sat down to write a letter[1] to the church. "You have here a full account of some remarkable things on our voyage," he began.

---

[1] The full letter text can be found at <http://bdhp.moravian.edu/personal_papers/memoirs/garrison/garrison.html>. The pdf format showing Captain Garrison's handwriting can be found at <http://bdhp.moravian.edu/personal_papers/memoirs/garrison/garrison.pdf >, both accessed on July 26, 2019.

59

The Successor

"That flag makes me nervous," Nicholas said. "But it would be nice to see if they have any spare tackle or coffee."

The *Irene* had continued to limp its way across the ocean. They had met more ships that assisted them and gave them news of the horrible results of the weather. Many ships had been lost. A ship from Newfoundland had given them a spare topmast. Now, a French ship was in sight.

"Ahoy there!" Nicholas called.

"Ahoy! You have run into some weather I see!"

"We have!"

The French captain came on board. He left them several pulleys and a barrel each of sugar and coffee. In exchange, Nicholas gave him several barrels of water.

When they finally reached Europe, Nicholas visited his friend Brother John Haidt, and this time he sat for his portrait.

"We almost waited too long," Nicholas said. "I did not think I would survive our last storm."

Nicholas chose two tools of his trade to include on the portrait. One was a ruler on which were written nautical abbreviations for navigation and wind. The other was a divider, the two-headed pointer joined by a hinge that enabled captains to measure and compare distances on charts. He dressed in his double-breasted brown coat.

Brother Haidt added a scene in the painting that looked like it was behind

Captain Nicholas Garrison
Moravian Archives Herrnhut, GS.375.
Used with permission.

Nicholas' left shoulder. It was a sea scene, half water and half sky, with the *Irene* sailing precariously between two rocks.

"I got the idea from the drawing your son Benjamin did," Brother Haidt told Nicholas later.

Benjamin still loved to draw. He had used India ink to draw the *Irene* in peril at sea. He had detailed the sailors on the deck and a wave sweeping higher than the deck. In the foreground and background, rocks threatened to tear the ship apart.

While there for the portrait, Nicholas got to see Brother Haidt's masterpiece, *The First Fruits*. More than twelve feet wide, the painting was a picture of Jesus in heaven with the first Moravian converts from across the world. A man from Greenland was dressed in sealskin. There were black men from St. Thomas and Indians from Suriname and America. All of these first converts had died, and Brother Haidt's painting pictured their joyous meeting with Christ.

Nicholas found his eyes resting on Sam, from Greenland. The man had died before Nicholas had gone to Greenland, but he had heard his story. When Sam found himself sick unto death, he had said that since he was the first of his people to give his life to the Savior, it was fitting that he should be the first to meet Him.

Nicholas also recognized some of the people from St. Thomas, including the black woman who wore the white cap of the Moravians and held a black baby in her arms.

Nicholas could not remember ever before seeing a painting with people of so many races and nationalities. It filled him with great joy in his service for the Moravian church. Despite Brother Ludwig's weaknesses, his enthusiasm and missionary zeal had taken the Gospel to places that other professing Christians from Europe had dismissed as unreachable.

In 1754, Nicholas transported forty-five Moravians to America, including two of his good friends, Brother Josef and Brother Haidt. Both Nicholas and Benjamin were part of the crew. It was a joy to have two of his best friends, two sons, and his wife on board.

"How long do you think you will operate as captain?" Brother Josef asked Nicholas one day as they drank coffee on the quarterdeck with Brother Haidt. It was a beautiful sunny day. The ocean lay around them nearly like glass and they were unable to move. Captain Garrison's quarterdeck welcomed visitors unless there was bad weather.

"I don't know, Brother," Nicholas said. "I love the sea, but I'm getting to be an old man. Fifty-three years old!"

"Ah, yes, that is quite old. I am still young."

The men laughed. Brother Josef was fifty and Brother Haidt fifty-four.

"I have enjoyed being captain of the *Irene*. Despite many close calls, she has been mercifully spared from disaster. I still anticipate the day when the longitude problem would be solved. I had great hopes in John Harrison's clocks, and I hear he is still making another. But it does take him a very long time!"

"He is a perfectionist if I ever knew one," Brother Haidt said. "I noticed that in the days when I engraved watch cases. If any man will solve it, it will be he."

"The lunar methods are more promising now than they used to be," Nicholas said. "But in storms, when you most need to establish your location, the moon cannot be seen. That is why I still hope for a sea-worthy timepiece."

Nicholas pulled the silver watch from his waistcoat pocket and rubbed its face with his thumb. It was a good watch, but it still never kept time on the voyages across the ocean.

"Have you thought of a successor for yourself, Captain?" Brother Josef asked. "Does one of your sons wish to be at sea full time?"

"I don't think so," Nicholas said. "I would like to give Nicholas a run as captain, but honestly, both of my boys enjoy drawing more than navigation. That is a gift they received from their mother."

"You have quite an eye yourself, Captain," Brother Haidt said. "I have seen your surveys."

"Ah, surveys. Those I can manage," Nicholas said. "They seem much easier than actual drawings. But as to a successor, Brother, I think Christian Jacobsen would make an excellent captain. I cannot forget him swimming across the deck to chop off the masts we were dragging on the Newfoundland seas. I believe he saved our lives."

Nicholas looked at Christian up in the rigging. He was watching the glassy sea for a cat's paw, the burst of ripples that would indicate a breeze that might push them forward.

"Thank God," Brother Josef said. "We have been blessed much by your presence on this earth! Even if the governor of Pennsylvania wishes that we would have a captain from Pennsylvania."

"What do you mean?"

"He has been asking why we always clear from New York. Perhaps I will visit him and remind him that our captain is from New York and is better able to secure paying freight from the merchants there."

"Aye, it's not just that," Nicholas said. "Most of the merchants in Philadelphia have their own ships. It's much harder to get cargo there to help pay for the voyage."

"Ah, yes, if I get the opportunity I will explain that to him."

Nicholas looked out across the water. He had spent most of his life at sea.

"You know, Brothers," he said. "I am a man of sensitive spirit. But perhaps you can shed light on this feeling. My entire career has been overshadowed by the guilt I feel toward my dying mother's wishes. She didn't want me to go to sea but I went anyway, only a few months after her death, and I have been at sea ever since."

Brother Josef's brow wrinkled as he looked calmly at Nicholas.

"Do you think your mother would be truly displeased with you, sir?" he asked.

"No, I guess not," Nicholas said. "It's just . . ." He sighed.

"For many years, I felt that my father blamed me for my brother's death. After I came to know the mercy of the Lamb, that guilt left me. But for some reason, the nagging thoughts about my mother's wishes have always remained."

"Ah, that is a common experience of believers," Brother Josef said. "Sometimes, our struggles are completely removed and we never worry about them again. Other times, we battle with them all our lives. Sometimes God wants to teach us more or show us His great mercy in a way we don't expect."

"We will pray for you, Captain," Brother Haidt said. "Like Brother Josef says, perhaps the Lord will show you something to touch your spirit on that matter."

Brother Josef conducted the services aboard the *Irene*. On Easter morning, they met on deck at 5 a.m. to watch the sun rise over the ocean. It was a splendid service. As weather permitted, song services, morning and evening devotionals, and love feasts were held each day. Sometimes, one of the boys played the cittern, which reminded Nicholas of Seagull Sal.

Communion was celebrated at sea as well. Before the special day, Brother Josef interviewed each of the men privately, asking them if they were right with their Savior and with the brothers. The leader of the women did the same with the sisters. As they ate the bread, Nicholas was filled anew with overwhelming gratitude for the sacrifice of the Son of God.

On a trip back to Europe, Nicholas loaded some cargo in Liverpool.

"Here to check your ship, sir. Captain John Newton."

"Captain Nicholas Garrison."

As the tide surveyor went over his ship, Nicholas felt he was being reminded of something he could not place. Then he remembered. Old Pete had worked as a tide surveyor in Liverpool! Could he have made it back? Could he still be here?

"Sir," he said to the man with the account book who was ticking off items with his pen. "Is there still a tide surveyor here by the name of Pete?" With shock, Nicholas realized that he did not even know Pete's last name.

John Newton looked up from his charts. "Pete was the name of the man whose place I took," he said. "I never met him, as he died suddenly. He was an old man, I believe, but everyone who knew him spoke highly of him. And—I don't know if it will interest you—but I found a New Testament with his name on it in the desk when I took over."

"Aye. He must have been old," Nicholas said, and tears sprang into his eyes. "And that is of great interest to me. He was a good friend of mine from my days of youth and foolishness."

"You had those too, then?" Captain Newton said.

"Ah, many. Only by the mercy of God have I found friends who put me on the right path and led me to the Savior whom I now serve."

"It is a pleasure to meet you," Captain Newton said. "My story is much the same! Except that besides friends, I had a faithful wife at home who continued to pray for me despite my indiscretions."

"Oh, but I did as well!" Nicholas said with a laugh.

They talked for much longer than the time needed to inspect the *Irene*. Captain Newton had been master of slave ships for some time. On a stormy night at sea, he had called out to God. After he and his crew survived the storm, Newton had given himself to the Savior. He had fallen back a few times but now was serving the Lord and writing poetry.

"I had a stroke recently," Captain Newton said. "I'm nearly recovered, but my days as a captain are over. I love hymns and poetry, and this job allows me time to write. One of my favorite songs is 'Amazing love, how can it be? That thou my God, shouldst die for me.' Charles Wesley wrote it, and it is the story of my life."

"I have heard the name Wesley," Nicholas said. "Truly, the work of Christ in the hearts of mere mortals is nothing short of amazing! What a pleasure to meet you!"

"If you get back to Liverpool, look me up!"

Around the same time, Nicholas gave his position to Christian Jacobsen. Nicholas Jr. had acted as captain for one voyage, but he did not enjoy it and the crew had found him indecisive.

Nicholas and Marianne retired in Herrnhutt, Germany. Marianne had grown up in Europe, and although she spoke fluent English, she preferred to stay there. Benjamin continued to serve with the crew of the *Irene* and traveled from continent to continent. Nicholas, Lambert, and Jan were in Bethlehem, where Nicholas was creating drawings of various Moravian communities in the New World, often asking advice of Brother Haidt.

Nicholas and Marianne had scarcely settled into their new house when he was asked to go to Suriname to take building materials to a new community of the believers there.

Nicholas had never been to South America, but it couldn't be that much more challenging than his many other voyages, and he agreed to go. The West Indies were close by, and he had been there many times.

Marianne, with a raised eyebrow, asked Nicholas if it was all right if she stayed home. She was quite sure that South America had large snakes. If the Lord asked her to go to a place where large snakes lived, she would go. Otherwise, she would stay at home.

60

The "Retirement" Trip

1756

Nicholas and his comrades were floating down a South American river through a black cloud of mosquitoes. Could anything be worse than the intense heat, the suspicious wails and cries from the green jungle, and the fearsome water creatures near their dugout canoe?

And then they saw it.

"Snake!"

Their Arawak guide slammed a pole into the water to check the canoe's progress and pointed into the leaves overhanging the water thirty feet ahead.

Nicholas would never have noticed the scaly body. By straining his eyes he could just follow the curve of the dark yellow reptile as it looped itself at a comfortable striking distance above the water. He could not see an end to the length of the snake.

"What do we do?" Nicholas asked.

The Moravian brother translated this question to the Arawak guide.

"We go on the other side of the river," the white man answered.

"That makes sense," Nicholas said. This would be quite a story to tell Marianne, if the privilege of returning to Europe were ever his.

Since leaving the shores of Europe, very little had gone well. First, they had encountered storms. Then they were becalmed in the heat of the tropics, tar oozing from the deck planks and sticking to the soles of their shoes. Then, one of the sisters had grown ill and died. They buried her at sea.

Nicholas had enjoyed the company of Brother Nyborg from Finland. This young man had packed his bags even before he was asked to accompany the group to Suriname, because he felt strongly that he would be sent to serve the Lord somewhere.

Johann, a brother who had lived in Suriname, had also accompanied them on the voyage and filled them in with stories of the Moravian efforts so far in Suriname. He would be happy to give directions and help with the language.

Johann told of a seasoned missionary who had once had a snake drop out of the rafters of his hut and wrap around him in his hammock. "He managed to reach for a piece of chalk," Johann said, "and he wrote on the table. He didn't want people to think that the Indians had killed him when really it was a snake. But then he called on the Savior to deliver him, and he was able to wrestle out of the grasp of the snake."

"I am glad my wife doesn't know that story," Nicholas said.

"She has probably heard some of the stories," Johann said. "The snakes can be two feet wide and fourteen feet long."

Johann had also told the men about the elderly lady who had been the first baptized convert in Suriname. "I wonder if she is still alive," he said. "She was so old that we told her she could not go with us because it was a three-day journey. Then, after we got back home, she walked out of the forest with her daughter. At the time I left Suriname, she could do nothing but pray. But pray she did, in her hammock, and one by one her children and grandchildren have been coming to the Savior."

Their ship had arrived at the mouth of the Coppename River, weeks after leaving Europe. A roar of delight had risen from the Arawaks who were camping and fishing there; they recognized their friend Johann.

The group had held a love feast there on the coast. But by the next day the newcomers were ill. Before a location could be chosen for the new Moravian community, Johann, the one most familiar with Suriname, had died.

They were going on without Johann, but Nicholas felt his loss keenly. Nicholas himself had been sick for over a week. He still felt exhausted, but it seemed he should work if he could. He clutched his canvas bag of surveying tools. If the canoe capsized, water creatures would probably eat the men inch by inch, but if he didn't die, Nicholas wanted to save his tools.

The huge snake remained on the other side of the river, and the party was able to pass. The next day they returned to their camp and started down a smaller river that cut across a plain along the ocean.

"Look at this!" Nicholas said. "I want to take readings on this plain. It looks like a good option for buildings."

They pushed through waist-high water grasses and up to drier ground. Nicholas determined the latitude and longitude of the plain. He checked his readings from multiple locations, and compared them to the few charts he had.

"I'm going to take a walk around the edge of the plain yet," he told Brother Nyborg, the Finnish believer. "Could you take the instruments back? I'll meet you at the canoe shortly."

A young Arawak boy stayed with Nicholas in case he should need assistance. Amid the heat and bugs, Nicholas felt annoyed by his presence, since he could not speak with the boy anyway. He tried to swallow the feeling. He took an inward glance at Christ. He looked at the sky, and the high clouds in the haze of rainy season brought him peace. As it had been since his childhood, looking up refreshed him. He recalled the sufferings Christ had experienced as He walked on this earth and realized that a boy with whom he could not speak was a trifling concern. Besides, he had once thought Joaquin a nuisance.

Nicholas climbed a little rise among the tangle of palm trees and jungle to get a view of the plain from a different angle. The small boy beside him began to chatter. Why was he being so noisy?

He turned to look at the boy but continued to walk forward. Too late, he realized his mistake. He walked directly into a hive of bees, breaking it loose from the limb on which it was fastened. The air turned black with furious, buzzing bodies, and Nicholas felt as if a multitude of candles were being burned into his skin.

Nicholas was stunned, but the fire of a hundred bees stinging him gave him a burst of energy. He leaped away from the hive. Clearly, the boy had seen it coming and had been desperately trying to warn him. He rolled into the hot grass, fire shooting through every exposed limb of his body. He sprang to his feet.

Across the plain, he saw the boy running as fast as he could with a small cloud of bees in pursuit of him as well. Nicholas ran too, toward the river which lay like a ribbon on the plain. The bees continued to pursue him, and he felt them crawling under his clothes.

He leaped into the river, tearing off his clothes piece by piece. He ducked his head into the water, staying under as long as he could. Not long before, he had been terrified of falling into the river for fear of what might be waiting to eat him. Now, the river was paradise.

Nicholas knew that he might die from the stings. At best, he would have a bad reaction. He must act quickly before the poison overtook him.

"Nicholas!" he heard Brother Nyborg shout. "Where are you?" Panting, Brother Nyborg came up on the bank with the boy, the rest of the party trailing them. "Brother!"

Nicholas looked at the air around him suspiciously. A few bees still buzzed, but most of the hive had lost interest. Nyborg slapped at the few bees that still clung to Nicholas' skin.

"Here, give me your clothes. Smear mud all over yourself and we'll get you back to camp."

With the help of the others, Nicholas smeared mud from the river bank thickly over his body, especially his face, neck, and arms. The men helped him back into his clothes after Brother Nyborg had declared them free of bees.

"I got stung only three times and it feels like I am burning up," Nyborg said. "I can't imagine how you are feeling, Captain."

How am I feeling? Nicholas asked himself. His neck was swelling as if it would soon crush his breathing pipe. His fingers were growing fat. His heart was pumping much too rapidly. Mostly, he still felt like he was on fire.

For the next few days, Nicholas suffered greatly. His face and hands swelled to grotesque proportions. His eyes swelled shut and he could see nothing. Those who were well kept exchanging the mud bandages to keep them as cool and wet as possible. They also applied frequent doses of aloe from the spear-like leaves of a tropical plant, which gave Nicholas more relief than anything else. Nicholas felt as if not only his skin, but his entire body inside was burning.

"Drink more," said an Arawak woman, holding a gourd of water to his lips.

Finally, after a week, the reaction subsided. Nicholas looked at his hands and found them to be hands again. He did not even want to think how his face must have looked. Though he missed Marianne, he was glad she had not needed to see his disfigurement.

When he had finally recovered and was able to rejoin the building effort, he thanked God. He particularly thanked God for the Arawak boy who had run for help after the attack of bees. It was odd, but this was the second time when a great blessing of God had come disguised as an annoying person.

The buildings were finished in time for a love feast at Easter. To Nicholas' dismay, his friend Brother Nyborg passed away to the Savior. He had been ill for many days. Weakened to delirium, he had been unable to speak English or German and only remembered Finnish. But his peaceful expression convinced them that his Finnish words were prayers to his best friend, Jesus Christ.

Nicholas arrived home from his voyage and found that his wife was living in Niesky, Germany, where a new place had been assigned them. He went to Niesky, hoping that this time he would truly retire from adventures.

61

The Last Voyage

Jonah was the English water spaniel Nicholas found nipping at his heels when he reached home after the trip to Suriname. Nicholas bent down and the brown and white curly-haired dog sniffed him suspiciously.

"Where did you—How did you—?"

"Ask your son," Marianne said crisply. "Although I must say I've gotten rather attached to the little thing. Benjamin said you had an English water spaniel as a child and he brought it from England."

"He really could be my old Jonah," Nicholas said. "As a sea captain, I should hardly name anything Jonah. Sailors call something a Jonah if they think it will bring bad luck. But I'm retired now, so I guess I can name him what I want!"

Jonah accompanied Nicholas on his nightly prayer walks through the woods. He sat by the little streams as Nicholas poured out his heart to the Savior, revisiting the many times when he had failed to live as a redeemed person should. It was a time of sweet fellowship with his best Friend, the Captain he had come to know and fully trust.

One night as a full moon rose in the east, Nicholas found himself standing by a haystack. The Scriptures of his childhood flooded his heart. He thanked God for parents who had taught him Scriptures, even if they had not known the Savior in a personal way. Had it not been for those Scriptures, he might never have been brought to a sense of guilt for his sin. Without that conviction, he would never have been attracted to the peace he had seen in Brother Josef and Brother Friedrich.

"O Lord," Nicholas whispered, "you have searched me and known me. I took the wings of the morning and went to the uttermost part of the sea, and even there your right hand led me. You were wounded for my transgressions and bruised for my iniquities and with your stripes I am healed."

Nicholas fell to his knees by the haystack and wept. Jonah curled up beside him and folded his paws properly under his muzzle, as if he understood that this was a sacred moment and no foolishness was permitted.

Even though he still wondered about his mother's desire that he stay on land, from that time on, Nicholas found a childlike dependence on the Savior that he had never before known. He walked with God day by day, moment by moment, not month by month or year by year. Life held many unanswered questions, but God was bigger than all of them, big enough to answer them.

Nicholas and Marianne spent six wonderful years in Niesky with the brothers and sisters in the church. In 1763, they moved to Bethlehem. Benjamin and his wife and child came with them from Europe. Jonah came too, becoming a favorite aboard ship.

It was hard for Nicholas to leave Brother Josef, who had first led him to saving faith in the Savior. Brother Josef had returned from America to Europe in poor health. He was now writing a biography of Count Zinzendorf, who had died in 1760.

Benjamin had wed Mary, the only surviving child of Thomas and Mary Noble. Benjamin's wife thanked Nicholas for allowing her to have the silver locket. She would pass it on to their first daughter, she said, in memory of the grandmother she had never met. As Nicholas played with his little grandson on the voyage, it was comforting to think that the boy was also the grandson of his old friend and employer, Thomas Noble. Nicholas was the only living grandparent the boy had.

They traveled with Captain Jacobsen on the *Hope*, which had taken the place of the *Irene*. Christian Jacobsen insisted on calling him *captain* the entire way across the Atlantic.

"It's been done, Captain, did you hear?" Christian Jacobsen had said when he first saw Nicholas in Holland. "John Harrison's chronometer, the size of a pocket watch, was taken on an 81-day voyage to Jamaica and lost only five seconds! Then they brought it back to England and it had lost only about two minutes for the entire voyage!"

"What was the original offer? Twenty thousand pounds to anyone who could accurately measure longitude within half a degree on a voyage to the West Indies?"

"Yes, half a degree, which on a six-week voyage means a watch could lose no more than an average of three seconds per day. Imagine! Only five seconds in 81 days!"

"What a wonderful thing for Mr. Harrison!" Nicholas said. "And for the world. He received the prize promised by Queen Anne, I hope?"

"I believe he received part of it," Christian said. "But I hear the Board of Longitude has been giving him trouble. Most of its members are astronomers who hoped to win the prize by charts of the moon and stars."

"They won't be very useful in the most critical weather," Nicholas said.

"Exactly. So I believe they asked Harrison to make a few more copies. We shall continue to wait, sir, but I think in our lifetime we may each get to handle a sea clock the size of a pocket watch—that actually works!"

In London, they picked up a fire engine that Captain Jacobsen had purchased for 43 pounds and 12 shillings. It was to be taken to the community in Bethlehem.

• •

The Treaty of Paris had been signed in February 1763 by dignitaries of Spain, France, and England. The treaty had granted all French territory in America to the British. Since the Seven Years' War[1] was over, the seas were a much safer place. Nicholas was still sad when he thought of the capture of the *Irene* during the war.

Captain Jacobsen invited Nicholas and Marianne to eat with him one night so he could tell them more details about the sad end of the *Irene.* While Nicholas was in Suriname, Captain Jacobsen had taken the *Irene* on her final voyage, leaving New York in November 1757. Nicholas had known that she was lost, as he was one of the trustees. But he wanted to hear the entire story from Captain Jacobsen.

"Andrew Schoute[2] was along on that voyage because he wanted to retire in Europe," Captain Jacobsen said. "Here, Captain, take more chicken than that! There is plenty."

Nicholas took a wing and bit into the flour-crusted skin. He shook his head, thinking of his own "retirement" voyage. "Andrew was a good sailor until his health kept him at home. How ironic that he took that voyage!"

"Yes, sir, he was a good sailor. He was so full of good cheer that I think he was a great asset considering what happened. And since I was taken from the ship, I owe most of the story to him. We were nine days out, in latitude 36 degrees north and 60 degrees west, not too far from Newfoundland, when a ship came down on us from the north. She flew the English flag, but we didn't believe the colors and crowded on all the sail we could.

---

[1] Also called the French and Indian War.
[2] Andrew Schoute wrote a detailed account of the loss of the *Irene,* which can be found in *Moravian Immigration to Pennsylvania,* 1734-1767, pp. 82–86, <https://www.jstor.org>, accessed on July 26, 2019.

"Once we started running, she brought down the English flag and hoisted the French flag and took up the chase. The *Irene* did well, but we lost our storm sails at eleven o'clock that night. We lost our edge and the French ship came up on us and started shooting her cannon, shot after shot, at least thirty times. Men on her deck were firing small arms too. We finally trimmed back our sails and they boarded us around midnight. I was immediately taken onto the French ship along with two of my men."

"Ah, yes," Nicholas said. "I remember that miserable feeling. Except for me as captain it was the Spanish who captured me both times."

"Andrew told me they were all stripped of their possessions. Then they began four weeks of wandering at the mercy of the wind and waves because the crew sent to command the *Irene* was inexperienced and unskilled."

"Ah," Nicholas said. "I am not surprised."

"Such a pity, is it not! They even asked Andrew and some of the other prisoners to help them occasionally. Then the food ran low and each of the prisoners was allotted a quart of water and three sea biscuits per day. Every night, the Moravians continued to have their time of worship even as we did on the *Margaret*. That was the name of the French ship where I was taken."

"Our boatswain came to Andrew and suggested that they attempt to overpower the crew and take back command of the *Irene*. He wanted to kill those who resisted and run her to the nearest English port. Andrew encouraged him to place his trust in God instead. Thankfully, the boatswain did not proceed with his plan.

"On January 12, there was a thick fog. They didn't know where they were, which was no surprise given who was in charge. They knew they must be off the coast of Newfoundland or Nova Scotia somewhere. The fog rose briefly and an island appeared beside them, so they backed away to the safety of open water. Then, the French had Mass around noon and decided to make for land."

"Did they have Mass in preparation for death?" Nicholas asked, raising his eyebrows.

"I don't know, sir," Captain Jacobsen said, "but Andrew begged them not to attempt landing in a fog. They refused to listen, and around 2 p.m. they found themselves in white water and soon struck a rock. Then they hit another one, breaking the rudder and ripping off part of the keel. In a short time, they had three feet of water in the hold."

Nicholas sighed, remembering the many days and weeks he had traveled safely on the *Irene*.

"The Frenchmen were so depressed that Andrew took charge and ordered the boat launched. Everyone fit into the boat and made it to land. The captain then fell on Andrew's neck and thanked him for saving their lives. They still didn't know where they were, but they went into a woods and built a fire to try to warm up and get dry. It was January, remember. After they built the fire they went back to the boat for more supplies and found it had drifted away."

"Oh, no," Nicholas said. He had not even finished his meal, so great was his interest in the fate of his beloved ship and its passengers.

"By morning they could see only the masts of the *Irene* sticking above the water. They walked along the shore and eventually arrived at Louisbourg, Nova Scotia, where I had been taken by the *Margaret*. I was sent to France and paroled. I had decent living conditions, but it was nine months until some of us were exchanged for French prisoners.

"Andrew became sick in Louisbourg, but he recovered and was hired as a gardener. Then the English invaded Louisbourg."

"I was thinking it had to be about time for that!" Nicholas said. The Siege of Louisburg had been a decisive victory for the English during the Seven Years' War. The news had even made its way to Niesky in Germany.

"What did the French do with the English prisoners?"

"They put them under guard below deck on one of the warships. Andrew's ship was riddled with shots, three hundred he estimated. He was sleeping behind a barrel of flour, and a ball shot through the barrel into the flour. Then the English set the French ships on fire. The prisoners managed to escape on boats but then fell back into French hands. Finally, the French surrendered, and Andrew and the other English prisoners were released."

Both Nicholas and Marianne let out a sigh of relief. Nicholas shook his head and picked up his cold chicken. "I don't think that's what Andrew was hoping for when he said he wanted to retire," he observed. "I had a retirement trip that was a little like that!"

"No, indeed, Captain," Captain Jacobsen laughed. "Andrew never made it to Europe. He changed his mind and went back to Bethlehem! But every time he tells the story he talks about the faithfulness of God."

The Truth

1763

On Staten Island, Nicholas marveled at the changes that had taken place in the few years he had been gone. There were more mills, more ferries, more taverns, more smithies, more trading posts, more churches and schools. The Garrisons stopped to visit the site of a new Moravian church in Staten Island. The foundation was in progress on one of the hillsides above Nicholas' childhood home, near the spot where he had asked Christina to marry him.

Nicholas and his family arrived at his sister Elizabeth's house. Elizabeth greeted them warmly.

"Is Mary still alive?" Nicholas asked when his old friend did not appear.

A sober look crossed Elizabeth's face. "I believe so," she said. "She is staying at her daughter Sarah's home, and is not well."

"May I borrow a horse?" Nicholas asked. It seemed of the greatest importance that he see Mary today.

"Why, of course," Elizabeth said. "Nicholas, you know she's ninety years old. I don't know anyone else on the island who is that old!"

Nicholas let the horse trot as he turned down the road, following Elizabeth's directions. As soon as he was out of earshot of the house, he kicked his heels, yelled at the horse, and let her gallop.

At Sarah's door, several little black children stared up at Nicholas in surprise. Nicholas smiled at them, realizing they must be Mary's great-grandchildren. How was he going to introduce himself to a woman who must remember him only vaguely from her childhood?

A dark face appeared at the door. For a second Nicholas thought it was Mary, but he realized it was her daughter Sarah. "Do you remember me?" he asked simply. "I'm Nicholas. I heard Mary is sick. I must see her."

"Oh, of course, indeed you must. Yes, I remember you, although you sure have deserted this island!" Then, in a secretive voice, she continued, "I would never tell any of your brothers or sisters, but I do think you were her favorite!"

Nicholas smiled, ducking as he entered the dark bedroom. A single taper candle burned on a chair beside the bed where a shrunken figure lay. Two white feathers from the down pillow had caught in the frizzled gray hair.

"Mary!" Nicholas knelt by the bed and reached for Mary's hand. Her hand picked at the edge of the cotton bedspread. "It's Nicholas! Do you remember me?"

"Do I remember my boy Nicholas?" The voice from the pillow quavered. "Now tell me, how am I gonna forget my boy Nicholas?"

Nicholas felt small children pressing in behind him, but he focused on the voice. Mary's eyes were gazing at the ceiling as if she was blind, but her voice was the same voice he had loved since childhood.

"Marianne and I are moving back to America, Mary. I stopped at Elizabeth's and they said you were sick."

"And now I knows why I couldn't die," Mary said emphatically. "Pine, he knew when to die at a ripe young age when ever'body going to remember him like the man he was. But old Mary, she been trying to die for two years, Nicholas, I have. And the preacher, he say, 'Is there someone in your family you are waiting on?' he do, and I say, 'No, my family is all here on the island.' But I was *wrong*, Nicholas, I was wrong! I had to say goodbye to my boy what been serving the Lord these many years on the sea!"

At the word *goodbye*, Nicholas felt the tears forming, but he forced them back, because he suddenly had something he wanted to say.

"I hope I have served the Lord on the sea, Mary," Nicholas said, "but I—"

"Hope!" said Mary sarcastically. "This is not a hope wish, Nicholas. You *did* serve the Lord."

"Well, I—but Mary, one thing has always troubled me . . . Mother didn't want me to go to sea, but I went anyway."

"And what do you mean, your mother didn't want you to go to sea?"

"Well, when she was dying and I went into her room to say goodbye—" Here Nicholas found his voice choking. He vaguely noted an adult behind him shooing children out of the room. He realized that his voice was choking partly from his memory of saying goodbye to his mother, and partly because he was saying goodbye to someone he loved—again. "She told me not to go to sea," he finished.

"She did *not,*" Mary said emphatically.

Nicholas would not have been more surprised if Mary had begun speaking Spanish. He grappled for a proper response, but he felt completely helpless. He couldn't even understand her statement.

"She did *not say you should not go to sea!*" Mary nearly shouted, and Nicholas feared her children would run into the room and expel him for exciting her.

"But—but—" Nicholas could hear himself stammering. "But you weren't there. I heard—"

"I was there," said Mary crossly. "I was there as much as you was. Do you think I let my Susannah die by herself, do you? Oh no, I would not do that. Oh no, I did not do that. And I remember every word she said, I do."

Slowly, Nicholas recalled the scene. He had not really thought of the details for years, only of the sense of guilt that he had disobeyed his mother's dying words. Yes, Mary would have been in the room. He remembered her now, at Mother's head, bathing her forehead with a cloth. But what could Mary mean?

"Mary, what do you mean? What do you think Mother said to me?"

Mary sighed, as if Nicholas were a forgetful child and her patience could scarcely endure the strain of basic review. "She say, 'Are you going to be like Daniel?' She wondered if you were going to go down that wicked path like your brother, that's what she asked. She said the sea led him astray.

"But your mama didn't care about a man's occupation, Nicholas. Oh no, she did not. My Susannah cared what was in a person's heart! She cared about a person spending their lives serving God, which is just what you done, Nicholas! So if I hear one more word—one more word, I tell you—about your mama telling you not to go to sea, I will—I will—"

"Beat me with your rolling pin?" Nicholas suggested.

"Now there you remember something right," Mary said, and she dissolved into a crackly chuckle. "And I suppose you don't remember how you answered her, neither. I suppose you do not. You said those Scripture verses to your mother, and do you know what she said when you left the room? She says to me, she says, 'Nicholas is going to be all right.' That's what she says to me, when you left the room. Nicholas, you was *wrong* in what you remembered, that's what you was. You was *wrong* all these years, feeling guilty about stuff that never was. As Pine says, there's no board painted so fine it can't get a chip out of it and show it's common wood underneath."

Later that evening, Nicholas sat by the fire at Elizabeth's. He puzzled over the painted board saying. He cried private tears onto the iron poker. He smiled widely, relief flooding his soul. The prayers of Brother Josef and Brother Haidt had been answered in a way none of them could ever have expected. Nicholas had heard his mother speak from half a century before. Nicholas, she had felt sure, was going to be all right.

Nicholas knew it was only by the grace of God that he was doing well. For many years he had not been fine. But never again would he struggle with the memory of his mother's death. What a wonderful, wonderful gift!

In the morning, Elizabeth was serving cheese and bread to her guests when there was a knock on the door and a young black man entered. He handed Elizabeth a note and withdrew. Elizabeth opened it, trembling.

"It's from Sarah," she said. "It says, 'Ma passed away this morning at sunrise.' "

63

The Final Years at Bethlehem

1763–1780

Bethlehem was a bustling town when Nicholas and Marianne arrived. Hundreds of people lived there, and the available lodging was filling up. Just the year before they had begun living more independently. Married people built their own homes if they wished, rather than living in assigned quarters. They could also rent rooms, as Nicholas found was the choice of his friend, Brother Haidt.

Brother Haidt met Nicholas and showed him the drawings done by Nicholas Jr. "I cannot convince him to paint," Brother Haidt said, "but your son has done excellent work with these views of our various settlements."

Nicholas and Marianne and Benjamin and Mary studied the sketches. Nicholas Jr. had traveled around the New World visiting the various Moravian colonies and sketching.

"Look at those details," Marianne said. "Why, he must have drawn every tree and shingle!"

"He has excellent detail," Brother Haidt said. "And for those who do not get out to the other settlements, it is a wonderful way for them to find out what those places are like. Here's his view of Bethlehem from 1757. Of course, more buildings have been added since then."

Nicholas Jr. had sketched Bethlehem from the hill on the south side of the Lehigh River. Most of the industries of Bethlehem were on the north side of the river, with water-dependent shops along the Monocacy Creek. The single brothers' house and the single sisters' house and the *Gemeinhaus* were near the center of the sketch. Neat rows of fruit trees lined the hills around the buildings. In the lower left hand corner, a farmer plowed a field with a team of two horses.

"Perhaps if he comes back to Bethlehem he will need to do an updated sketch," Brother Haidt said. "Why, the town has expanded so much since then. You passed the Sun Inn on the way here, did you not?"

"We ate there," Nicholas said. "A very nice place. Just built last year, right?"

"Two years ago," Brother Haidt said. "Though it was in process for a few years."

Nicholas Jr. had sketched small scrolls at the top of some of the drawings and written the name of the place on them. *Donegal* in Lancaster County showed the Mt. Joy Moravian Center with slanting dormer windows and a split rail fence. Nicholas Jr. had captured the light and the shadow on the fan folds of the fence, with the light source coming onto the drawing from the left.

"Even though he does not wish to paint," Nicholas said, "I think he learned many things from you, as did Benjamin. Did you know he has done several drawings of our old ship the *Irene?*"

"Yes, I believe I saw one before we came to America," Brother Haidt said. "Remember, I used his idea for the background of your portrait."

Nicholas and Marianne settled into life at Bethlehem, renting an apartment as the Haidts did. In many ways it was similar to life in Niesky and Marienborn. The morning and evening worship services, the love feasts, and the song services were the same. The 24-hour intercessory prayer continued, and Nicholas and Marianne both took slots of time to help pray through the night. Nicholas could see his sons more often, including Nicholas Jr. and his family who lived in Philadelphia.

In 1758 Nicholas Jr. had married Grace Parsons, the daughter of a well-known Philadelphia man who was a friend of Benjamin Franklin. Nicholas Jr. and Grace had moved to Philadelphia in 1762.

Nicholas took Brother Haidt's old role of *Fremdendiener*. This made him the official tour guide for the town. Visitors were intrigued by the orderliness, simplicity, and peace of Bethlehem. Nicholas explained which services they were allowed to attend, which services would be preached in English, and where they could stay for the night. He explained the rites of feet-washing and the kiss of love. Visitors enjoyed seeing Haidt's paintings and the sketches done by Nicholas Jr.

By this time more than sixty trades were practiced in Bethlehem. Nicholas showed visitors the dye house, the slaughter house, the tannery, the sawmill, the soap makers' work room, the orchard, the nailsmith and locksmith, the bakery, the wheelwright, and the pottery house.

The waterworks at Bethlehem were the first in the American colonies, although similar pumps had been used for many years in Europe. Nicholas told them how the oil mill and bark mill had burned only four days before the trial run of the new fire engine.

Nicholas' role gave him a chance to meet people of all classes: wealthy seekers from Philadelphia, poor farmers from the frontier, and native Americans from across the mountains. He made it his goal to greet each of them with the love of Christ.

In his private time, Nicholas roamed along the Lehigh River with Jonah. Together they enjoyed the sky, the water, and the forest. Nicholas spent time in conversation with his best Friend. The peace he felt here reminded him of his blessed period of rest in Niesky.

After Jonah died, Nicholas built a small arbor on a hill overlooking the river. Here he prayed and worshiped in the privacy of nature. He called the hill Niesky Hill, and the other members of the community began to use the name as well. When he received word in 1770 that his son Lambert had been lost in a shipwreck, he retreated to his place of quietness to grieve and to refresh himself in the Lord.

During the early 1770s, a few American colonists were stirring up trouble with the British. They felt that the new tax laws were unfair. The Sun Inn at Bethlehem was frequented by leaders of the rebellion who were passing through. George Washington and his wife stayed at the inn on several occasions, even attending church services. Benjamin Franklin and Alexander Hamilton breakfasted at the inn.

When war broke out with Great Britain, Nicholas faced a new challenge. "Marianne," he said one evening, "how will I explain nonresistance to those who visit here? Some of our neighbors are angry at us for refusing to join the war effort."

"God will give you wisdom, will He not?" his wife encouraged. "Remind them that Christ teaches us to provide for anyone who is in need."

Because of its location near New York and Philadelphia, Bethlehem became a thoroughfare to and from the war. First, American soldiers passed through heading north. Then, British prisoners came through heading south. Four wagonloads of the wives and children of the prisoners came into Bethlehem on a bitterly cold day in January 1776. The Moravians collected blankets and clothing to warm the sufferers. Bethlehem also took in refugees from Philadelphia. Its population swelled.

Bethlehem received the wounded and several times acted as a field hospital. The Brethren's house, designed to house two hundred men, was crammed with more than six hundred patients. The conditions were not safe, but there was nowhere else to go.

Nicholas watched as a cart rumbled through the streets, carrying away the bodies of the men who had died in the night. At first the Moravians nailed together simple coffins for the dead, but finally there were too many. The cart traveled to a bluff across the Monocacy Creek and the bodies were buried in trenches.

As he grew older, Nicholas experienced increasingly painful attacks of gout. He continued to stay active as much as possible, keeping to his bed only on days when the pain was too great for walking.

It was time to write his *Lebenslauf.* The Moravians expected each person to write a brief story of their life to be read at their funeral. Nicholas had heard these memoirs read many times. One morning, he collected his writing case, and making sure he had several good quills and a quantity of ink, he made his way to Niesky Hill. He brushed a few leaves off the arbor and sat down.

The water flowing below in the river brought to mind the endless days and nights he had lived at sea with the sound of the waves against the sides of the ships. He had read the temperament of the sea just by listening from his cabin.

He gazed into the sky. In all his adventures from the West Indies to Greenland to Holland to Suriname to Pennsylvania, the sky had been his friend and clock. It had reminded him of his mother and the Bible verses she had taught him.

With tears flowing, he began to write.[1]

In the cold of 1780, Brother Haidt finally got his wish and passed on to the Savior. Nicholas wept at the memories over the many years they had known each other, but he could not help rejoicing too. Brother Haidt had suffered a stroke a few years before. Although he had recovered somewhat, he had suffered and had been longing for some time to go to the Savior.

Nicholas and Marianne joined Brother Haidt's wife Catherine and the rest of the congregation in the *Saal,* where many of Brother Haidt's paintings were on display. After a short address, an abbreviated version of Brother Haidt's *Lebenslauf* was read. Nicholas smiled, remembering how Brother Haidt had told him that he had written 38 pages.

The minister added details of Brother Haidt's life that had taken place after he wrote the memoir, emphasizing his patient suffering and loyalty to the Savior through his last illness. He talked about the painter's joy in capturing the birth, suffering, death, and resurrection of the Savior with his brushes. The eyes of the congregation moved to the paintings around them as the minister spoke.

At the end of the service, the congregation moved up the hill to the snow-covered graveyard where a grave had been dug. In the married men's row, Brother Haidt's body was laid to rest. Nicholas looked on down the row, his foot aching with gout. How long would it be until he would be called home? Although he

---

[1] Nicholas Garrison's *Lebenslauf* can be found at <http://bdhp.moravian.edu/personal_papers/memoirs/garrison/garrison. html>, accessed on August 2, 2019. The English translation can be found in Addendum II on page 367.

wanted to be faithful as long as he had life, he could not keep back a twinge of eagerness.

Later the same year, Nicholas Jr. and his family moved back to Bethlehem as refugees rather than loyal Moravians, due to Nicholas Jr.'s active involvement in the war effort. Nicholas Jr. was one who had not remained neutral. Had his eagerness for war been ignited during his stay on Admiral Vernon's warship as a teenager? Perhaps if Nicholas had stayed in Jamaica with his son, they could have returned together to Staten Island. But Nicholas had come to understand that unhealthy regret was not worthwhile, and this he also committed to the Lord in his favorite spot above the river.

Nicholas was on his back with pain the day his son's family arrived. Nicholas Jr. came to visit. "Good to see you, my son," Nicholas said. "I'm sorry I can't welcome you properly. This pain makes me long to go to the Savior!"

"Father," Nicholas Jr. said. "I brought you something from Philadelphia that I think you will find interesting." He slipped a round piece of metal into Nicholas' hand. Nicholas inspected it.

"A chronometer, Father. Made by a Mr. Arnold in England. It's almost a miracle we managed to get it through in this war. Mr. Arnold is taking on John Harrison's effort."

"Oh!" Nicholas said, distracted from the pain by the small miracle in his hands. "I heard about the voyages of Captain Cook. I thought he liked the Harrison-style better than the Arnold ones."

"I believe he did, but Arnold tried again, and he is doing a really good job. His chronometers never lose more than three seconds a day."

In the summer of 1781, Nicholas was walking up the steep slope of Market Street. Bethlehem had quieted down from the busy days of the war hospital, but the war was not over. The British had won a great victory in March and had gathered in Yorktown, Virginia. Everyone expected that a siege would be laid on Yorktown by the Americans and French, but no one could tell how the war would end. Nicholas felt weary of the long war.

His foot was aching, and he misstepped as a horse and wagon careened past him downhill. The wagon struck his hip, throwing him to the street. He was unable to rise, and had to be carried home on a stretcher. He felt confident that he would recover after a few weeks, but the injury became infected. He lived each day in terrible pain, longing for release to his true home.

"You will be all right when I'm gone," he told Marianne. "The Savior will not abandon you."

Benjamin came to see him. "I hate to see you suffering, Father, even though you don't complain. As much as I will miss you, I see that you really want to go."

After a moment, Benjamin reached into his pocket. "I brought something to read to you that I thought you might like," he said. "It's a song written by a former sea captain by the name of John Newton."

"Ah!" Nicholas said, his eyes brightening despite the pain. "I met him years ago in Liverpool! We shared very similar journeys, and he told me how much he liked the hymn by Charles Wesley about the amazing love of Christ."

"I will read Newton's song about grace," Benjamin said, "and I will give it to your choir group to sing for you when they visit. Is there any other song you would like me to mention to them?"

"Yes," Nicholas said, " 'Oh God, Our Help in Ages Past!' The song we sang in prison. I would love to go to the Lamb with such music in my ears."

As Benjamin read, tears of worship and thankfulness filled Nicholas' eyes.

> Amazing Grace! How sweet the sound
> That saved a wretch like me.
> I once was lost, but now am found,
> Was blind, but now I see.
>
> Twas grace that taught my heart to fear,
> And grace my fears relieved;
> How precious did that grace appear
> The hour I first believed.
>
> Through many dangers, toils, and snares,
> I have already come.
> Twas grace that brought me safe thus far,
> And grace will lead me home.
>
> The Lord has promised good to me,
> His Word my hope secures;
> He will my shield and portion be
> As long as life endures.

"Thank you, Jesus!" Nicholas whispered when he could speak. Marianne squeezed his hand. "That is indeed the story of my life!"

Afterword

2018

Nicholas Garrison passed into the arms of his Savior on September 24, 1781. Nearly 237 years later, on September 10, 2018, I search for his footprints. "Where would he have walked?" I wonder.

I splash through puddles and stroll through scattered orange leaves in Bethlehem, Pennsylvania. I walk the concrete paths of the cemetery on the hillside overlooking the Lehigh River. I search for the place that Nicholas Garrison might have come to spend time with God.

Five white-tailed deer, one with a rack of antlers, bound ahead, stopping to look back and check on my progress. A red fox steps across the path where the hill drops to the river. Across the river, the specter spires of Bethlehem Steel stand silent, memorials to a century of steel production.

Maybe it was just like this, minus the steel mill. Maybe it was here that he stopped to pray. Maybe on the rainy days, he was reminded of the ocean's salt spray, and the creaking of the masts in a storm.

Soon I hear water squishing in my shoes. I need to go back to my car. Even though I still don't know exactly where Nicholas sat on this hill, I feel a connection to him through the things that have not changed.

The hill is the same. The quietness of the 1700s continues here. And the name that Captain Garrison gave this place, in honor of his relationship with God and his old home in Niesky, Germany, is still etched on the gate: Nisky Hill Cemetery.

A few days later I approach an older cemetery, just a few blocks from the one on the hill. My husband Marnell is with me this time, and the sun is shining.

At the older cemetery, giant oaks have grown up over the rows of flat white grave markers. Acorns and tree foliage, mixed with dirt, have mingled with wind, snow, and rain to erode the simple words etched on the markers. Will anything be legible now, in 2018?

This is the first cemetery of the Moravian church in Bethlehem. Here, we meet historian Peter Hoover and his assistant, Chris. Together, we search for the grave of Nicholas Garrison. The papers in our hands that tell us Nicholas Garrison is buried in Section A, Row 1. We have an unclear photo of his grave marker, which makes us fear we may not be able to identify his grave. On the photo, it looks as if the marker has been dug from under a layer of dirt, and we cannot decipher the words.

Adult men are buried in Row 1. Young boys, such as little Seger, are buried in Row 6. Seger's stone is also unreadable on the photo. Marianne's grave is in the women's area, Section C, Row 1.

"Samuel, Lance, John," Marnell says, walking down the row of adult men.

No Nicholas. No Garrisons.

Historian Hoover points out the grave of a Mohican Indian who joined the Moravian Church. We find the grave marker of Marianne Garrison.

But still, no Captain Nicholas Garrison.

I meander back to the men's row. 1780. 1781. These men died at the same time as Garrison, so surely one of these unreadable stones would be his. But where? Which one?

This is the painful thing about research. Sometimes, we need to be content without knowing.

I stop under a large tree and look down at the twigs and acorns scattered in the muddy earth. This tree, large as it is, was likely not even a sapling in the time of Nicholas Garrison. But perhaps the stone on the paper photo was under a tree, and that's why someone needed to scrape it clean. I see a hint of gray.

Is that a stone there?

I scrape earth away with my shoe. More stone. Flat stone.

I bend down, pick up a twig, and scrape away more mud. The gray stone widens. It's definitely a grave marker.

"I wonder . . ."

But a lot of people died in 1781. Across the graveyard, the men's voices murmur as they continue searching for those two dates: 1701 and 1781.

I scrape the stone a little longer. Then I call to them.

"I wonder about this one under the tree?"

The men head my direction. The historian, arm bandaged from a fall in a cemetery the previous week, arrives at the scene.

"I hope we find it," he says.

Marnell comes from the boys' section, where Seger's grave cannot be identified. Assistant Chris looks down at the muddy stone.

"But . . . according to the picture we have you won't be able to read anything."

"Yeah, you're right," I agree, "because this one is actually showing up a little bit."

"Aha!" says the historian. "Any words that one can pick up?"

"Well, this one says 1781," I reply. "But so are the others in this area. I wish I had a—"

"Do you need my Leatherman?" Marnell asks.

"Or maybe a wash cloth," I say. "I'm afraid I see a B there, which isn't a good thing."

There is no B in Garrison.

"Or maybe it's another R! I think this is him. Look, it says Garrison!"

"I do believe it does," Chris says.

"Are you serious!" the historian cries. "That is *so* amazing!"

I keep scraping, and there is the word at the top: Nicolaus.

Marnell bends down and helps scrape dirt off with a credit card. More letters appear and I try to put them together.

"Depart, September 24. Born, 1701, 23rd, is it May? It looks like there's a Y. It looks like July. It's July!"

NICHOLAUS
GARRISON
Born July 23
1701
at Staten Island
depart Sept. 24
1781

"It's not even a question," the historian agrees. "There it is just clear and bright. We will have to thank the Lord that we discovered this."[1]

And so, in September 2018, perhaps for the first time since September 24, 1781, a prayer goes up to the throne of God from the grave of Nicholas Garrison.

"We are very grateful, Lord," the historian prays, "that we actually figured it out. In 1781, this brother was buried right here. All the journey, all the things that happened were behind him. All the exciting things that took place—being kidnapped in Cuba and spending much time there in prison, all those sailings—to South America and to Greenland and into Germany and wherever all he went all over the ocean through the years—and now he lies here, awaiting the resurrection. Thank you so very much, that we can actually see this grave. So we are very grateful, Lord, and we just pray that somehow this story could be a powerful witness as Katrina writes it. So thank you very much for the opportunity of being here. In Christ, Amen."

That is still my prayer today. Amen!

[1] <https://www.findagrave.com/memorial/68505278/nicholas-garrison>, accessed on July 26, 2019.

Author's Notes

While I thoroughly enjoyed writing *Captain Garrison*, historical fiction always raises questions. I will list some of the questions you may have about this book, and answer them as well as I can.

- Is this book fiction or nonfiction? *This book is fiction. However, whenever I could find facts about the real Nicholas Garrison, I tried to stay true to that information.*

- What sources did you use to find information about Nicholas Garrison? *The Lebenslauf of Nicholas Garrison is my primary source and can be found in Addendum II. If there was a conflict between Garrison's words and the words of someone else, I considered his document to be the final word.*

- What are the facts? *Nicholas Garrison shares almost nothing about his childhood. He does tell us he had godly parents who tried to teach him the truth of Scripture. He says his brothers led him astray, and that he went to sea at age twelve, after his mother died. After he is saved and becomes a member of the Moravian Church, he gives much more detail about his life. Therefore, in this story, the last half of his life contains more nonfiction than the first half.*

- Did you make up the names of Captain Garrison's family? *For the most part, no. Genealogy websites provided family names, although some records conflict. We did contrive the name of one of his daughters, Katie, because there were not enough names to account for the twelve children whom Garrison claims.*

- Did you make up the names for Pine and Mary? *Both names are included on the Staten Island census of 1706. However, the characters are fictional.*

- Did Seger really drown? *Probably not. He is listed on the 1706 Staten Island census but disappears a few years later. We can be fairly sure that he met a tragic, early death. We also know that Nicholas had two sons named Seger, both of whom died at a young age.*

- Was Nicholas imprisoned in a Cuban prison? *Yes. See his detailed description of these events in his* Lebenslauf.

- Did you make up the names of the Moravians? *Here is where the story got tricky. I did not make up the names of Moravians, but I did incorporate fictional details. Brother Haidt was a painter from London who moved to Germany and then to Bethlehem. I do not know if he and Nicholas were close friends. I did not find documents to prove that they were not, but such documents may exist. I do not read German, and there is a large volume of documents about the Moravians that has not yet been translated into English.*

Please email me at Katrina@500-words.com with further questions or comments or new research on Nicholas Garrison. I will do my best to answer you!

Addendum I
Garrison Family Records

Lambert Garrison (1660–1725) married in 1683 to
Susannah Morgan (1662–1713), daughter of Charles and Catherine Morgan.
Charles died in 1667 and Catherine remarried Capt. Nicholas Stillwell in 1671.
Catherine died in 1698.

Lambert and Susannah's children:

1. Lambert   1686–1770, d. Bethlehem, Pa. Married Elizabeth.
2. Charles   1688; married Susan and died in Pa.
3. Susannah   1690; married Hance. Died May 5, 1719 or before.
4. Catharine   1693–1733; married Abraham Crocheron
5. Daniel   1696–1725(?)
6. Seger   1698–1708(?)
7. **Nicholas**   1701–September 24, 1781; married **Christina Van Woogelum**
8. Isaac   1703–1783; married Maria
9. Jacob   1705–1774
10. Elizabeth   1708; married Matthys Inyard

Nicholas Garrison (1701–September 24, 1781) married in 1725(?) to
Christina Van Woogelum (April 1707–1747).

Nicholas remarried to Marianne Brandt, December 1747.

Nicholas and Christina's children:

1. Nicholas Jr.   June 26, 1726; married Grace Parsons
2. Susanna   January 28, 1728–March 12, 1745, 17 years old
3. Jan   September 14, 1729
4. Lambert   August 13, 1732–1770
5. Benjamin   born and died 1733(?)
6. Garret   born and died 1734(?)
7. Benjamin   1735; married Mary, Thomas Noble's daughter
8. Catharine (Katie) 1736–1747, 11 years old [1]
9. Seger   August 12, 1738–1742
10. Blandina   June 15, 1740–1744(?)
11. Seger   September 14, 1742–1745
12. Abraham   September 18, 1744–1745

---

[1] One source indicates that an eleven-year-old child died in 1747. The name was not given.

Addendum II
Nicholas Garrison's
Lebenslauf

Source: Bethlehem Diary, Moravian Archives. Original transcription and translation from German by Katherine E. Carté. Minor editing done for clarity. [1]

Our dear Brother Nicholas Garrison recorded the following of his life's events:

I was born in the year 1701 on Staten Island, in New York, and enjoyed a God-fearing upbringing from my parents in the English Church. Beginning in my childhood, they taught me about the Holy Scriptures, which I liked to read, and from my most tender years I worried about my eternal well-being. Unfortunately, it was only too early, and I was pulled into worldly ruin by my dear brothers. Yet my dear Lord followed me so faithfully, that I always felt remorse for my sins, and promised to improve. I was twelve years old when my dear mother blessedly left this world. The impression of what she had told me about the suffering and death of the Savior stayed with me through my entire life.

Soon after her passing, my father let me go to sea at my own request. Eight years passed before I tired of the mean and godless life among sea-people and returned home. During that time, I was taken prisoner three times, and was amazingly rescued from various dangers. There was one time in particular when I swam to

[1] Bethlehem Diary, Vol. XXXIII, Beth Cong 33, Moravian Archives, Bethlehem, Pa., Copyright 2000-2009, Bethlehem Digital History Project, <http://bdhp.moravian.edu/personal_papers/memoirs/garrison/garrison.pdf>, accessed on July 18, 2019. Used by permission.

another ship in order to escape, and I was nearly drowned. I had to conceal myself on the new ship until it sailed into open sea.

Not long after my return home, my father passed away. I now decided to marry and lead a godly life. I entered into marriage with the daughter of a neighboring, God-fearing family. The Lord blessed this union with twelve children, which I tried to raise after my understanding.

Despite all my efforts, diligent reading, prayer, and fasting, and the outward appearance of piety, I remained a slave of sin, and my own heart and conscience damned me. I decided to return to sea in order to better my worldly circumstances. So far, I was successful, but my soul's distress followed me and grew ever greater. Since I could not resist sin, I became very scared for my soul.

It was in this condition that, on the island of Eustatius, I came together with Brother Spangenberg, who had been on a visit to St. Thomas. From there [Eustatius], he went with me to New York, which I afterward saw as the guidance of the Savior. We had a very pleasing sea-journey; his lifestyle and behavior, as well as the sermons that he gave on board ship, were a blessing to my people and me. I looked on him as a man of God and tried to follow his example, but it was all in vain because I still followed in my own judgment, and had no clarity over the reconciliation through the blood of Christ.

In May 1737, on my next voyage to the West Indies, I was sick and I doubted that I could reach Antigua. It pleased the Savior then to extract me from my own judgment. I saw myself naked and bare; all of my sins were before my eyes, and my supposed good works were to me like a sullied cloak, made of pure hypocrisy and deception. There I stood as a condemned sinner, expecting soon to go into eternity without consolation and full of damnation because I had sinned against my own convictions. I received such a fear of hell that I cannot describe it.

As I wanted to break down under this burden, it was as if I heard myself say that there was help for me in the blood of Christ, upon which I was comforted a little. Because I was still under the law, however, my sins seemed too great, and I found it hard to believe that they could be forgiven. Yet, I thought, if God preserved my life this time and gave me a reprieve for penance, I would look on it as a sign that He would handle me with mercy.

This [plea] He granted me in grace. Because I had come to know the Brethren through Brother Spangenberg during my last trip, I now hurried to them. Brother Friedrich Martin took care of me faithfully, and during my long sickness I enjoyed love-filled accommodations in the house of Mr. Carstens.

After my recovery, I set out with Mr. Carstens on my return journey to New York, where, through a new attack of my illness, I arrived much weakened. Brother

Joseph visited me, and rejoiced over the changes that I had undergone. He was a great comfort to me. I did not neglect to express to my acquaintances with cheerful courage how I had previously cheated them and myself through my own will, and how the Lord in grace had opened my eyes, which information had a good effect on some of them.

My firm resolution not to go to sea again changed before two years were out, because I felt an irresistible pressure in my heart to become a good example to sea-faring people, and to win them for the Savior. I had the joy of seeing that my efforts in this direction were not without result, in some cases.

Around the end of the year 1738 I had the pleasure of seeing the blessed Count von Zinzendorf in St. Thomas and of sharing a house with him. Right from the first moment I received a strong impression from him, and his company was to me like a veritable blessing for my heart.

In May 1740, I undertook to please some merchants, and took a trip to Jamaica against my inclination, particularly as I had not yet fully recovered from my last sickness. Prayers and tears accompanied the parting from my wife and dear children. My oldest son I took with me.

Near Jamaica I was taken by a Spanish warship (from which I previously had had retribution) and was brought to the island of Cuba. I was put on the Spanish warship, among mean and godless sailors. I had no other bed but the floor (the deck of the ship) and the most miserable diet. The thought that I might never again see my family, who lay very close to my heart, made me very sad, yet I held by my dear Lord in the conviction that nothing could happen to me without His will.

The doctor on the ship took special care of me, and I found in him a man who loved the Savior. Since he had been compelled by force to serve on the ship, and the mean society was very burdensome to him, as it was to me, he comforted me, shared his bed with me, and did everything he could to ease my condition. Thus, it affected us very much when we had to part from one another.

I was put on land with my people [sailors] and other prisoners, in order to be taken by convoy 150 miles inland to Byam.[1] The first day we had to go 30 miles through a thick forest, without coming across either water or a house. My fourteen-year-old son, who grew sick from the intense heat and thirst, had to be carried in turns by my people, until they were themselves no longer in any condition to continue. They hurried farther, because of great thirst, and left us behind without help, when it was already nearing evening in the thick woods. In this emergency, I went, like Hagar,[2] a bit from the boy, and cried to my Savior. I was assured of His hearing, took my son by the hand, and in a half hour we were again with our group and revived by a little creek.

Before night we came to a house, where we were given over into the hands of an old man who was to take us farther. He treated us with friendship, and granted my request that we be allowed to rest on the following day, as the next station was a hard day's journey through the forest. Among the prisoners, of which there were twelve, I was the only [one] who could speak some Spanish, which came in handy.

I was allowed to go to a house a quarter mile away to get some sugar cane. The man inquired very kindly about my circumstances, and regretted much that the next day we were to be taken on by a party of hunters who would probably murder us. These same men had alarmed us very much the previous night, and from their conversation one could gather their plans only too clearly. He [the man] allowed himself to be moved by my urgent plea that he travel with us for our security, and was, as will be shown hereafter, our guardian angel. When we were in the middle of the forest on the way to the next station, [the hunters] wanted to carry out their evil deed. But our faithful companion, who in any case was well armed, declared that he would defend us to the end and that they would have to kill him first. He remained steadfast until they gave it up, and so we safely reached our quarters late in the evening.

Our companion did not want to leave us until we had been brought to Byam safe and sound and had been handed over to the governor with a special recommendation. He then tearfully parted from us. After passing a difficult night in a narrow room, my son, my helmsman, and I were brought to a room with other English captains, some of whom had already been sitting there for a year. Even as I entered I heard what sort of company I had now come into, and would have wished rather for death. I asked the prison overseer to find me a separate room, and he gave me some hope.

During the night I dampened the floorboards, which were my bed, with tears for my heart's melancholy. And so it went also the next three nights, until the Savior, who saw my tears, comforted me mightily, and gave me the assurance that He wanted to rescue me from here and bring me to my family. The rest of that night I wept tears of love and gratitude.

The next morning my fellow prisoners set into me as usual, but whereas previously I had remained silent and full of grief, now the Lord opened my mouth so that I could speak my mind with confidence and courage. I held as emphatic a sermon for them as they had probably ever heard. They were so struck by it that they could not respond with a single word. Thus, I left them, and went on for myself alone.

One of them, however, a Captain Toler, came after me and testified that I had spoken the truth. He told me his whole life's story, how he had once been thoroughly awakened, but had afterwards become unfaithful and now feared that he had missed his hour of mercy. I encouraged him and he sought and found mercy in the Savior, so that we were both very pleased with one another. Together we read and sang for our edification. This came as a blessing to the others as well, who were won over by and by.

When I became very miserable from this bad and unusual life, the Savior decreed that a certain young man who had inquired closely over my circumstances formed a special love for me. He visited me every day, and during my imprisonment cared for me in every way possible. I also enjoyed from some others much useful friendship, which I ascribed to the true and loving care of my dear Savior.

After five months had passed, an uncomfortable circumstance came to pass. Although the prisoners were thrown into a tougher prison, a separate room was provided for me and my son alone, through the intercession of my good friend. It did not last long, however.

On the accusation that I had an understanding with the governor's son, who was at odds with his father, to escape together, I was put into the prison with the others. Yet the hand of the Savior was also here, as this was the reason that all the other prisoners came out of this unhealthy dungeon. When I became deathly ill from the dankness and the intolerable stink, my friend could not receive permission to bring me to the hospital.

So with the help of the king's attorney, he procured an order for all seventy prisoners to be transferred to St. Jago,[3] a port on the island. He also took care of everything necessary for my good transfer, both by land and by ship. On his recommendation the captain handled me with respect, made me the overseer of the prisoners, and on our arrival in St. Jago he found for me, through an English man in the castle, good board and lodging for me, my son, and the above-mentioned Capt. Toler.

After a stay there of six months, we were freed by Admiral Vernon, who was in Jamaica. I enjoyed much friendship on his ship for six to eight weeks, and received permission to return to New York on a warship.

On September 16, 1741, I came to land on Staten Island, three miles from my home. I hurried to pour out my heart's gratitude before the good Lord: that His promise to me had been so mercifully fulfilled, that He had let me see so many examples of His charity and faithfulness during my imprisonment, that I wondered at every consideration, and that I would hereafter celebrate this day as a day of thankfulness, until He took me to Him. I then made my way to my family, by whom I was welcomed with great joy after an absence of fourteen months.

Around the end of that year, the blessed *Jünger*[4] spoke in my house, and I accompanied him as far as Brunswick on his trip to Pennsylvania. In the next year I made my last trip to the West Indies. I took my dear Friedrick Martin back with me and went with him to Bethlehem, where I stayed for a few days and then returned home. In addition, after some time I brought three of my children to Bethlehem to live.

In 1743, the blessed *Jünger* gave me the task of traveling with him and a group of twenty people to Europe, in order to bring a number of Brethren to America, which assignment I accepted with joy. I also received permission to take my oldest daughter, who was fifteen years old, with me. On this journey, we were in great danger of wrecking on the reef of Scilly, where a storm pushed us with great force. The blessed Count, who, to my amazement, was very cheerful . . . said to me that we would all come safely to land, and that the storm would be over in two hours. After the passage of that time, he sent me on deck and in a few minutes, the storm was over. A favorable wind brought us out of any danger. This remarkable occurrence can be read about in detail in the blessed Count's biography, page 1,470.[5] It made a great impression on me and filled me with a particular admiration and love toward this servant of Jesus.

On my arrival in England, I also found my son, who had just come from Jamaica with Admiral Vernon. I took him with me to Germany, and we reached Marienborn at the end of March.

On April 27, I was taken into the *Gemeine* by the blessed *Jünger*. By the next *Abendmahl* I achieved the enjoyment of this great good [communion], to my great humility before my dear Savior's grace and mercy. In June, I went to London with a few Brethren who understood sailing, in order to acquire a ship and, as captain, to take a number of Brethren to America.

In August, I found myself in a position that I had often wished for but never believed I would experience: at sea on a *Gemeine* ship that was being used by the Brethren. We were 132 people in all, and sailed from Rotterdam to New York, where we arrived on November 25.

From there, I accompanied this group to Bethlehem. The trip cost me many tears afterwards, however, because I could not show the necessary faith, and I could not console myself over this until the dear Savior gave me assurance in my heart that He had forgiven me everything.

On the return trip to Europe, with a few Brothers and Sisters, we were taken by a Spanish warship and brought to St. Sebastian in Spain, from where, however, we soon went to London with an English cartel ship, and from there to Germany. After a short sojourn, I was sent with Brother Joseph and several other Brethren back to America, with the task of ordering a community ship built. In October

1744 we reached New York.

In March, after the necessary shipbuilding arrangements had been made, I sailed for England with Brother Peter Bohler and his congregation, as well as with my wife and two children, one of whom was still nursing and went home [died] in Marienborn. As we were reaching the end of our trip, we were seized by two French warships and taken to St. Malo.

From there we traveled by land to Havre de Grace, sailed to Holland, and reached Marienborn in June of the same year, full of praise and thanks for our Lord, who had shown us so much mercy. Now I had the joy of seeing myself and my whole family in the *Gemeine*, which exceeded all my expectations. My wife soon achieved being taken into the *Gemeine* and admitted to the Holy *Abendmahl*.

In 1747 I brought building materials for a *Gemien-Haus* in New Herrnhut to Greenland. On the return trip, we had two Brethren and five Greenlanders with us, whom I accompanied from Amsterdam to Marienborn. There I was met with the news that my wife and eleven-year-old child had gone to the Savior.

At the end of the year 1747, I was bound in holy matrimony with my current wife [Marianne], who was born in Bandtin. We traveled the next year to America in order to outfit the newly built *Gemeine* ship, the *Irene*, with tackle work, and then to take over the place of captain of the ship.

I remained in this position for eight years, and had the joy of experiencing much wonderful protection by the Savior, who had an especially merciful eye on this ship. Among other occasions, [He protected] us three times from the danger of sinking, once in a thick fog on the reef of Scilly, the same in the ice in the Davis Strait,[6] and also during a strong storm in the Channel, as well as others.

In 1756, I gave my position to my former helmsman, Captain Jacobsen, and the *Irene* was now used as a merchant ship. I traveled with my wife to Herrnhut, but was in the same year sent to Suriname in order to find two pieces of land for settlements for the Brethren. This was my last and hardest sea journey in the service of the *Gemeine*, yet with the help of the Lord everything proceeded well, regardless of all the onerous struggles that we experienced in the rivers and forests, and through sickness.

After my return to Herrnhut in August 1757, I was assigned to a little place in dear Niesky, where my wife had already been for some time. Here I had a blessed period of rest, enjoying the blessings of the *Gemeine* and the love of my dear Brethren. I thought over my whole life's course before the Savior at this time. With many tears, I confessed to Him all my sins, negligences, infidelities, and my insufficient application of all the graces and good deeds He granted to me. He made me an especially merciful and friendly visit, and assured me of His forgiveness, love, and mercy, and my call and election to His people. From this time on, I lived in a very blessed way, in childlike dependence on my best Friend, as He had maintained me before.

In April 1763, after a five-year stay in this dear *Gemeine*, I traveled one more time under the direction of our good Lord, with my son Benjamin and his wife and child, to Holland and England, and from there among a community of Brethren with Captain Jacobsen to New York. We reached there happily in October, and continued on to Bethlehem. In memory of my dear Niesky, I named the little place on the banks of the Lehigh, which I made into a comfortable spot for solitude and silent meditation in conversation with the Savior, with the name Niesky. There I completed this essay on the merciful guidance of the Lord through my whole life, and often thanked Him for my election.

So far his own composition.

• •

What concerns his [Nicholas'] life among us, we can say nothing but that he had a heart that was devoted to the Savior and penetrated through and through by Jesus. He expressed this on many occasions with heartfelt feeling and humility. The duty of *Fremdendiener*, which he faithfully performed for many years, gave him frequent occasions to give an emotional witness of the foundations of our salvation to those both high and low. This was, for some, not without real blessing, and we miss him very much in this capacity.

Above all, his relations with every man were affectionate and filled with love, his whole progress and development exemplary and edifying; it laid close to his heart to follow the customs and laws of our Lord and to change honorably for the Gospel. The *Gemeine* gatherings were for his heart a blessed pasture, and he never lightly neglected one. Regardless of his advanced age, he was still quite lively and healthy, except that he once in a while had attacks of podagra. . . .[7]

The occasion for his last, serious illness was that he was hit in the hip by a passing cart and had such a bad fall that he had to be carried home. Outside of a minor wound in the foot, there was no visible sign of injury, and, at the beginning, it [the accident] seemed not to be of great consequence. But then the podagra set into his toe and finally spread to his body, so that it appeared this could be the time of his salvation. Everything was used for his recovery, but he became worse from day to day. He longed for his passing because of his great pain, which he often professed to those who visited him. In the end, it went so far that his whole throat was inflamed, so that he could not take anything in and talking came with great difficulty.

He took an affectionate parting from his wife a few days before his passing, and he comforted her that the dear Savior would not abandon her. He was very calm despite his great pain, and looked with yearning and silent sigh towards the blessed moment when he would be released from all need, and could refresh himself in Jesus' wounds. In this mood, he recommended himself to the memorials and prayers of the *Gemeine*. This desire was granted to him on Monday the 24th in the third hour, when he went over blessedly into the arms of his Redeemer, during the singing of several verses and with the blessing of the *Gemeine* and his choir. It was the 81st year of his life.

• •

Notes

[1] Probably the town of Bayamo, on the southeastern end of the island.

[2] Hagar was the mother of Ishmael, Abraham's son. This story is related in Genesis 21:9–21.

[3] Santiago, Cuba.

[4] *Jünger* is the term the Moravians used for Count Zinzendorf.

[5] Spangenberg's *Leben des Herrn Nicolaus Ludwig Grafen und Herrn von Zinzendorf*, published in Barby between 1773 and 1775.

[6] Davis Strait connects Baffin Bay to the North Atlantic, southwest of Greenland.

[7] Podagra is a gouty inflammation that often begins in the big toe and can spread to other parts of the body if left untreated for too long.

About the Author

A lifetime writer, Katrina is the author of six previous books including *Blue Christmas, Shatterproof, Inferno in the Lost Pines,* and *Faces of Syria.* She grew up in Stratford, Wisconsin, with two brothers and three sisters, all of whom developed a love for words through the coaching and example of their parents.

Katrina loves reading, especially inspirational books and historical fiction. She enjoys visiting Lake Michigan at Promontory Point, Chicago, where her husband Marnell proposed in 2017.

Katrina and Marnell live in Elkhart, Indiana, where they seek to join God's work with the members of their small urban Anabaptist church. At press time, they are sharing their home with two teen boys in need of a safe environment.

Visit katrinahooverlee.com to find out more about the Lees or to read Katrina's Saturday night blog. She enjoys hearing from her readers and can be contacted at Katrina@500-words.com. You may also write to her in care of Christian Aid Ministries, P. O. Box 360, Berlin, Ohio 44610.

About Christian Aid Ministries

Christian Aid Ministries was founded in 1981 as a nonprofit, tax-exempt 501(c)(3) organization. Its primary purpose is to provide a trustworthy and efficient channel for Amish, Mennonite, and other conservative Anabaptist groups and individuals to minister to physical and spiritual needs around the world. This is in response to the command to ". . . do good unto all men, especially unto them who are of the household of faith" (Galatians 6:10).

Each year, CAM supporters provide 15–20 million pounds of food, clothing, medicines, seeds, Bibles, Bible story books, and other Christian literature for needy people. Most of the aid goes to orphans and Christian families. Supporters' funds also help to clean up and rebuild for natural disaster victims, put up Gospel billboards in the U.S., support several church-planting efforts, operate two medical clinics, and provide resources for needy families to make their own living. CAM's main purposes for providing aid are to help and encourage God's people and bring the Gospel to a lost and dying world.

CAM has staff, warehouses, and distribution networks in Romania, Moldova, Ukraine, Haiti, Nicaragua, Liberia, Israel, and Kenya. Aside from management, supervisory personnel, and bookkeeping operations, volunteers do most of the work at CAM locations. Each year, volunteers at our warehouses, field bases, Disaster Response Services projects, and other locations donate over 200,000 hours of work.

CAM's ultimate purpose is to glorify God and help enlarge His kingdom. ". . . whatsoever ye do, do all to the glory of God" (1 Corinthians 10:31).

The Way to God and Peace

We live in a world contaminated by sin. Sin is anything that goes against God's holy standards. When we do not follow the guidelines that God our Creator gave us, we are guilty of sin. Sin separates us from God, the source of life.

Since the time when the first man and woman, Adam and Eve, sinned in the Garden of Eden, sin has been universal. The Bible says that we all have "sinned and come short of the glory of God" (Romans 3:23). It also says that the natural consequence for that sin is eternal death, or punishment in an eternal hell: "Then when lust hath conceived, it bringeth forth sin: and sin, when it is finished, bringeth forth death" (James 1:15).

But we do not have to suffer eternal death in hell. God provided forgiveness for our sins through the death of His only Son, Jesus Christ. Because Jesus was perfect and without sin, He could die in our place. "For God so loved the world that he gave his only begotten Son, that whosoever believeth in him should not perish, but have everlasting life" (John 3:16).

A sacrifice is something given to benefit someone else. It costs the giver greatly. Jesus was God's sacrifice. Jesus' death takes away the penalty of sin for all those who accept this sacrifice and truly repent of their sins. To repent of sins means to be truly sorry for and turn away from the things we have done that have violated God's standards (Acts 2:38; 3:19).

Jesus died, but He did not remain dead. After three days, God's Spirit miraculously raised Him to life again. God's Spirit does something similar in us. When we receive Jesus as our sacrifice and repent of our sins, our hearts are changed. We become spiritually alive! We develop new desires and attitudes (2 Corinthians 5:17). We begin to make choices that please God (1 John 3:9). If we do fail and commit sins, we can ask God for forgiveness. "If we confess our sins, he is faithful and just to forgive us our sins, and to cleanse us from all unrighteousness" (1 John 1:9).

Once our hearts have been changed, we want to continue growing spiritually. We will be happy to let Jesus be the Master of our lives and will want to become more like Him. To do this, we must meditate on God's Word and commune with God in prayer. We will testify to others of this change by being baptized and sharing the good news of God's victory over sin and death. Fellowship with a faithful group of believers will strengthen our walk with God (1 John 1:7).